A CITIZEN'S GUIDE TO AIR POLLUTION
Second Edition

A CITIZEN'S GUIDE TO AIR POLLUTION

Edited By:

**DAVID V.BATES, MD (Cantab), FRCP,
FRCPC, FACP, FRSC
Professor Emeritus of Medicine
University of British Columbia
Vancouver, BC**

**ROBERT B. CATON, Ph.D., QEP
Project Director
RWDI West Inc.,
Vancouver, BC**

SECOND EDITION

**Vancouver, BC
Canada**

David Suzuki Foundation
2211 West 4th Ave., Suite 219
Vancouver, British Columbia, Canada
V6K 4S2

Canadian Cataloguing in Publication Data
Bates, David V. (David Vincent), 1922-

A citizen's guide to air pollution
Includes bibliographical references

ISBN 0-9689731-2-4

1. Air - Pollution. I. Caton, Robert. II. David Suzuki Foundation. III. Title.
TD883.B28 2002   628.5'3   C2002-910663-X

Jacket and text design by Deirdre O'Brien

Printed and bound in Canada by Friesens

Every attempt has been made to trace accurate ownership of copyright material in this book. Errors and omissions will be corrected in subsequent editions, provided that notification is sent to the publisher.

This volume is dedicated to
the late Pat McInnes of Fort McMurray, Alberta
and to Pamela Graham of Vancouver, BC —
two citizens who made a difference.

Table of Contents

LIST OF FIGURES

LIST OF TABLES

A CITIZEN'S GUIDE TO AIR POLLUTION

Foreword

Air is a substance that is absolutely vital to our lives; we need it every minute from our first gasp at birth until the last breath at death. Deprived of air for more than a few minutes, we suffer permanent brain damage or death.

With each inhalation, we take air deep into our lungs, where it fuses with the surfactant lining some 300 million alveoli so that whatever is in that breath is absorbed into our bodies. At my age, I calculate I've inhaled more than 300 million times, filtering the contents before returning each breath to the atmosphere. Clean air is a vital part of our survival and well-being, and access to it ought to be a universal basic human right.

For most of human history, nature, including the atmosphere, was vast and endlessly self-renewing. Humanity understood that we were deeply embedded in and dependent on the natural world. Our rituals, ceremonies, and prayers reaffirmed our place in nature and our responsibility to act properly to keep it all going. We have always used the air as a free depository for the volatile debris of our activity as if it were limitless. But now with the explosive growth in human numbers, technological prowess, consumptive demand, and a global economy over the past century, we have overwhelmed the absorptive and detoxifying capacity of our surroundings. It should be obvious that whatever is placed into air, water, and soil will end up in living organisms, and that as a species at the apex of the food chain, we will have bioamplified levels of pollutants in our tissues.

Despite impressive progress in 20th century science, our understanding of how the human body works and interacts with the environment is primitive at best. The fact is, we don't know the long-term impact of most pollutants, the threshold of effects, or synergistic interactions. Rather than trying to manage the impact of chemical compounds once they are generated and circulating through the biosphere, we should be striving to eliminate them from production or release in the first place. Meanwhile, we must deal with those that are created and with us.

Air is something we can no longer take for granted; informed and responsible citizens and parents have to know how air behaves, the nature of our interaction with it, and its impact on our health and lives. To have a measure of control over our lives, we have to be informed, and for anyone who wants to understand the nature of air pollution and how best to manage it, this book is an excellent place to start.

David Suzuki
Vancouver, BC
October 2001

Preface to the First Edition (1972)

Existing texts on air pollution may be divided into two broad classes, those that are primarily technical monographs or books containing detailed summaries of existing knowledge, and those which are in the general category of polemic texts. It is unfortunate that the cost of the former is often prohibitive and the technical accuracy of the latter is not infrequently questionable.

Proper legislative controls of air pollution must be built on the basis of an informed public opinion. Efforts to reduce significantly the present burden of air pollution are bound to have an effect on economic standards and on personal convenience, and it follows that decisions can only be taken in the presence of a general understanding of the reasons for adopting particular legislation at a particular point of time.

This short book has been written to act as a primary text for the many individuals who have a special responsibility in relation to air pollution. It is to be hoped that engineers, physicians, school teachers, and businessmen in general will acquire enough background knowledge on this contemporary problem to be able to understand the issues with which it deals. I do not share the opinion, expressed by some scientists concerned about environmental pollution, that it is necessary deliberately to exaggerate if any impact on the public or the politicians is to be achieved. If such a policy were to become general amongst the scientific community, far more would have been lost (the essence of science itself) than would have been gained.

The text has not been written with the conviction that air pollution is our most pressing problem, nor in the belief that the health risks associated with it are in any way comparable to the enormous burden of disease occasioned by heavy cigarette smoking. Nevertheless, it has become increasingly clear that unless problems of air pollution are dealt with now, they can only get worse in the future, and since the legislative and control processes will inevitably be slow, there is every reason to urge that the present time is an appropriate one to begin to deal with air pollution. The text affords the reader every opportunity to delve into technical monographs and original sources of material, but such references are not by any means exhaustive. Finally, the reader will find that he is not given pre-packaged answers to the question of whether air pollution legislation is required, but he may be able to understand the components of the question as a basis for formulating his own answer.

November 1971
Montréal, PQ

NOTE: *The volume received a Special Citation of Merit from the Canadian Meteorological Association in 1973.*

Preface to the Second Edition

When the first edition of this volume was prepared in 1971, air pollution consisted of major emissions of black smoke (controlled by baghouses, for the collection of particles, and banning of open coal burning), huge emissions of sulphur dioxide (controlled by scrubbers or by switching to low-sulphur coal or other fuels), and, in a few locations such as Los Angeles, significant pollution from automobile emissions. The industrial West dealt with the first two of these successfully; in contrast, the totalitarian regimes of Eastern Europe, while protesting their dedication to "the Environment," permitted their factories to continue to operate in the traditional uncontrolled manner, with gross air pollution as a result.

Our current problems, which are detailed in this book, consist of continuing difficulties in curtailing ground-level ozone pollution, which originates from nitrogen oxide emissions and hydrocarbons, and efforts to understand how to limit the emission or formation of fine particles. These two questions may necessitate a rethinking of urban transportation. The problem of CO_2 emissions and the build-up of this greenhouse gas in the earth's atmosphere was mentioned in the first edition, but at that time seemed to be eclipsed by shorter-term problems.

It is clear from a review of the history of air pollution and its control that in a free society, an informed (even indignant) public opinion has been an essential factor in legislation aimed at reducing pollution exposure. The problems now confronting us are more complicated (and less easy to understand) than was the case 30 years ago; and it has been this realization that has prompted us to prepare this second edition. We have not been concerned to develop a large volume of technical data, but rather to provide a framework in which it can be understood by an informed reader — a citizen.

Political interest in air pollution control is highly variable, and recent conservative governments in the free world have declared their intention of putting such environmental issues on the back burner, and of reducing expenditures on departments of the environment or agencies of environmental protection. In some instances, this has been defended (mistakenly) as necessary for economic development. It is noteworthy that the communist world achieved very high levels of air pollution and virtual economic collapse at the same time. Recent attempts in the United States and Canada to express, in dollar terms, what has been achieved by reduced air pollution have unanimously concluded that Western society has so far saved far more dollars in reduced (real) costs than it has spent on air pollution control.

The general field of air pollution and its effect on human health has become immensely more complicated since the first edition was written. For this reason, this edition has to contain much more technical detail and methodologic discussion on this subject than appeared in the first edition. The imperative of some public understanding of the issues involved remains the same.

In the text that follows, we have not referenced every individual study that lies behind a generalization, but we have listed for the reader general reviews of the literature which have provided useful summaries of the effects of air pollutants. References will be found at the end of each chapter.

D.V. Bates and R.B. Caton
Vancouver, British Columbia
November 2001

Acknowledgements

In the preparation of this edition, the editors have been helped by the discussions at the Air Quality Advisory Committee Meetings of the Greater Vancouver Regional District, and by the informal dinner meeting discussions of the Air Pollution Discussion Group in Vancouver. Members of the Physical Effects Review Panel under the chairmanship of Dr. Mort Lippmann, convened by the Science Advisory Board of the US Environmental Protection Agency, provided insight into the problems of costing the adverse effects of air pollution.

Dr. Michael Pain of Melbourne read an early first draft of the text, and Prof. Frank Speizer of the Harvard School of Public Health wrote many useful comments and suggestions in the margin of it.

We are greatly indebted to the excellent work of Karla Adam, Frank Chow and Deirdre O'Brien who were retained by the David Suzuki Foundation and David Hocking to prepare the manuscript for publication.

Editors and Authors

DAVID V. BATES, MD, FRCP, FRCPC, FACP, FRSC
Professor Emeritus of Medicine, University of British Columbia

KAMAL K. BHATTACHARYYA, Ph.D., P.Eng.
Air Quality Consultant, Victoria, BC

MICHAEL BRAUER, Sc.D.
Associate Professor, School of Occupational and Environmental Hygiene
University of British Columbia

ROBERT B. CATON, Ph.D.
RWDI West Inc., Vancouver, BC

BOHDAN W. HREBENYK, M.Sc.
SENES Consultants Ltd., Vancouver, BC

IAN G. McKENDRY, Ph.D.
Associate Professor, Atmospheric Science Program, Department of Earth
and Ocean Sciences, University of British Columbia

MORRIS MENNELL, B.A.Sc, M.Sc., P.Eng.
Policy and Planning Department, Greater Vancouver Regional District

BRIDGET A. MILLS, B.Sc., P. Eng.
SENES Consultants Ltd., Toronto, Ontario

VICTOR C. RUNECKLES, Ph.D.
Professor Emeritus of Plant Science, University of British Columbia

DOUW G. STEYN, Ph.D.
Professor, Atmospheric Science Program, Department of Earth and Ocean
Sciences, University of British Columbia

SVERRE VEDAL, MD
Professor, Respiratory Division, Department of Medicine, University of
British Columbia (Currently Senior Research Scientist, National Jewish
Hospital, Denver, CO)

JAMES ZIDEK, Ph.D.
Professor, Department of Statistics, University of British Columbia

Preamble

The preparation of a volume on a subject like air pollution, in which there are a large number of highly technical considerations, necessarily involves many compromises if it is to be kept at manageable length. We have been guided by our judgement as to what is basic and essential information; what one can reasonably expect an informed lay reader to explore in more detail if necessary; and what a small volume designed as a guide for the interested citizen has to contain. It has been difficult to meet these requirements and be sensitive to the balance within the volume in terms of the length devoted to each of the many topics that have to receive recognition. We have used local or Canadian examples where possible, but there has to be coverage of important work done in the United States and Europe; and in some instances special problems in the developing world also require mention.

In free societies, there are many non-technical citizens involved in air pollution issues. When a specific question arises in some region, and where air pollution issues are involved, there is always intense local interest in whatever process takes place to decide whether the environmental impact should be considered as acceptable. In such situations, extreme statements are often encountered on both sides of the argument; we are hopeful that this volume will help to restore a sense of balance.

This book is intended for the informed citizen who wishes to know more about the science of air pollution and its effects and how this body of information relates to air quality management strategies and policies.

The editors have encouraged the individual chapter authors to address the subject from a perspective of their own experience and judgement in preparing material of this nature for general, informed readers. The treatment of each subject, then, varies from author to author. The chapters are essays on the subject from a technical specialist in each field. The reader will find more scientific detail and citations of the primary literature in some chapters (notably, the chapter on health effects, judged to be of paramount interest to most readers) and less in others. In all cases references to generally accessible literature are also given for further reading and research.

Chapter 1
Historical Introduction

David V. Bates

Brimblecombe's excellent volume [2] traces the early history of air pollution in Britain, and shows that concern about its effects extends as far back as the 14th century. A major landmark was the publication by John Evelyn in 1661 of "Fumifugium, or The Inconveniencie of the Aer and Smoak of London Dissipated ..."

Evelyn was a member of the Royal Society, and his interest in air pollution may have derived from actions taken by Archbishop Laud who had fined brewers in Westminster for emitting coal smoke. It was the increasing coal consumption of London that triggered the problems. Brimblecombe provides the following figures for the imports of coal into London:

Year	Tonnage of coal
1585	23,867
1605	73,984
1614	91,599
1637	142,579
1667	264,212
1680	361,189

Table 1.1: Imports of coal into London from 1585 to 1680.

Captain James Cook in the mid-1700"s got his sailing apprenticeship on colliers bringing coal from Whitby in Yorkshire to London. It has been estimated that at the time he enrolled as a seaman at the age of 18, there were 400 vessels engaged in this trade. The great English painter J.M.W. Turner in the 19th century painted the offloading of coal in the Pool of London by moonlight in one of his greatest canvases, which can be seen in the National Gallery of Art in Washington. At the end of the 19th century, a London fog had caused the death of animals in the city; this was noticed by a veterinary journal, but apparently did not have any other impact [1].

It was Claude Monet, who spent four months of the winter of 1901 in London, who captured on canvas for the first time the complex interplay of light and pollution emissions in the London atmosphere [3]. He went back to Paris with 96 canvases of views from the balcony of his hotel room at the Savoy, and of the House of Commons painted from across the river from St. Thomas' Hospital. He regarded these paintings as one of his major achievements, but they are rarely discussed in art books, and now are scattered round the world in different galleries. His 36 views of Waterloo Bridge are especially noteworthy. Two of these are shown in Figures 1.1 and 1.2; in the painting in the National Gallery in Ottawa, the combination of mist and pollution makes the bridge almost invisible.

Figure 1.1: Claude Monet; 1903; "Waterloo Bridge, Gray Day," from the Chester Dale Collection. Reproduced with permission from the National Gallery of Art, Washington, DC. Note the horse buses crossing the bridge.

Figure 1.2: Claude Monet; 1903; "Waterloo Bridge: le soleil dans le brouillard." Reproduced with permission from the National Gallery of Canada, Ottawa.

A severe industrial pollution episode in the Meuse Valley in Belgium in 1930 alerted the world that industrial emissions were capable of inflicting severe loss of life; and a similar episode in Donora, Pennsylvania, in 1948 served to confirm the fact. Donora had only one industry, a nail mill, located on a horseshoe bend in a river valley surrounded by low-lying hills. The pollution episode there caused about 50 excess deaths in a two-week period. Citizens in Pittsburgh in 1946, a major steel-making town, pioneered legislation to restrict emissions, basing their campaign on the fact that the physicians in that city were convinced that air pollution was having adverse health effects, though there were no studies to show this [1].

It was the London episode in December 1952 that clearly indicated that pollution episodes not associated with specific industrial emissions were responsible for excess mortality. It was shown within three weeks of the episode that deaths were much higher in London compared with other cities in Britain during and after the week of the severe pollution [1]. It has always been stated that the excess mortality was about 4,000 people, but a recent BBC historical documentary (first screened on television in September 1999) revealed that this figure was based on a decision by the British cabinet that all deaths after December 20th would be officially attributed to influenza. However, there was no influenza anywhere else in Britain, and the World Health Organization (WHO) in Geneva was not notified of an influenza outbreak. If the elevated mortality is counted up to January 1, about 8,000 people died as a result of this episode; if the date is prolonged until the daily mortality returned to a normal level, the total is about 12,000 people. An aroused public opinion pushed a reluctant government (in July 1953) to appoint a special committee to report on the causes of pollution; and this committee proposed legislative action to deal with the problem. As Lord Ashby pointed out [1], the action they recommended was to enable local authorities to ban open coal burning; this was a feasible proposal because there were smokeless fuels available. These fuels greatly reduced the particulate burden from coal burning, but were still a significant source of sulphur dioxide (SO_2). No-one was sure whether reduction of smoke was more or less important than reductions in SO_2 emissions but this discussion was put on one side. The British Clean Air Act was passed in 1956. Open coal burning was progressively reduced over the whole country, with Glasgow in Scotland being the last major city in Britain to adopt such legislation.

Hearings in the US Senate in 1967, ably led by Senator Edmund Muskie, led to the writing and passage of the first US Clean Air Act in 1970. This was designed to limit both particulate and SO_2 emissions, but the problems of automobile emissions and tropospheric ozone formation, which had been described in Los Angeles in 1952, were also discussed. There was no doubt that the legislation was based on the perceived need to protect public health. This was the case in both Britain and the United States.

These measures preceded the adoption of similar controls in Canada and in most European countries. Overall, the emissions of smoke and, to a lesser extent, of SO_2 were greatly reduced over the next 20 years throughout the industrial West. No comparable actions were taken in the communist world, where any investigator who made a public statement about the adverse health effects of pollution was liable to be silenced. By 1972, when the first edition of this book appeared, the major reductions in smoke emissions in London, where smoke indices fell to one-third of their previous value between 1958 and 1968, could be documented; similarly, in Manhattan the reductions in SO_2 levels achieved between 1965 and 1969 were also highly significant.

There has always been a close relationship between economic conditions and actions to prevent air pollution. Representatives of industry have usually claimed that if they are unduly penalized by pollution controls, they will lose their international competitiveness and their future will be jeopardized. In the US, the period of stricter controls, which began in 1970, was followed by an examination of alternative strategies; this culminated in the Clean Air Act Amendments of 1990, a very complex document of several hundred pages. The program outlined aimed at a 10 million ton reduction in SO_2 emissions from 1980 levels. Emissions of SO_2 were allocated among the states and their sources, which were then allowed to "trade" them like stocks and bonds. At the time of writing (2000) it seems clear that this program has worked, and SO_2 emissions have been reduced by rather more than was anticipated (and at a significantly lower cost than originally estimated).

During the period between 1975 and the present, however, a different problem was moving onto centre stage. Worldwide, the population per car declined from 29 people in 1960 to 12 people in 1990 [4]. In the industrialized West, this period has seen a major increase in vehicle traffic everywhere. By 1990, there were 11.3 people per car in Eastern Europe, 2.5 in Western Europe, 2.1 in Canada, and 1.7 in the US. Although more and more stringent emission standards have been imposed on vehicles in the US and Canada and total emissions of pollutants from the vehicle fleet have fallen dramatically, the expansion of the fleet has been such that emissions have reached a minimum for the period 2000-05 and are predicted to increase again. This is true even with the more stringent vehicle emission standards that are to come into force after 2004 in the US and Canada. The problem faced by the state of California is illustrated by the following statistics:

Year	Number of vehicles (millions)	Vehicle miles travelled (millions)	Estimated NOx & VOCs emissions (million tons/year)
1940	2.8	24	Not available
1950	4.5	44.5	Not available
1960	8.0	71	Not available
1970	12	110	1.6
1980	17	155	1.6
1990	23	242	1.4
1995	26	271	1.1

Table 1.2: Vehicle emissions in California, 1940-95

The fall in emissions between 1970 and 1995, when vehicle miles travelled more than doubled, was due to increasingly strict emission controls.

In 1952, Haagen-Smit in Los Angeles had shown that tropospheric (ground-level) ozone was formed from oxides of nitrogen in the presence of sunlight when hydrocarbons were also present. By the mid-1980s, it had become clear that this was a continental problem by no means confined to Los Angeles, and also that control of this type of air pollution was going to present major difficulties [5], not only because noone emitted ozone directly but also because the reductions that had been obtained in vehicle emissions were beginning to reach their limit of feasibility.

The period between 1960 and the present was also distinguished by the development of significant studies of the acute effects of air pollutants on volunteer human subjects. This research showed that asthmatic subjects were much more sensitive to SO_2 than others; that ozone in very low concentrations (lower than those encountered in many regions) caused a progressive fall in lung function in normal subjects, and that this was attended by the induction of inflammation in the lung; and that exposure to one pollutant often enhanced the response to another. All of this research had a major effect on the standards being set for the protection of public health, and provided a strong underpinning to air pollution control efforts.

By 1985, following a few pioneering studies in Britain 20 years earlier, the study of the epidemiology of air pollution had begun to reinforce the laboratory data. Indices of adverse effects on the population other than mortality began to be investigated, and computers made the analysis of large banks of data such as hospital admission, a relatively easy matter. A surprising development was that levels of pollution by small particles (illustrated in Plate 2 of the first edition of this book, and in Figure 3.2 in this edition) in the urban environment were found to be associated, on a daily basis, with mortality rates and also with evidence of effects on a variety of morbidity indicators.

The air pollution problems in 1972 were primarily associated with smoke emissions and SO_2 from stationary sources; today the issues concern particles and tropospheric ozone formation, both of which are primarily the consequence of vehicle emissions. The present situation is that health concerns seem likely to have an impact on future transportation planning, and that urban planners (and the public) are beginning to recognize that "more of the same," in terms of more or larger freeways and more vehicles, is not a viable proposition. Another recent development has been a serious attempt to estimate the costs, in health terms, of present levels of air pollution. These will be used as a guide to policy, no doubt; but their calculation presents serious difficulties. These issues are discussed in the relevant chapters below.

Reviewing the problem of air pollution and its control as it has evolved from 1956 to the present, it is possible to make some generalizations, as follows:

1. It is much easier to control single, the large point sources of air pollution that have been the focus of regulatory control for most of the past 45 years than multiple, dispersed sources such as motor vehicles or community space heating. In this situation, air quality management requires a more sophisticated information base to inform public debate and policy development.

2. Public opinion, access to information, and free publication are essential components of the politics of air pollution control. It is often difficult for the public to learn what the important questions are. Even in free societies, governments may be expected to prepare reports that may conceal rather than illuminate important contemporary problems — to protect their vested interest in maintaining control of the public agenda.

3.   Excess mortality in specific episodes is an easily documented outcome of air pollution, and its political impact is considerable; less dramatic but important effects on morbidity and disease are harder to understand and easier for the politicians to disregard. The finding of increased morbidity, as indicated by such outcomes as hospital admissions, reinforces the validity of mortality data.

4.   In a free society, false economic estimates, unrealistic prophecies of the economic impact of control measures, and blaming air pollution on periodic meteorological events (summer heat in the case of ozone, and temperature inversions in winter) are all to be expected. There is always a danger that the agenda of air pollution control will be pre-empted by narrow interests, and that the objective of public health protection will be tacitly abandoned.

5.   There are increasing air pollution problems in developing countries, mostly related to the growth of vehicle traffic but also derived from industrialization without pollution controls. The traditional burning of biomass or fossil fuels without adequate ventilation leads to very high levels of particulate pollution inside a dwelling (a problem as old as man). Relevant data are given in Table 10.1 (see Chapter 10). This is an important factor in the high mortality and morbidity from respiratory disease in children in such locations.

6.   The past few years have provided examples of the "universality" of the air we breathe. The radioactive dust from Chernobyl affected reindeer in Finland and sheep in Wales; and PCBs (principally from Eastern and Northern Europe) have gotten into the natural food chain of people living and fishing in the Canadian Arctic. If we had not realized it before, it has now become abundantly clear that the earth's atmosphere is universally shared, and therefore the importance of "clean air" has become everyone's responsibility.

These considerations have led the present authors to put together a volume designed to be of use to anyone involved in air pollution concerns.

REFERENCES

[1] BATES, D.V., Environmental Health Risks & Public Policy, University of Washington Press, Seattle & London. 1994. Pp 117.

[2] BRIMBLECOMBE, P., The Big Smoke: A History of Air Pollution in London since Medieval Times, Methuen, London & New York. 1987. Pp 185.

[3] SEIBERLING, G., Monet in London, High Museum of Art; University of Washington Press, Seattle & London. 1988. Pp 103.

[4] FREUND, P. & MARTIN, G., The Ecology of the Automobile, Black Rose Books, Montreal, New York, & London. 1993. Pp 213.

Chapter 2
Sources, Emissions, Concentrations, Exposures, and Doses

Michael Brauer

INTRODUCTION

In this chapter, the major outdoor air pollutants and their sources are described. In order to understand the complex relationships between multiple air pollution sources and exposure of human beings, we first describe the major features involved in air pollution measurements and modelling, and outline the pathway from source to receptor — the human respiratory system or natural ecosystems.

Emission of pollutants into the air is the release of a pollutant from a particular source or category of sources. This quantity is often expressed in units of mass of pollutant per amount of fuel burned or energy produced (in the case of power plants), or mass of pollutant per distance travelled (in the case of motor vehicles). Emissions data are used as inputs to air quality models that can evaluate the impact of control and management strategies on air quality. Emissions data are also used in the regulation of specific sources of air pollution such as industrial releases, and motor vehicle emissions standards. In fact, nearly all regulation of air pollutants is based upon the amount of pollution released into the environment; regulations based on the coupling of emissions information to the amount of contact between people and these pollutants are much less common. Emissions data are frequently available in public databases such as the Toxic Release Inventory (http://www.epa.gov/t) — a more toxic compound and a major precursor of photochemical smog. NO2 concentrations in urban areas rarely exceed air qualit data are important for air quality modelling and may be useful in ranking different pollutant sources, they cannot be used to directly assess health and other environmental impacts, because they do not incorporate atmospheric dispersion and transformation of pollutants.

The **concentration** of air pollutants describes the amount of pollutant actually present in the air at a given location. This is the measurement most frequently reported by air quality management agencies and is the basis of air quality standards and air quality indices throughout the world. Ambient air quality concentrations are also the most common measurement used in epidemiological studies of the health effects of ambient air quality. Factors affecting the concentration of pollutants include the proximity to their sources, meteorological conditions (for example, wind speed, wind direction, and temperature), and atmospheric chemistry (see Chapter 3).

Exposure refers to the intersection of individuals with these pollutant concentrations and therefore incorporates both concentration and time terms (i.e., how much time the person spends in a setting with the specified concentrations). In order to understand the potential health risks associated with air pollution, one must first understand the variables affecting exposure to air contaminants. While much emphasis is placed on the regulation, control, and health effects associated with outdoor sources of air pollution, it must be recognized that the majority of exposure to air pollution occurs indoors (Chapter 10). This is due to the simple fact that individuals, particularly those in developed countries or in urban areas, spend the vast majority of their time indoors. Therefore, while the distinction between indoor and outdoor sources is important from a regulatory perspective (outdoor sources are typically subject to regulations while most indoor sources are not), from a health impact perspective both must be considered. Evaluation of the indoor environment and the various sources of air pollutants, including those from outdoors, that affect indoor air quality is an essential component in the evaluation of health effects associated with air pollution.

Exposure may be affected by human activities such as the amount of time that an individual spends in particular "microenvironments" and by the fate of the pollutant in these microenvironments. Since human activities are different for different people, demographic factors are major determinants of exposure.

Dose refers to the amount of air that is actually inhaled — in some cases it may also mean a delivered dose — the amount of pollutant that reaches a specific tissue where it may cause damage. Dose is affected primarily by inhalation rate as well as the chemical and physical characteristics of the pollutant in question. Dose is the ultimate quantity linked to adverse health outcomes.

To describe the relationship between emissions, concentrations, exposures, and doses, the concept of **exposure effectiveness** is useful [1]. Exposure effectiveness describes the dose received by an individual or a population as a fraction of the amount that is emitted. For example, essentially all of the smoke emitted from a cigarette is inhaled by a smoker. A "passive" smoker inhales a lower fraction. Individuals living near traffic sources inhale a greater fraction of traffic emissions than do those who live at some distance from traffic sources. Exposure effectiveness therefore provides a framework by which different pollutant sources may be compared on the basis of their ability to result in an inhaled dose. Use of exposure effectiveness terms may help to identify particularly useful management strategies. As an example, indoor emissions or those that occur inside moving vehicles have much greater exposure effectiveness than do releases of contaminants outdoors from a variety of sources [2]. In reality, however, nearly all air quality management is conducted on the basis of emission reductions, often with some assessment of the impact on ambient concentrations but with little emphasis on exposures.

SOURCES OF AIR POLLUTANTS

In addition to natural sources of air pollution such as volcanic eruptions, dust storms, and naturally occurring vegetation emissions and fires, major human-generated sources of outdoor air pollution are often classified as either stationary (comprising both point sources and distributed area sources) or mobile sources. Inventories of emissions are often broken out into point, area, and mobile source categories. Major stationary sources include rural sources such as agricultural production, agricultural burning, mining, and quarrying; industrial sources such as manufacturing and power generation; and community sources such as residential home heating and municipal waste incinerators. In many urban areas, mobile sources are the single largest contributors to air pollution emissions. These include any form of combustion-engine vehicles such as gasoline-and diesel-powered cars, trucks, motorcycles, and buses, as well as aircraft and marine vessels.

In this chapter, the discussion is limited to primary emission sources, that is, those sources that emit air pollutants directly to the atmosphere. But secondary pollutant sources are major contributors to the degradation of air quality. Secondary pollutant sources emit precursor compounds that react within the atmosphere after emission to produce new chemical products, some of which are harmful. These secondary pollutants are discussed in more detail in Chapter 3. It is important to note that while the regulation of primary pollutant emissions is straightforward — the emissions may be measured and compared with emission standards — the regulation of secondary pollutants and the ultimate management of air quality is more complicated. This is due to the difficulties inherent in understanding the complex atmospheric reactions that convert primary emissions into secondary pollutants and in evaluating the influences of meteorology, topography and other factors that affect the atmospheric transformations and dispersion of pollutants.

Important sources of indoor air pollution include infiltration of polluted outdoor air; combustion products from unvented indoor combustion devices (stoves for heating and cooking; consumer products such as perfumes, hairsprays and cleaning products; and emissions from building materials such as paints, furniture and carpets). In addition, indoor air may be contaminated with elevated levels of biological pollutants such as dust mites, pet allergens and fungal spores that propagate on moist or water-damaged surfaces. These are discussed in more detail in Chapter 10.

EMISSIONS

General

Emissions inventories provide some estimates of the relative importance of different major emissions sources in a particular location or region. For example, Figure 2.1 depicts primary emissions of carbon monoxide (CO) in the Greater Vancouver area of British Columbia, Most major urban areas have assembled similar emissions inventories.

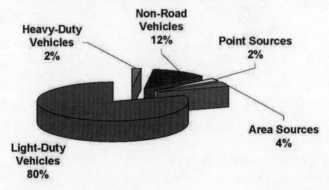

Figure 2.1: Primary carbon monoxide (CO) emissions for the Lower Fraser Valley Airshed, British Columbia, Canada. *Source*: 1999 Emission Inventory Update for the Lower Fraser Valley Airshed. Greater Vancouver Regional District Air Quality Department / Fraser Valley Regional District. 2000.

The figure depicts a typical breakdown of emissions categories. The light-duty vehicle category includes passenger cars, light-duty trucks, and motorcycles. Heavy-duty vehicles are buses and trucks, while the non-road category includes aircraft, marine vessels, railroads, and agricultural and construction equipment. Often the light-duty, heavy-duty, and non-road categories are combined into a mobile source category. Point sources are specific large emissions sources such as industrial facilities and power plants. Area sources include smaller, broadly distributed industrial, agricultural, and residential sources that do not require a specific emission permit. For example, this category includes agricultural sources, natural ("biogenic") sources, small industries, space heating, gas stations, and restaurants.

As can be seen from Table 2.1, mobile sources account for the majority (94%) of overall CO emissions for this airshed. While this value may differ between areas depending upon the particular mixture of emissions sources, population, climate, and geography, it illustrates the primary importance of mobile sources as local contributors to air quality degradation in most North American cities. Within Canada on a national basis, the estimated contribution of gasoline - and diesel - powered vehicles is as shown in Table 2.1 below [3].

Pollutant	Percentage of total emissions in Canada
Carbon monoxide	60
Nitrogen oxides	35
Volatile organics	25
Benzene	50
Carbon dioxide	20
Particulates[1]	5-60

Table 2.1: Estimated contribution of motor vehicles to national emissions of selected pollutants.

It is important to note at this point, however, that regional and even urban air quality is a combination of such local emissions and the contribution of air pollutants that are transported over large distances from distant sources. The impacts of this long-range transported air pollution may be substantial in many locations. For example, a significant fraction of the air pollution throughout the US northeast and southern Ontario, Canada, originates from emissions in the Midwestern US [4]. It has recently been discovered that the Pacific Northwest is even subject to air pollutants that are transported across the Pacific Ocean from sources in Asia [5].

Motor Vehicle Emissions

In recognition of the important impact of motor vehicle emissions[1] on urban air quality, regulatory agencies devote special attention to the mobile source category in the development of air quality management programs. At a national level there are regulations governing the emission of CO, nitrogen oxides (NOx), hydrocarbons, and particulate matter from vehicle tailpipes. Automobile manufacturers must provide test data to certify that new vehicles comply with emission standards. These standards are given in units of grams of pollutant per distance travelled for a vehicle over the expected duration of use. These standards are frequently updated and strengthened as new technology to reduce emissions becomes available.

Tier 1 standards in the US and Canada have been in use since the 1994 model year. Tier 2 standards have been introduced and will be phased in for all new vehicles in the US and Canada between 2004 and 2009. These Tier 2 standards will require all passenger vehicles, including sport utility vehicles (SUVs), pickup trucks, and vans to meet the same range of emissions standards as cars. The Tier 2 standards comprise a series of "bins" or classes of emission levels that will be averaged over a manufacturer's product lines to meet a target average emission level in new vehicle sales. An optional US federal program and a mandatory state of California program has introduced new categories of allowable vehicle emissions, including (in order of stringency) Low Emission Vehicles (LEV), Ultra Low Emission Vehicles (ULEV), Super Ultra Low Emission Vehicles (SULEV), and Zero Emission Vehicles (ZEV). Numbers of vehicles in each class will be phased into use either through voluntary or mandatory programs as a mechanism to improve overall air quality. Currently, vehicles of all types are available for sale in California and several other locations (http://www.arb.ca.gov/msprog/ccbg/ccbg.htm). For an example of the

---

[1]The contribution of motor vehicles to fine particle emissions and to fine particle concentrations is difficult to quantify as particle emissions result from direct emissions within vehicle exhaust as well as from secondary formation of particles in the atmosphere resulting from motor vehicle emissions of sulphur dioxide, nitrogen oxides and volatile organics. Vehicles also emit particles from brake and tire wear and from resuspension of dust that has settled on roadways ('road dust'). The latter two categories of emissions will dominate future particulate emissions associated with motor vehicles, since direct tailpipe emissions are being reduced dramatically.

application of vehicle manufacturing data for consumers, the US Environmental Protection Agency (EPA) publishes a *Vehicle Emissions Guide* (http://www.epa.gov/autoemissions/) which ranks new vehicles in different classes on the basis of their emissions. Natural Resources Canada (NRCan) provides similar information athttp://autosmart.nrcan.gc.ca/online_e.htm.

Because of the evidence that emissions from diesel vehicles may have distinct health effects (see Chapter 4), vehicle emissions have been the object of special studies [6] and of special regulatory efforts [5a]. Additional regulations govern the quality of fuel used by motor vehicles. An important consideration in recent years has been the sulphur content of gasoline and diesel fuel. The introduction of "low sulphur" fuel (<0.05%) into the heavy-duty vehicle fleet allows for newer catalytic converters to be used to reduce emissions of CO and NOx and also has the additional benefits of reducing emissions of fine particulates and sulphur dioxide from these vehicles by up to 90% [3]. Both the US and Canada plan to require gasoline and diesel fuel to have reduced sulphur content to 15-30 parts per million (ppm) by 2005-06. Engine manufacturers have argued in favour of more stringent fuel quality standards to enable the new engines to meet their emission standards.

While emissions standards for new vehicles are one measure to reduce the impact of motor vehicle emissions, another component of many air quality management programs is the inspection and maintenance (I&M) program. I&M programs involve periodic testing of in-use vehicles and are a way to evaluate the real-world performance of vehicles that are currently in use, incorporating engine modifications, vehicle age, engine failures, and variable maintenance programs of drivers. These programs typically require vehicles to be tested regularly for emissions of major primary air pollutants. Those vehicles with emissions that exceed the specific I&M criteria for their airshed are required to invest in engine repairs to reduce the emissions and then be retested for compliance. At present, I&M programs are in effect in 27 US states and in two Canadian provinces.

The combined efforts of increasingly stringent vehicle emission standards and inspection and maintenance programs have had positive results in North American urban areas [3]. Unfortunately, these decreases in the emissions per vehicle kilometre (or mile) travelled have been offset by large increases in the total numbers of kilometres (or miles) driven and by the introduction of larger, less fuel-efficient vehicles, which now comprise about 50% of new vehicle sales in North America. Therefore, without continued emphasis on improved motor vehicle emissions, total emissions from the North American vehicle fleet are expected to reach a minimum about 2010 and then increase slowly to 2020 [3]. Very recent emission modelling indicates that emissions from the on-road fleet (light - and heavy-duty) will continue to decrease toward 2020 as the new engine and fuel technologies penetrate the on-road fleet. By 2020, it appears that the regulatory requirements will have reduced on-road vehicle emissions from their current dominant position to perhaps 25% of emissions in some airsheds (perhaps 10%, if CO is excluded). These percentages vary widely from region to region, but the implications for future air quality management and exposure reduction strategies are significant.

EXPOSURE

Research conducted over the past 30 years has led to the conclusion that individuals within a population differ considerably in their exposure to air pollutants [6a, 13]. This is relevant because nearly all routine monitoring and regulation of air pollution are based upon measurements that are conducted at fixed locations. Assessment of exposure to air pollution is concerned with individual and population patterns of contact between humans and air pollutants, and with understanding the sources of variation in exposure between individuals. In some cases, outdoor monitoring at a single location within an urban area may be a good indicator of the exposure of the entire population, whereas in other instances there may be very little relationship between outdoor concentrations and the levels that individuals are actually exposed to. Information on exposure is therefore important in understanding the applicability of monitoring network data to the assessment of health risk and to the identification of population subgroups who may be at increased risk. Information on additional sources of air pollution exposure, such as exposures due to indoor sources, is also important in this context. Personal monitoring studies, in which individuals are equipped with small air-monitoring devices, have revealed some clear patterns regarding how individuals come into contact with air pollutants that are useful in evaluating the relative importance of outdoor air pollutants.

Time-activity surveys have indicated that, on average, individuals in North America spend approximately 87% of their time indoors, most of this in residential environments. Approximately 7% of time is spent in transit and only 6% outdoors [7]. Studies of specific population groups, for example, the elderly or those with pre-existing disease, have confirmed the general patterns of time-activity, but have also revealed differences according to age and location [8, 9, 10]. This predominance of time spent in indoor environments had led to increased attention towards exposures that occur indoors.

When indoors, individuals are exposed to outdoor air pollutants that penetrate inside, as well as air pollutants produced from indoor sources. Penetration of outdoor pollutants indoors is a function of the air exchange rate — the rate at which outdoor air replaces indoor air. Air exchange is determined by building construction, open windows, outdoor temperatures and the presence of air-handling equipment (ventilation systems, air conditioners, etc.) among other factors. Major factors which determine the impact of indoor sources are the specific sources present, the level of emissions from those sources, the volume of the indoor space, and the air exchange rate.

For particles, it is estimated that 70% of outdoor fine particles penetrate indoors in the absence of air conditioning [11]. If particles as small as 1 micron are considered (and vehicle particulate emissions and other combustion particles are all of such a size), the correlation between indoor and outdoor particle concentrations is very high. Air conditioning may limit this penetration to as low as 30%, although there is substantial variability between building types. Major indoor particle sources include smoking, cooking, vacuuming, and cleaning activities as well as the burning of candles, incense, and firewood. For nitrogen dioxide, approximately 50-70% infiltrates indoors from outdoors. Major indoor sources are unvented gas combustion appliances, especially gas stoves. Ozone has relatively few major indoor sources in homes; photocopy machines and laser printers generate ozone, but high levels are not produced unless usage is very high and ventilation is very poor. Indoor levels of ozone are approximately 70% of outdoor levels in non-air-conditioned homes. In homes with air conditioning this value decreases to 10-30%. Personal monitoring studies have shown that the level of ozone exposure is directly related to the amount of time spent outdoors [12].

For volatile organic compounds (VOCs), indoor sources are far more important contributors to exposure than outdoor sources. In a series of groundbreaking studies conducted in the 1970s and 1980s, the US EPA demonstrated that indoor levels were higher than outdoor levels, even in those communities with the highest outdoor concentrations [11]. Surprisingly, the major sources of exposure were ordinary consumer products and not the chemical emissions of hazardous waste facilities that had previously been the subjects of extensive regulations and attention. These investigations uncovered smoking, dry-cleaned clothes, air fresheners, cleaning agents, deodorizers, the pumping of gas, and the use of chlorinated water as major contributors to volatile organic compound personal exposures. These studies have led to estimates of source contributions to that population exposure to benzene, a known human carcinogen. According to these estimates, 45% of the population exposure results from smoking, 36% from inhaling gasoline (while refuelling) and other common products (glues, for example), and 16% from other household sources such as paints, while only 3% was due to industrial pollution [13]. This is in contrast to regulatory attention placed on emissions from motor vehicles and industrial sources. Accordingly, to most effectively reduce exposure, actions directed towards smoking and/or the presence of benzene in household products ought to be considered instead of the current regulatory emphasis principally on gasoline composition and industrial releases.

Both carbon monoxide and sulphur dioxide penetrate indoors with high efficiency. Indoor sources of sulphur dioxide are uncommon, while unvented combustion, attached garages, poorly ventilated furnaces and fireplaces, and smoking are important indoor sources of carbon monoxide exposure. For such indoor pollution sources, increased ventilation is an effective means of reducing exposure. For carbon monoxide, fine particles, and nitrogen dioxide, proximity to major roads appears to lead to higher levels of exposure.

DOSE

As the primary route of exposure for most air pollutants is via inhalation, the factors that affect the deposition of pollutants within the respiratory system are important.

Routes of exposure other than inhalation may also be important for compounds emitted into the air; for example, airborne lead is deposited on soil and can then be ingested via contaminated food or via soil ingestion by infants or toddlers. Pesticides that are emitted into the air may be inhaled, ingested in contaminated food or soil, or absorbed through skin which comes into contact with contaminated materials. Some compounds, such as mercury emitted from coal burning and dioxins from municipal waste incineration, may be deposited in fresh water and then ingested.

In addition to understanding the major routes of exposure for individual pollutants, for those pollutants where the primary route of exposure is via inhalation, an understanding of pollutant respiratory deposition is important. Assessment of pollutant respiratory deposition patterns can help in the evaluation of the relative impacts of different pollutants. For example, the deposition of pollutants in different regions of the respiratory system leads to different effects — some regions are more sensitive than others. Among the factors that affect the location of pollutant deposition in the respiratory system are the breathing rate and the amount of air inhaled per breath. An average adult breathes approximately 13,000 L/day (15 breaths/min; 500-600 mL/breath); inhalation rates increase during exercise and decrease during sleep. Whether air is inhaled through the nose or mouth also affects the respiratory deposition, since the nasal cavity is an effective scrubber of many gases and particles. The majority of people breathe though their nose except when exercising; however, approximately 20% of the population are habitual mouth breathers and therefore may be more susceptible to the effects of air pollutants, since the filtering effect of the nasal passages is bypassed. In addition to the concentration of the pollutant and the duration of exposure, the physical and chemical characteristics of pollutants also affect their ability to lead to adverse effects.

For gases, solubility affects the location of deposition and therefore their mechanism of action and toxicity. The Henry's Law constant (H) from thermodynamics expresses the ratio of the concentration of the gas in the gas phase to the concentration in the liquid phase. The smaller the value of H the more soluble is the gas in the liquid phase. The less water-soluble the gas, the further down the respiratory tract will be the major site of absorption or toxic effect. Some values of Henry's Law constant are given in Table 2.2. A limited number of gases at very high concentrations actually cause suffocation (hypoxemia) by reducing the amount of oxygen that can be inhaled. Examples are methane, nitrogen, and carbon dioxide in levels that may be encountered in confined spaces as part of occupational exposure. Other gases are called toxic asphyxiants as they cause suffocation by direct toxic mechanisms. For example, carbon monoxide, which is an insoluble gas with low reactivity, is hazardous due to its specific ability to bind to hemoglobin in the blood and reduce the ability of hemoglobin to deliver oxygen to tissues. Fat-soluble gases such as petroleum hydrocarbons are absorbed into the blood through the alveolar membrane and therefore may lead to systemic effects such as peripheral neuropathy.

Gas	Henry's Law constant	Predominant site of lung deposition
Nitrogen dioxide	8.8	Alveoli and bronchioles
Ozone	6.4	Alveoli and bronchioles
Formaldehyde	0.56	Upper airway
Sulphur dioxide	0.05	Upper airway
Ammonia	0.0011	Nose

Table 2.2: Henry's Law constant for five pollutants.

Soluble irritant gases exert their effects in the upper respiratory tract and eyes, and may lead to sinus congestion, headache, nasal irritation, and throat irritation (dry cough, hoarseness). Examples of these are ammonia, nitric acid, and hydrochloric acid. Moderately soluble and highly or weakly soluble irritant gases in high concentrations exert effects in the mid respiratory tract (the tracheobronchial region) and may lead to chest tightness and difficulty in breathing. Examples of these gases are sulphur dioxide and chlorine. Low-solubility gases exert effects in the deep lung (the alveolar region) and may lead to severe conditions such as pulmonary edema and pneumonitis. An example of such a gas is nitrogen dioxide, which may be present in high concentrations in agricultural silos and in locations where combustion occurs with poor ventilation (tunnels, mines, ice skating arenas, gas cooking). Ozone is a weakly soluble but highly reactive, gas that reacts throughout the respiratory system. Other factors that affect pollutant toxicity are the physical geometry of the airways and the ability of the body's defence mechanisms to clear and/or detoxify the pollutant once it isdeposited.

Particle deposition is a function of airway geometry, particle size, and breathing pattern (particles "stick" when they contact tissue). Of these, particle size is the best understood. Very large particles may not travel far from a source to reach human receptors at all or are removed in the nose. Smaller particles, often termed "inhalable particles," are removed in the throat and upper airways, while even smaller particles, the "respirable" fraction, may be deposited in the deep lung. Due to the important impacts of particle size in evaluating health risk, most air pollution standards for particles specify a range of applicable particle sizes in addition to a concentration. Recent attention has also been focused on the smallest particles, the ultrafine particles. Particle size is described in more detail in the section "Particulate Matter (PM)."

Actual dosimetry of the airways can be calculated based on physical principles and knowledge of the diameters of the human airways as the branching occurs from the trachea downwards. Almost all the particles between 10 and 100 microns in size will be deposited in the nose or upper airway; deposition in the lower respiratory tract starts to increase with particles less than 0.25 microns in size and rises to a rises to a maximum at a size of about 0.02 microns, and thereafter declines. A recent British report [14] contains a well-written account of particle dosimetry.

The lung has the ability to clear particles deposited in it through a variety of mechanisms; the actual particle load at any one time will be determined by the rate of deposition and the rate of clearance. A recent study of autopsy lungs in residents of Vancouver not occupationally exposed to dusts showed that there were $PM_{2.5}$ particles in the lung connective tissue [15]; the composition of these was mostly metals. Ultrafine particles were noted to be very infrequent. A similar analysis of autopsy lungs from Mexico City, a location with much higher levels of air pollution, found significantly higher concentrations of particles in lung tissue, including large quantities of ultrafine particles [15a].

MAJOR AMBIENT AIR POLLUTANTS

One of the reasons why air pollution science has become more complex is the recognition that today's air pollution is the result of multiple sources of pollutants, and the understanding that the pollutants emitted from these sources may interact to form new compounds after they have been emitted. "Natural" sources, such as windblown dust from dry soil or resuspended dust from road surfaces, may be intermixed with combustion particles, which are believed to be much more harmful.

In the sections that follow, examples have been selected to illustrate the common sources of important emissions.

Particulate Matter (PM)

Airborne particles are a complex mixture of solid particles and liquid droplets suspended in the air ("aerosol"). Particles in outdoor air have numerous sources with varying chemical and physical composition. Typically particles are classified according to their size (Figure 2.2); particle size affects deposition in the respiratory tract and consequently the potential to cause health effects.

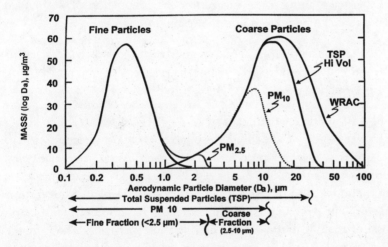

Figure 2.2: Idealized fine and course mode particle mass. The dotted lines represent the mass captured by different monitors; for example, PM_{10} mass would be proportional to the portion of the coarse mode under the curve (coarse fraction) and all of the fine fraction. "Ultrafine" particles are defined as all particles less than 0.1 micron in size — their mass is very small although their numbers and surface area are large. Data from the US EPA Criteria Document for Particulate Pollution.

Several measurements can be made that reflect different aspects of particulate matter. The expression of particulate emissions in terms of "tonnage" is no longer considered useful; substantial reductions in tonnage may occur, but the actual concentrations of the smaller particles ($PM_{2.5}$) might have increased. For this reason, emission licences for industrial plants that specify only the permitted tonnage of particulate emissions are not protective. The following terms are in current use:

PM_{10}: The concentration, by mass, of particles less than 10 microns in size (effective aerodynamic diameter), expressed as micrograms per cubic metre ($\mu g/m^3$); often called the "inhalable" fraction of airborne particles. The fraction of particles between 2.5 and 10 microns is often called the "coarse" fraction. "Coarse" particles include mainly those originating from soil material such as resuspended road dust and windblown dust, and from materials handling, crushing, and grinding operations. PM_{10} includes fine (and ultrafine) particles and a major portion of the suspended coarse particles, and is meant to reflect the proportion of suspended particles that can be inhaled into the respiratory tract.

$PM_{2.5}$: The concentration, by mass, of particles less than 2.5 microns in size (effective aerodynamic diameter), expressed as $\mu g/m^3$. Thus, $PM_{2.5}$ is a fraction of PM_{10}.

The $PM_{2.5}$ fraction encompasses all of the particles capable of entering the alveolar region of the lung ("respirable" or "fine" fraction). $PM_{2.5}$ includes mainly particles produced in fuel combustion (motor vehicles, power plants, industry, home heating), fireplaces, and wood stoves, and via atmospheric reaction of gases (sulphur dioxide, nitrogen oxides, some volatile organic compounds). Recent attention has also been focused on a subset of the fine particle class, the "ultrafine" particles. These are the smallest particles (smaller than 0.1 micron) and are formed directly in combustion exhaust. Over time they aggregate and coagulate to form fine particles. When particles are counted by number, the ultrafine category accounts for the vast majority of all ambient particles, although their contribution to particle mass (the usual quantity for measurement) is rather small. Particles less than 2.5 microns in size are thought to be the greatest contributors to health risk (see Chapter 4), due to their size and consequent deposition in the respiratory tract, as well as to their common origin in combustion processes. Figure 2.3 shows the deposition characteristics of the human respiratory system.

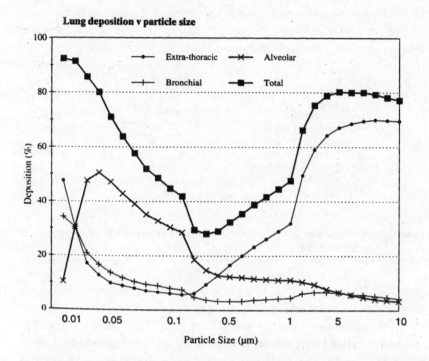

Figure 2.3: Deposition of particles in the human lung. Note that alveolar deposition reaches a maximum (of about 50%) at a particle size of about 0.05 micron in size — their mass is very small although their numbers and surface area are large. Data from the US EPA Criteria Document for Particulate Pollution.

Total suspended particulates (TSP) or total particulate matter (TPM): This is the gravimetrically determined mass loading of suspended airborne particles, measured with a high-volume air sampler. This fraction includes both PM_{10} and $PM_{2.5}$ as well as even larger particles (up to about 40 microns) which are likely not inhalable and therefore of less relevance for health impacts. For this reason TSP is no longer used as the sole measure of particulate matter in most locations.

Black smoke: This measures non-reflective (dark) particles associated with a smoke stain method of measurement.

Coefficient of haze: Black staining of a filter paper through which air is drawn usually for a 24-hour period.

Emission inventories provide some estimates of the relative importance of the emission sources. Table 2.3 shows the estimated emission sources for PM_{10} in Great Britain in 1993 [19].

Source	Percent of total
Diesel vehicles	19
Power stations	15
Domestic heating	14
Mining and quarrying	11
Miscellaneous industrial processes	11
Iron and steel fabrication	8
Other industrial combustion	7
Petrol vehicles	5
Refineries	3

Table 2.3: Estimated emission sources of PM_{10} (particles less than 10 microns in size) in Great Britain in 1993.

Although trends in air pollutant concentrations vary by location, several sources can be examined to evaluate general patterns. Among these, the US EPA publishes an annual trends document that describes trends in emissions and ambient air concentrations for the criteria air pollutants as well as several air toxics. These reports are available at <http://www.epa.gov/airtrends/>. Note that these trends are based on available monitoring data that is biased by the location of monitors primarily in urban areas. The number of monitors within an urban area is not standardized within the US and Canada or between countries. The EPA's trends database now includes the results of the IMPROVE network of fine particle monitoring in remote areas (national parks and similar locations), which includes about 50 sites. Figure 2.4 shows the distribution of $PM_{2.5}$ 98th percentile concentrations across the US for 1999.

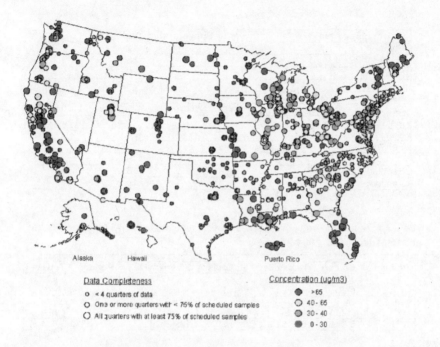

Figure 2.4: 24-hour average PM$_{2.5}$ concentrations in different regions of the US. This map is on the US EPA Web site: see reference [19].

Local air quality management districts often also conduct similar trend analyses. For example, in Vancouver, trends have recently been analyzed for the 1987-96 period and are updated in an annual air quality monitoring network summary. These trends generally follow those described in the US EPA report for the entire US, although there are some local differences [17]. Based on the EPA trends reports, nationwide inhalable particulate concentrations decreased by 18% between 1990 and 1999. Insufficient data were available to estimate trends for fine (respirable) particles. Where data are available, the decreasing trend in PM$_{10}$ ambient concentration appears to have levelled off in most regions of both the US and Canada in recent years.

Table 2.4 shows average concentrations for selected US and Canadian cities based on data from 1994-98. These cities are located in the west and Midwest; urban concentrations of some pollutants, especially particles, are higher in many eastern North American cities.

Metropolitan area	Concentration ($\mu g/m^3$)
Phoenix	41.2
Los Angeles	35.3
San Diego	30.5
Denver	26.2
Sacramento	23.8
San Jose	22.9
Minneapolis–St. Paul	21.4
San Francisco–Oakland	21.0
San Antonio	20.3
Portland	19.1
Seattle	18.6
Vancouver	14.0

Table 2.4: Annual average of inhalable particulate matter (PM_{10}) for selected US and Canadian cities, 1994-98.

Pollutant	Boston	Knoxville	St. Louis	Steubenville	Portage	Topeka
$PM_{2.5}$	15.7 (9.2)	20.8 (9.6)	18.7 (10.5)	29.6 (21.9)	11.2 (7.8)	12.2 (7.4)
PM_{10}	24.5 (12.8)	32.0 (14.5)	30.6 (16.2)	45.6 (32.3)	17.8 (11.7)	26.7 (16.1)
SO_4	6.3 (4.7)	8.8 (5.6)	8.1 (6.0)	12.4 (9.6)	5.2 (4.7)	5.0 (4.3)

Table 2.5: Particulates and sulphates (in $\mu g/m^3$) in six US cities that formed the Harvard School of Public Health Six-Cities Study.

Table 2.5 shows average concentrations of particulate matter and sulphates in cities in the Harvard School of Public Health Six-Cities Study. The ratio of $PM_{2.5}/PM_{10}$ was about 65% in all centres except Topeka (a rural site), where it was 50%.

Cities in different parts of the world have very different patterns of particulate pollution. Those in dry and dusty regions will have a high proportion of crustal windborne dust as a constituent of PM_{10}. Delhi, the capital of India, measured hourly PM_{10} levels as high as 460 $\mu g/m^3$, and this may have a large component of blown dust. In other cities, such as Santiago, Chile, vehicles are the major particle source [16].

One of the major air pollution control success stories has been the reduction in particulate lead emissions from motor vehicles due to the elimination of leaded gasoline in North America. This reduction has led to a sharp reduction in the levels of lead in the blood of the population [20]. Similar reductions have also occurred elsewhere in the world, although airborne lead levels are still high in many developing countries where lead has not been removed from gasoline.

Ozone

Ozone is a gas that occurs naturally in the stratosphere, where it has the important function of filtering out UV radiation. At ground level it is the prime oxidant ingredient of smog in cities and many rural areas. Ground-level ozone is a secondary pollutant, meaning that it is formed as the product of atmospheric reactions of primary emissions; nitrogen oxides and volatile organic compounds in the presence of sunlight lead to its formation, which is accelerated by higher temperatures (warmer than about 25°C/77°F). As ozone requires atmospheric reactions in order to be formed, ozone levels are strongly dependent upon meteorology. The highest ozone levels are typically found during periods of high pressure, warm temperatures, and light winds. On a day-to-day basis, ozone concentrations follow a distinct daily pattern which follows that of available sunlight and the patterns of morning motor vehicle emissions (see Figure 2.5).

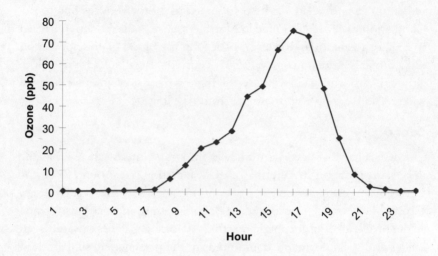

Figure 2.5: A typical example of the diurnal ozone concentration pattern as measured in Abbotsford, in the Fraser Valley of British Columbia. Data from August 3, 1993.

Ozone concentrations begin to rise in the late morning as rush hour emissions are transformed in the atmosphere. The levels typically peak in the late afternoon, when solar radiation is highest, and begin to decline after the evening rush hour and as the sun sets. The dependence of ozone on atmospheric conditions is also responsible for the regional characteristics of elevated ozone concentrations. As ozone precursors are transformed in the air, they are also dispersed with prevailing winds. It is often rural areas downwind of urban centres that experience the highest ozone concentrations. A typical example is shown for Vancouver in Figure 2.6. An even more extreme example is seen in national parks in the northeastern US, which often exceed the US National Ambient Air Quality Standards (NAAQS) a result of transported emissions from the Ohio Valley and southeastern states and the eastern seaboard.

O3 (8hr avg) - 1998 Summer

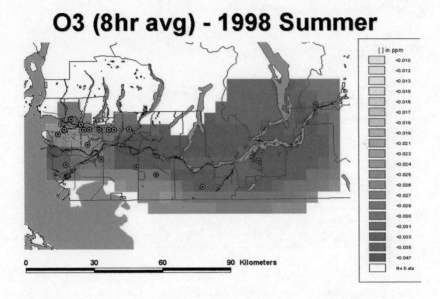

Figure 2.6: 8-hour average ozone concentrations in the summer of 1998 in the Vancouver, BC, airshed. The urban area is located closest to the coastline at the left of the figure, while the highest ozone concentrations are in the suburban-rural Fraser River Valley located to the right of the figure. The circles denote air quality monitoring stations.

The dependence of ozone levels on two main categories of precursors, volatile organic compounds (VOC) and nitrogen oxides (NOx), and upon meteorological conditions makes the management of ozone difficult. Regulatory efforts have been directed at VOC and NOx emission reductions, although these have been only marginally successful. The emphasis on NOx or VOC control needs to be carefully balanced and is different for different locations.

Although ozone concentrations vary greatly between years due to different meteorological conditions, there has been a general decrease in peak ozone levels in urban areas in North America over the past 20 years, although ozone levels still exceed health-based standards on occasion (Table 2.6). In contrast, ozone concentrations in US national parks have increased during the past 10 years. The average annual ozone concentration globally has been increasing slowly over recent years.

Metropolitan Area	Concentration (ppb)
Los Angeles	241
Sacramento	154
San Francisco–Oakland	149
San Diego	144
San Jose	142
Seattle	135
Phoenix	130
San Antonio	126
Portland	108
Denver	107
Vancouver	106
Minneapolis–St. Paul	N/A

Table 2.6: Ozone (O_3) concentrations in selected US and Canadian cities. These are the maximum of the second highest maximum reported concentrations taken over all sites within the metropolitan area over five years from 1994-98 [21a].

Air quality management policies and measures in ozone management are discussed in Chapter 9.

Volatile Organic Compounds

Volatile organic compounds are a varied group of compounds that are present in the atmosphere mainly as gases at typical temperatures. These compounds include a variety of hydrocarbons such as alkanes, alkenes, alkynes, aromatics (such as benzene and toluene), aldehydes, ketones, alcohols, esters, and some chlorinated compounds. The contributions of individual VOCs to ozone formation vary widely according to their photochemical reactivity, which further complicates management of their sources. The sources of VOCs are diverse, and include fossil fuel evaporation and combustion, solvent use, and industrial processes. Chemical manufacturing, petroleum production, and the use of industrial solvents represent important sources of emissions. Gasoline handling, such as refuelling and fuel transfer, is also responsible for significant emissions unless strict programs are implemented. This is one reason for the introduction of vapour recovery technology either within vehicles themselves or at locations where vehicles are refuelled.

Natural sources of VOCs are also significant in many areas. Vegetation and forests (particularly conifers) may emit large amounts of VOCs, especially when temperatures are high. Since VOCs are a major precursor to ozone, the importance of natural VOC sources complicates efforts to control ozone production.

Benzene is one VOC which has received much attention due to its carcinogencity. The main sources of benzene emissions are vehicle fuels, although in most cases exposure is dominated by indoor sources such as environmental tobacco smoke, stored fuels, and paint supplies, as described previously in this chapter. General population exposure in urban areas depends on the amount of benzene in the gasoline used in the area [21]. Other aromatic compounds, such as toluene (a common constituent of alkyd paints and other coatings), are more chemically reactive than benzene and thus contribute more significantly to ozone formation. Aromatics such as toluene also contribute more significantly as precursors to secondary organic aerosol formation than lower molecular weight VOCs, principally because of the effect of molecular weight on volatility of the secondary products. The heavier and less volatile the photochemical reaction products, the more likely they are to be found in condensed phase in or on airborne particles.

Sulphur Dioxide

Sulphur dioxide (SO_2) is an irritant gas and produces bronchoconstriction; as noted in Chapter 4, individuals with asthma are much more sensitive than others to these effects. SO_2 is released into the atmosphere primarily as a result of combustion of sulphur-containing fuels such as coal, oil and vehicle fuels, and in the heating of materials that contain it, such as occurs in the manufacture of some types of cement. The emission rate depends on, among other factors, the sulphur content of the fuel. In urban areas, particularly those with many diesel vehicles, vehicular sources (diesel cars, buses, and trucks) are also a significant source of SO_2. As SO_2 can be transported over long distances and converted to sulphate particles and potentially to acidic particles and acid rain, non-urban emissions are also important. These particles are important components of the ambient fine particle burden.

The major regional sources are large coal-fired power plants and non-ferrous metal smelters. Historically, SO_2 was implicated in several of the more significant historical air pollution episodes (the 1952 London fog, for example). Today, the highest concentrations are found in cities in China where coal is burned for residential heating and power generation, and around very large smelters, as at Mount Isa in Australia. SO_2 levels have decreased dramatically in most urban areas in North America, and cases where air quality standards exceeded are now rare.

In the US, actions taken under the 1990 Clean Air Act Amendments have led to substantial declines in SO_2 emissions. Related agreements between the US and Canada under the 1991 Canada-US Air Quality Agreement on control of acid rain precursors have led to similar reductions in Canada. Since 1991 there have been commitments to further reductions in acid rain precursors in both countries.

Carbon Monoxide

Carbon monoxide (CO) is produced by the incomplete combustion of fossil fuels, mainly from mobile sources. Concentrations in urban areas depend upon traffic density, topography, and weather conditions. As noted in Chapter 10, accidental indoor exposure is responsible for a significant number of deaths in many countries. Carbon monoxide levels in urban areas display a distinct daily pattern that follows that of traffic patterns (Figure 2.7).

In many ways, carbon monoxide has become one of the simpler air pollutants to categorize. Emissions from vehicles have been much reduced as a result of fuel injection technology and more efficient combustion and exhaust gas cleaning.

Despite a US 30% nationwide increase in vehicle miles travelled in the US, CO concentrations decreased by 36% between 1990 and 1999. This decrease was due to the improvements in vehicle emission standards, as described above.

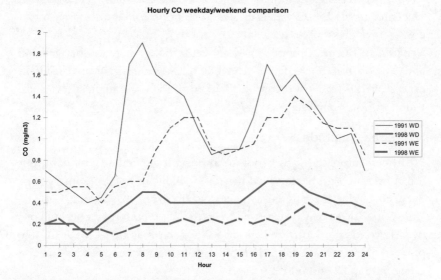

Figure 2.7: Carbon monoxide (CO) hourly profiles measured in Erfurt, Germany, in 1991 and in 1998 for weekends (WE) and weekdays (WD) separately. The significantly lower levels in 1998 relative to 1991 are due to German unification and subsequent modernization of the vehicle fleet. Note the concentration peaks during 1998 morning and evening weekday rush hours that are absent during weekends.

Nitrogen Oxides

Oxides of nitrogen (NOx) are produced by high-temperature combustion of fossil fuels for transport, heating, and power generation. They are formed by oxidation of nitrogen in the air and by oxidation of nitrogenous compounds in the fuels themselves. Initially, almost all of the NOx emission is in the form of nitric oxide (NO). NO is then oxidized in air to nitrogen dioxide (NO_2) — a more toxic compound and a major precursor of photochemical smog. NO_2 concentrations in urban areas rarely exceed air quality standard levels (except in Los Angeles), and are mainly of concern as indicators of ozone precursor concentrations and of vehicle exhaust. While NO_2 concentrations have generally decreased over the past 10 years, this decrease appears to be levelling off.

In most cities, daily ambient NOx levels are approximately 50 ppb (parts per billion) or lower, but severe inversion conditions can lead to a rapid rise in concentrations when traffic density is high. In London in December 1991, NOx values exceeded 400 ppb for eight hours on two consecutive days [22]. In a city of about 1 million people, such as Vancouver, BC, maximum hourly concentrations fluctuate between 40 and 60 ppb for most of the year, but on a few days, hourly levels in excess of 120 ppb are recorded [23]. In the US, the highest levels are found in Los Angeles.

Hydrogen Sulphide

Hydrogen sulphide (H_2S) is not an important general air pollutant, but it can become significant when there is a "blowout" of a "sour" gas or oil well. Under these circumstances, as occurred in Alberta, Canada, large populations may be exposed to levels of 1.0 ppm (parts per million) (well beyond the odour detection level, which may be as low as a few ppb) for days or weeks. Other potentially significant sources include Kraft pulp mills and oil refineries.

Air Toxics

Air toxics are loosely defined as compounds that are known or suspected causes of serious health effects other than respiratory disease, such as cancer, birth defects, immediate death, or other serious illnesses. In general, attention is directed towards compounds that are released to the air in large enough amounts to be acutely toxic and that reach many people. In this section we describe several example air toxics. The US Clean Air Act specifies compounds that are considered to be "hazardous air pollutants." A list of these in available at http://www.epa.gov/ttn/uatw/pollsour.html. Special attention is often directed towards persistent toxic compounds — those compounds that are toxic and known to persist in the environment for long periods of time, so that they are deposited in soil and water bodies, thereby entering the food chain and possibly also drinking water supplies.

Benzene exposure and the importance of indoor sources, especially environmental tobacco smoke, has been noted earlier. In terms of outdoor sources, benzene is considered important as it is a known human carcinogen. The major outdoor sources are motor vehicle emissions and, in some locations, industrial sources. Although trend data are not available for most air toxics due to very limited monitoring, benzene has been monitored for sufficient duration and in enough locations for trends to be apparent. Between 1993 and 1998 there was a 39% decrease in benzene levels in US urban areas (http://www.epa.gov/airtrends). This decrease has been attributed to the lower benzene content of fuels. A similar decrease in urban levels in Vancouver and other Canadian cities occurred between 1989 and 1993 [24].

Toluene is one of the more widespread hydrocarbons present in ambient air due to its predominant use in petrochemical products. The major sources of toluene emissions to outdoor air are motor vehicle exhaust and evaporative emissions of gasoline. As with benzene, indoor levels are much higher than those outdoors due to environmental tobacco smoke and the common presence of toluene in many consumer products. Toluene exposure has been associated with human central nervous system dysfunction.

1,3 Butadiene is used in the manufacture of synthetic rubber and is also emitted to outdoor air in vehicle exhaust. Elevated levels may also be found in the vicinity of petrochemical facilities. It is of concern as it is thought to be carcinogenic to humans.

Persistent Organic Pollutants (POPs) and Heavy Metals

A subclass of air toxics, these pollutants are toxic and known to persist for long periods in the environment. POPs are of great international importance as their environmental persistence facilitates their atmospheric transport over great distances. Recent reports have shown that these compounds may be transported from northern Europe, the southern US, and even South America to the Arctic. In many cases the routes of human (or animal) exposure may include air as well as ingestion or dermal exposure via contaminated food or soil. Many of these compounds tend to accumulate in foods, reaching higher concentrations higher up in the food chain.

Twelve high-priority compounds have been identified as part of a recent international treaty that aims to eventually eliminate the compounds from the environment. These 12 POPs include seven pesticides — aldrin, chlordane, dieldrin, endrin, heptachlor, mirex, and toxaphene — all of which have been slated for banning between approximately 2001 and 2005. An additional pesticide, DDT, is also listed in the treaty . The use of DDT in some locations has been argued to have a net positive public health benefit as it is effective in the control of malaria-carrying mosquitoes. The treaty specifies an ultimate goal of elimination of DDT, while in the interim ensuring that is used only for disease vector control in accordance with World Health Organization guidelines.

The remaining POPs are two industrial chemicals, polychlorinated biphenyls (PCBs) and hexachlorobenzene (also a pesticide) and two byproducts of combustion and industrial processes, dioxins and furans. For these compounds elimination is a long-term goal of the treaty. While the global POPs treaty is directed toward organic pollutants, heavy metals are also toxic and known to persist in the environment. The US-Canada Binational Toxics Strategy aims to eliminate persistent toxic compounds from the Great Lakes basin. As part of this effort, the strategy identified 12 types of compounds for highest-priority action. This list includes many of the compounds specified by the global POPs treaty:

Aldrin and **Dieldrin**, which were used primarily as pesticides, are no longer made in either Canada or the United States. Dieldrin is a probable human carcinogen, and may affect fertility and fetal development.

Benzo[a]pyrene (B[a]P) is a polycyclic aromatic hydrocarbon (PAH) which is formed during incomplete combustion and during the production of steel and coke. B[a]P is also formed when garbage is burned or when coal is liquefied or turned into gas. Wood burning is known as a major PAH source along with forest fires,[2] cigarette smoke, vehicle exhausts, agricultural burning, and hazardous waste sites. Cooking meat or other foods at high temperatures increases the amount of PAHs in the food. PAHs are of concern due to their carcinogenicity. They are generally found attached to fine particles in ambient air.

---

[2]See US-Canada Binational Toxics Strategy. Draft Report on Benzo[a]pyrene (B[a]P) Sources and Regulations (November 1999).
http://www.epa.gov/glnpo/bns/baphcb/stepbap.html.

Chlordane is a mixture of more than 50 chemicals, and has been used as a pesticide, primarily for termite control, since the late 1940's. Chlordane was banned in the US in 1978 for most uses, and specifically for termite control in 1988. Chlordane was discontinued for use in Canada in 1990. It is considered to be a hazard to human health because it accumulates in body fat. Most health effects in humans that may be linked to chlordane exposure are on the nervous system, the digestive system, and liver. Chlordane is measurable in the fat of most people [25]. While insufficient human evidence is available to indicate that chlordane is carcinogenic to humans (http://www.iarc.fr) , animal studies suggest that chlordane may well be a human carcinogen. It is persistent in the environment and a danger to wildlife. Chlordane exposure is therefore quite common as a result of years of common use, and research surveys have indicated that chlordane is present in the air of approximately 75% of US homes [25]. The highest exposures of people today result from living in houses that were treated with chlordane for termites, from eating foods prepared from plants grown on chlordane-treated fields, and from eating the fat of meat and milk from animals that eat grass from chlordane-treated pasture.

DDT was introduced to North America as an insecticide in 1946. Although it has been banned for most uses in the US since 1973 and in Canada since 1985, DDT is still used elsewhere in the world and continues to be transported to North America through the atmosphere. As noted above, among other uses DDT is an effective agent for control of malaria-carrying mosquitoes.

Hexachlorobenzene (HCB) was originally manufactured as a fungicide for crops and generated as a byproduct when pesticides were manufactured. The use of HCB was discontinued in Canada in 1976 and in the US in 1984.

Alkylated lead was produced mainly as a gasoline additive. Today, levels of alkylated lead compounds are decreasing as leaded gasoline has been phased out in many countries, but alkylated lead is still in use in developing countries. Ambient particulate lead levels in North America have dropped significantly since tetraethyl lead was banned as a fuel additive in the 1980s.

Mercury and mercury compounds — In the past, mercury was widely used in the pulp and paper industry and in the manufacture of chlorine and caustic soda. Additional uses include batteries, electrical equipment (switches), medical equipment, thermometers, thermostats, pesticides, preservative,s and dental amalgam. Many uses (for example, as a fungicide in paint) have been discontinued, but mercury is still used in some products and processes. Currently its largest use in the US is in the production of chlorine gas and caustic soda. Mercury is also released into the environment when natural materials containing mercury (coal, wood, and metal ore) are processed, when garbage is burned, and by vaporization from landfills.

Mirex — All uses of this extremely persistent insecticide and flame retardant have been banned in the US and Canada for more than 20 years. The human health impacts of mirex exposure are not well known. It is known to be highly toxic to a variety of marine crustaceans, including shrimps and crabs, and to accumulate in marine life if released into water.

Octachlorostyrene (OCS) — There is no known use for this compound, which is identified in the Binational Toxics Strategy Document [26], but it is a byproduct of processes involving chlorine, organic chemicals, and heat. Identified sources of OCS include past production processes of the chlor-alkali industry, incineration, combustion, and metal smelting operations, and the production of chlorinated solvents. Since OCS appears to be formed in the same processes that lead to the formation of dioxins, furans, and several other potentially toxic chlorinated hydrocarbons it is thought to be a useful indicator of their general presence in the environment. The reduction of OCS may indicate the simultaneous reduction of a range of co-generated compounds. The toxic properties of OCS are not well understood, although OCS does accumulate in the biosphere [27].

Polychlorinated biphenyls (PCBs) — Although these compounds are no longer produced in North America or used in the manufacture of new products, they are still widely dispersed in sealed electrical and hydraulic equipment. Therefore, the major sources of airborne levels of PCBs today are from PCBs already present in soil and water. PCBs may also be released to the air from PCB disposal sites and incineration of PCB-containing wastes. Long distance transport and deposition both occur, and these compounds have been detected in the Canadian Arctic and its population. PCBs are of concern due to irritation, developmental effects, and possible carcinogenicity associated with chronic exposure.

Dioxins (PCDD) and furans (PCDF) — Dioxins are stable complex chlorinated compounds formed mainly as byproducts of chemical reactions and during the combustion of chlorine-containing compounds, such as during waste incineration. The term "dioxin" usually refers to polychlorinated dibenzo dioxins (PCDD) as well as the related compounds polychlorinated dibenzo furans (PCDF). One early example was the generation of dioxins as byproducts in the production of Agent Orange, a defoliating agent that was used extensively during the Vietnam War. Even though the relative amount of dioxins formed during Agent Orange production was small, they are exceedingly toxic compounds and these exposures have been associated with a large number of health impacts in military personnel and in civilians who were exposed to Agent Orange. Today, the major emission sources are municipal waste incinerators [28]. Metal processing, chemical and pulp and paper manufacturing, and wood burning are other sources that may be important in some locations. Dioxins are also produced as a byproduct by pulp and paper mills that use chlorine in their bleaching process (increasingly rare in North America as non-chlorine-based processes are replacing traditional methods), or when chlorophenoxy herbicides are produced and chlorinated waste is incinerated. Furans are structurally and chemically similar to dioxins and are a byproduct of waste incineration and the same industrial processes that produce dioxins. Dioxins are extremely toxic, are carcinogens, and may also be important endocrine disrupters.

The insecticide **toxaphene** was widely used in North America until late 1982, when its use was discontinued in Canada and the US. It is still used in developing countries. It is known to be very toxic to fish. Toxaphene exposure of humans has been associated with effects on the lungs, nervous system, liver, and kidneys; and animal studies have shown evidence of carcinogenicity.

REFERENCES

[1]   SMITH, K.R. Fuel combustion, air pollution exposure and health: The situation in developing countries. Annual Review of Energy and Environment 1993; 18:529-66.

[2]   LAI, A.C.K., THATCHER, T.L., & NAZAROFF, W.W. Inhalation transfer factors for air pollution health risk assessment. Journal of the Air and Waste Management Association. 2000; 50:1688-99.

[3]   CCME(http://www.ec.gc.ca/oged-dpge/level3e/ccme3/ccme1_2e.htm).

[4]   NORTHEAST STATES FOR COORDINATED AIR USE MANAGEMENT (NESCAUM). The long-range transport of ozone and its precursors in the eastern United States, March 1997 (http://www.nescaum.org/pdf/transport.pdf).

[5]   JAFFE, D., ANDERSON, T., COVERT, D., KOTCHEN RUTHER, R., TROST, B., DANIELSON, J., SIMPSON, W., BERNTSEN, T., KARLSDOTTIR, S., BLAKE, D., HARRIS, J., CARMICHAEL, G., & UNO, I. Transport of Asian Air Pollution to North America. Geophysical Res. Ltrs. 1999; 26(6):711.

[5a]   US ENVIRONMENTAL PROTECTION AGENCY. Heavy duty engine and vehicle standards and highway diesel fuel sulphur control requirements. EPA 420-F-00-057. 2000 (http://www.epa.gov/otaq/regs/hd2007/frm/f00057.pdf).

[6]   SOUTH COAST AIR QUALITY MANAGEMENT DISTRICT. Mobile air toxics exposure study (MATES II). 2000 (http://www.aqmd.gov/matesiidf/matestoc.htm).

[6a]   OTT, R. Human exposure assessment: the birth of a new science. Journal of Exposure Analysis and Environmental Epidemiology. 1995; 5(4):449-72.

[7]   KLEPEIS, N.P., TSANG, A.M., & BEHAR, J.V. Analysis of the National Human Activity Pattern Survey respondents from a standpoint of exposure assessment. US EPA: Las Vegas, Nevada. 1996.

[8]   EBELT, S.T., FISHER, T.V., PETKAU, A.J., VEDAL, S., & BRAUER, M. Exposure of chronic obstructive pulmonary disease (COPD) patients to particles: relationship between personal exposure and ambient air concentrations. Journal of the Air and Waste Management Assoc. 2000; 50:1081-94.

[9]   BAHADORI, T., SUH, H., & KOUTRAKIS, P. Issues in human particulate exposure assessment: Relationship between outdoor, indoor, and personal exposures. Human & Ecological Risk Assessment. 1999; 5(3):459-70.

[10]   ROJAS-BRACHO, L., SUH, H.H., & KOUTRAKIS, P. Relationships among personal, indoor, and outdoor fine and coarse particle concentrations for individuals with COPD. J Expo Anal Environ Epidemiol. 2000; 10(3):294-306.

[11]   WALLACE, L.A. Human exposure to environmental pollutants: A decade of experience. Clinical and Experimental Allergy. 1995; 25(1):4-9.

[12]   BRAUER, M. & BROOK, J.R. Personal and fixed-site ozone measurements with a passive sampler. Journal of the Air and Waste Management Association. 1995; 45(7):529-37.

[13]   OTT, W.R. & ROBERTS, J.W. Everyday exposure to toxic pollutants. Scientific American. February 1998; 86-91.

[14]   COMMITTEE ON THE MEDICAL EFFECTS OF AIR POLLUTANTS, DEPARTMENT OF HEALTH. Non-biological particles and health. Her Majesty's Stationery Office, London. 1995. Pp 141.

[15]   CHURG, A. & BRAUER, M. Human lung parenchyma retains PM2.5. Am J Respir Crit Care Med. 1997; 155:2109-11.

[15a]   BRAUER, M., STEVENS, B., VEDAL, S., AVILA-CASADO, C., FOURTOUL, T.I., & CHURG, A. Air pollution and retained particles in the lung. Environmental Health Perspectives, in press, 2001.

[16]   OSTRO, B., SANCHEZ, J.M., ARANDA, C., & ESKE-LAND, G.S. Air pollution and mortality: Results from a study of Santiago, Chile. J Exposure Analysis & Environmental Epidemiology. 1996; 6:97-114.

[17]   GREATER VANCOUVER REGIONAL DISTRICT. Trends in ambient air quality 1987-1996. July 1998.

[18]   BRAUER, M., BRUMM, J., & EBELT, S. Evaluation of ambient air pollution in the Lower Mainland of British Columbia: Public health impacts, spatial variability, and temporal patterns. Report to the Administrative Council of Lower Mainland Medical Health Officers. May 15, 2000 (http://www.southfraserhealth.com/Images/Whats_Happening/PDFs/Air%20Quality%20Report%20-%20Final.pdf).

[19]   EPA map of PM2.5 data (Figure 2-53, 1999 Air Quality Trends Report) (http://www.epa.gov/airtrends/).

[20]   PIRKLE, J.L., BRODY, D.J., GUNTER, E.W., KRAMER, R.A., PASCHAL, D.C., FLEGAL, K.M., MATTE, T.D. The decline in blood lead levels in the United States: The National Health and Nutrition Examination Surveys (NHANES). JAMA. July 27, 1994; 272(4):284-91.

[21]   MENESES, F., ROMIEU, I., RAMIREZ, M., COLOME, S., FUNG, K., ASHLEY, D., & HERNANDEZ-AVILA, M. A survey of personal exposures to benzene in Mexico City. Arch Environ Health. 1999; 54:359-63.

[22]   THE HEALTH EFFECTS OF AN AIR POLLUTION EPISODE IN LONDON DECEMBER 1991. Report commissioned by the Department of Health, London. 1995.

[23]   BATES, D.V., BAKER-ANDERSON, M., & SIZTO, R. Asthma attack periodicity: A study of hospital emergency visits in Vancouver. Environ Research. 1990; 51:51-70.

[24]   DANN, T.F. & WANG, D.K. Ambient air benzene concentrations in Canada (1989-1993) - seasonal and day of week variations, trends, and source influences. Journal of the Air & Waste Management Association. 1995; 45(9):695-702.

[25]   AGENCY FOR TOXIC SUBSTABCES AND DISEASE REGISTRY (ATSDR). Public Health Statement for Chlordane.1989(http://www.atsdr.cdc.gov/ToxProfiles/phs8906.html).

[26]   http://www.epa.gov/glnpo/bnsdocs/98summ/ocs/ (Binational Toxics Strategy Document)

[27]   http://www.on.ec.gc.ca/glimr/lakes/superior/ninechem.html

[28]   US ENVIRONMENTAL PROTECTION AGENCY, NATIONAL CENTER FOR ENVIRONMENTAL ASSESSMENT. Draft exposure and human health reassessment of 2,3,7,8-tetrachlorodibenzo-p-dioxin (TCDD) and related compounds.2000 (http://www.epa.gov/ncea/pdfs/dioxin/part1and2.htm).

Chapter 3
Meteorology and Chemistry of Air Pollution

Douw G. Steyn and Ian G. McKendry

INTRODUCTION

Air pollution is defined as a state of the atmosphere in which substances that harm human or plant health or corrode materials exist in concentrations above their normal or background levels. As this implies, air pollutants are generally not "foreign" substances that are introduced into the atmosphere, but are substances that are generally found in the atmosphere because they are emitted by "natural" sources. A clean atmosphere contains pollutants, but they are at concentrations so low that they do not produce undesirable effects. Substances that distrub the biogeochemical balances that prevail on Earth (such as the greenhouse effect enhancement caused by accumulation of carbon dioxide) are generally not considered pollutants.

Table 3.1 displays the most commonly recognized pollutants, their typical concentrations in clean and polluted air, and their major natural and anthropogenic sources. As can be seen from the table, the major anthropogenic sources are related to the combustion of fossil fuel for energy production, for transportation, or for a variety of industrial processes, while natural emissions arise from a highly varied set of biological processes, or a range of geological processes. Pollutants can be emitted from point sources (such as large industrial installations or volcanoes) or area sources (such as the combined emissions of a fleet of motor vehicles travelling around a city, or emissions of ammonia from bacterial action in a field).

Pollutant	Clean air	Polluted air	Sources
SO_2	1-10	20-200	Power generation, smelting
CO	120	1000-10,000	Internal combustion engines, cars
NO	0.01-0.05	50-750	Combustion processes
NO_2	0.1-0.5	50-250	Combustion processes
O_3	20-80	100-500	Secondary atmospheric reactions of precursor NOx and hydrocarbons
HNO_3	0.02-0.3	3-50	Atmospheric reactions of NOx
NH_3	1	10-25	Natural processes, agriculture
TSP	20	60-200	Soil, forest fires
PM_{10}	20	60-200	Combustion processes, industrial processes
$PM_{2.5}$	5	50-200	Combustion processes

Table 3.1: Concentrations of pollutants in clean and polluted air. Units are parts per billion (ppb) for gases, and $\mu g/m^3$ for total suspended particulate matter. PM_{10} = particulate matter less than 10 microns, $PM_{2.5}$=particulate matter less than 2.5 microns.

Anthropogenic air pollution has its prehistoric origins in smoke emitted as a result of land clearance and agricultural practices by prehistoric peoples. Much later, pollutants were primarily emissions of smoke from space heating and cooking in settlements, and simple industrial emissions from metalworking, tanning, and spinning processes. This pattern of rather diffuse, small point sources changed dramatically with the rise of industrialization in the late 18th century, as industrial areas developed in which a myriad of sources of varying sizes were located in a single region, resulting in substantial emissions spread over often quite wide areas. The emissions arose from space heating, power generation, ore processing, and a variety of heavy industrial applications, and consisted largely of smoke and sulphur dioxide. The realization that these emissions were undesirable led to the development of emissions control technology and legislation which has largely curbed the most blatant examples of such pollution. More recently, it has been discovered that the combined emissions of many motor vehicles (both private and commercial) concentrated in large cities are the source of pollutants that have significant human health effects. These pollutants are a complex mixture of gases and fine particles that are collectively called *photochemical smog*.

The pollutants discussed above all occur in the outdoors. By strong contrast in terms of chemical composition and typical maximum concentrations are air pollutants that occur indoors. The chemical composition is different because the industrial combustion processes that result in the pollution of ambient air generally are not allowed indoors. Indoor air pollution arises mainly from emissions of gases from building and furnishing materials in the developed world, and from cooking fires in the developing world. Concentrations of indoor pollutants can be very high because of the limited dilution available to pollutants trapped inside buildings. The health effects of indoor pollution can be quite severe because people can be exposed to continuously high concentrations without relief for many hours.

More details about pollutants and their sources are provided in Chapter 2.

Emissions of air pollutants can vary widely in both space and time. The most notable variation in time is the diurnal cycle evident in the emission of pollutants from automobiles. This variation generally occurs as emissions peaks during morning and afternoon rush hours, with relatively low emissions through the middle of the day and at night. Many industrial emissions have a diurnal variation that corresponds to the working-day levels of activity. Emissions arising from power generation in countries that have significant heating and/or cooling load have strong annual cycles. Ambient pollutant levels resulting from temporally varying emissions generally reflect their source variation, albeit in a somewhat modulated way due to mixing and transport in the atmosphere.

Spatial variations of pollutant emissions are as varied as the types of landuse encountered on Earths surface — emissions, both quantity and type of pollutant, can vary widely in space. The most intense emissions arise from large industrial complexes made up of a number of large smokestacks surrounded by a large number of smaller individual sources. Such complexes can be many kilometres in spatial extent, in which case they are the source area for a plume of pollution that can cover many hundreds of square kilometres of surrounding countryside. There exist a number of very large industrial installations whose pollutants are emitted from a single large smokestack. The commonest examples of such installations are power generation facilities and smelters. Since the stacks are tall, pollutants are emitted well into the lower atmosphere (up to 300 m above ground level) and as a consequence can travel up to hundreds of kilometres before being diluted or absorbed. All examples of air pollution have spatial and temporal dimensions that are essential parts of both the problem and its solution.

Pollutants emitted into the atmosphere are ultimately returned to Earth's surface. This return can occur by direct absorption of the pollutant onto surface materials, or can be mediated through incorporation of the pollutant into rain, snow, fog, or cloud droplets. In many cases, pollutants undergo chemical reactions in the atmosphere (with other pollutants or with constituents of the clean atmosphere) before returning to the surface. The products of such reactions are called *secondary* pollutants, to distinguish them from *primary* pollutants, whose sources are readily identifiable. The most important secondary pollutants are photochemical smog, and the mixture of sulphate and nitrate ions that are active in acid rain.

THE SPREAD OF POLLUTANTS IN THE ATMOSPHERE

Once emitted, a pollutant will spread into the atmosphere and be diluted by atmospheric motion at a variety of scales. It is convenient to consider the spread of a pollutant along the direction of mean wind (called *advection*) as separate from the crosswind mixing in both horizontal and vertical directions (called *diffusion*). This perspective allows us to understand the commonly observed phenomenon of plumes of smoke issuing from tall smokestacks. The small-scale atmospheric motions called turbulence are responsible for the often rapid crosswind spread of the plume of pollutant as it is advected along the direction of the mean wind. The two processes of diffusion and advection combine to dilute the pollutant concentration by mixing pollutant with cleaner air. It is thanks to this process of dilution that emission of any pollutants can be bearable. All smokestack design is conducted with the objective of ensuring that dilution in the atmosphere is sufficient that ground-level pollutant concentrations surrounding the stack remain at levels low enough to provide adequate protection to human and plant health and from material corrosion. A significant portion of the subject of air pollution deals with understanding the dispersion of pollutants into the atmosphere so that predictions can be made about the pattern of ground level pollution concentrations for regulatory purposes.

The ground-level concentration pattern is clearly determined by the intensity of turbulent diffusion (stronger diffusion reduces the concentration) and mean wind advection (stronger advection reduces the concentration). Mean wind is largely determined by large-scale weather systems and local topography. The intensity of turbulent diffusion is determined by the strength of atmospheric turbulence, which is simply a manifestation of the constantly fluctuating wind speed and direction. These fluctuations are largest under strong wind conditions and/or when Earth's surface is strongly heated by solar radiation, and smallest under light wind conditions and/or when Earth's surface is cooling due to loss of heat to the night sky.

The propensity of the atmosphere to mix vertically is termed *stability* and is closely tied to the vertical temperature stratification. Atmospheric stability plays a very important role in the dispersion of pollutants. Volumes of air rising or sinking in the atmosphere tend to change temperature according to known physical principles. For example, a volume of rising dry air will cool at a rate of 9.8°C/km due to the energy utilized in expansion as it encounters lower pressures. It is the difference in temperature between rising (or sinking) volumes of air and surrounding (ambient) air at the same level, that determines the depth of vertical mixing. If air that is rising and cooling remains warmer than surrounding (ambient) air at the same level then it will be less dense and positively buoyant. This is called an *unstable* atmosphere and will promote vertical mixing. The opposite case is termed *stable* and is associated with suppressed vertical mixing. At night, the lower atmosphere is often stable (due to surface radiational cooling) and weak mixing is confined to a shallow layer (often producing high pollutant concentrations). Daytime heating produces a mixed layer that is typically 1-2 km deep (called the mixing height). Consequently, pollutants may be dispersed into a much larger volume than during nighttime. The mixed layer is capped by a relatively shallow layer in which temperature increases with height (such a layer is very stable and is called an *inversion* as it represents the opposite of the typical cooling with height observed in the atmosphere). The presence of this capping inversion generally prevents pollutants from being mixed higher into the atmosphere.

To summarize, in stable layers where ambient temperature decreases only slowly with height (or actually increases in the case of inversions), turbulence and the diffusion of pollutants are suppressed. In unstable layers where ambient temperature cools rapidly with height, turbulence and the diffusion of pollutants are enhanced. These effects are most noticeable when observing individual smokestack plumes. A plume that undergoes large vertical excursions and appears to form large loops as it moves downwind is diffusing into an unstable atmosphere. By contrast, a plume that spreads horizontally in a thin layer with hardly any vertical movement is diffusing into a stable atmosphere. In the intermediate case, atmospheric neutrality leads to a plume that spreads in a cone with both vertical and horizontal mixing. While the behaviour of individual plumes is important, emission conditions are seldom so simple as to result in a ready identification of an individual plume with its source.

Plumes exist on a variety of scales, depending on amount and height of emission, and chemical and physical properties of the emitted substances. For single, moderately large smokestacks, individual plumes are identifiable over tens of kilometres, and extend up to a few hundred metres above the surface. Very large stacks can result in plumes that are detectable for up to a few hundred kilometres downwind, and up to 2 km above the surface. The smaller of these plumes will appear to move in a single direction, while the larger are notably meandering due to variations in wind direction over their length. Large industrial complexes with many sources, or very large conurbations, can result in plumes that are detectable up to 1,000 km downwind. Extremely large sources such as volcanic explosions, entire industrial regions, or large deposits of mobile dust (such as the loess plateau of Asia) produce plumes that cover half the globe. Air pollution thus ranges from local to global in scale.

Complex topography and coastal effects can significantly alter the behaviour of pollution plumes. Plumes can become trapped in deep valleys, resulting in highly concentrated pollution choking the valley. This effect is particularly severe in conditions of strong capping inversions, when the pollution is trapped both vertically and horizontally. In coastal regions, the layer into which pollutants can spread is severely limited in depth, often resulting in quite severely polluted conditions in the immediate coastal zone. This effect is often exacerbated by the presence of sea (or lake) breeze conditions that can recirculate and trap pollutants in the coastal zone.

While patterns of pollutant emissions tend to vary relatively little from day to day, the ability of the atmosphere to disperse, transport, transform, and remove pollutants varies considerably at a range of timescales. Consequently, meteorological variability is the main factor contributing to variations in pollutant concentrations and visibility. Clearly, any discussion of air quality trends must give due consideration to demographic and technological change as well as meteorological variability. The first two factors in particular are responsible for complex and linked spatial and temporal trends which make it difficult to identify temporal trends in air quality alone. Furthermore, from year to year, annual frequencies of weather patterns conducive to the development of episodes of poor air quality are strongly modulated by year-to-year atmospheric variability associated with such phenomena as ENSO (El Niño Southern Oscillation) and the Pacific Decadal Oscillation (PDO). It is therefore essential that time series (i.e., historical monitoring records) of pollutant concentrations are "declimatized" when temporal trends in air quality are considered. Otherwise, it is difficult to determine whether long-term trends in pollutant concentrations can be attributed to control strategies or are simply a result of yearly or decadal climate variability.

THE CHEMICAL TRANSFORMATION OF CHEMICALS IN THE ATMOSPHERE

Earth's atmosphere is made up of oxygen, nitrogen, water vapour and a large number of other gases, some of which are considered to be air pollutants. Most of the gases that make up the atmosphere are able to take part in chemical reactions, whose reaction products may be pollutants themselves. Pollutants formed in this way are called secondary pollutants to distinguish them from primary pollutants, which have a well defined source. Because secondary pollutants are amongst the most important in terms of human and plant health effects, and because control of these pollutants requires particular considerations, it is important to understand the nature of chemical processes that produce the pollutants.

Combustion of fossil fuels (in which hydrocarbons are burnt in air) results in the emission of water vapour, oxidized nitrogen (primarily nitric oxide [NO] and nitrogen dioxide [NO_2]), and sulphur dioxide (SO_2). The SO_2 results from the oxidation of trace amounts (0.5 to 3%) of sulphur found as an impurity in current fossil fuels. The SO_2 is oxidized to sulphuric acid (H_2SO_4) in the atmosphere by a fairly complex chain of reactions in which a hydroxyl radical (OH) is consumed and finally regenerated, with the net effect of producing H_2SO_4 from SO_2, and maintaining a background concentration of OH. The H_2SO_4 produced in this way dissolves in atmospheric liquid water, to produce acidified precipitation. This phenomenon is commonly called acid rain, and has a significant effect in reducing forest growth by disrupting the chemical processes whereby plants access their nutrients. Acid Rain is also responsible for the acidification of many lakes in eastern North America and Western Europe, with the resultant death of many lakeborne fish populations.

The NO and NO_2 mixture produced in all combustion processes is commonly called NOx. When emitted into the atmosphere, this mixture of oxidised nitrogen undergoes an important set of chemical reactions when it is exposed to the ultraviolet (UV) radiation which is part of solar radiation. NO_2 in the NOx mixture absorbs a UV photon to produce NO and a highly reactive monatomic oxygen, which reacts with molecular oxygen to produce ozone (O_3). The O_3 produced in this way reacts with NO to produce NO_2 and molecular oxygen. These three reactions form a cyclical system which can reach a stationary steady state. The concentrations of O_3 and NO_2 in this state are determined by the initial amount of NO_2 and the amount of UV radiation. O_3 concentrations for typical conditions are seldom more than 50 parts per billion (ppb). If any of a variety of volatile organic compounds (abbreviated VOC) are also present, the stationary state can be significantly perturbed so that ozone concentrations are significantly higher (up to 400 ppb in the worst cases). The ozone in such cases is accompanied by a wide range of sulphates, peroxides, nitric acid, and organic nitrates, including peroxyacyl nitrates. This mixture is generally called *photochemical smog* and is a common phenomenon around large cities whose emissions include NOx and VOCs.

Under many conditions, the complex chain of chemical reactions that results in photochemical smog includes chemical reactions that lead to gaseous pollutants reacting to produce solid or even liquid particles (see "Aerosols as Air Pollutants" below). These particles are extremely small (usually less than 1 micron in size) because they are produced from reactions between molecules. The chemical makeup of these aerosols can be very complex, depending on which VOCs are involved, but often include organic nitrates and sulphates. Since the chemical reactions responsible for these pollutants occur over finite times, the pollution does not occur immediately at the point of emission but is encountered some distance downwind. This distance varies, depending on wind speed, temperature, the details of VOC species emitted, and the ratio of VOC to NOx, but can be tens to a few hundred kilometres. Clearly, in conurbations larger than these distances, this kind of pollution occurs in the downwind urban areas. Natural sources of NOx (mainly wildfires and actions of bacteria in soils) and VOCs (mainly substances evaporated from certain species of plants) add to anthropogenic sources, and can, in some places, form an important component of total emissions.

The only means of reducing ambient levels of photochemical smog are the curtailment of anthropogenic emissions of NOx and/or VOCs. While it is clear what must be done, just how to achieve acceptable air quality in specific cases is an extremely complex question because the relationship between emissions levels and ambient concentration of pollutants is extremely complex. Not only is it unclear just what fraction of emissions must be reduced, it is also not clear what the relation must be between NOx and VOC emission reductions in order to achieve a desired improvement in a given region which experiences photochemical pollution. To further complicate matters, meteorological variability has an extremely strong effect on the severity of individual episodes of polluted air. The total emissions of a given city vary by less than 5% from day to day (though weekday-to-weekend variations are measurable and well documented), while ambient pollution concentrations can vary by a factor of 10 from one summers day to the next due to differences in meteorological conditions. Any emissions reduction strategies must take into account the vagaries of weather.

While regional photochemical smog occurs in most cities with populations exceeding roughly 2 million, two notable examples are to be found in and around the cities of Los Angeles and Atlanta. The case of Los Angeles is notable because the smog resulting from emissions in its basin became notoriously bad in the mid-1970s. Strenuous effort at emissions reductions have largely ameliorated conditions but not completely solved them. This example shows that the matter is tractable, though far from simple. The second interesting example is the significant photochemical smog found in the southeastern United States around the city of Atlanta. The problem is widespread in its extent, as indicated in Figure 3.1, which shows the ozone "lake" that was observed around the Atlanta area during the US Southern Oxidants Study in 1990.

Southern Oxidants Study

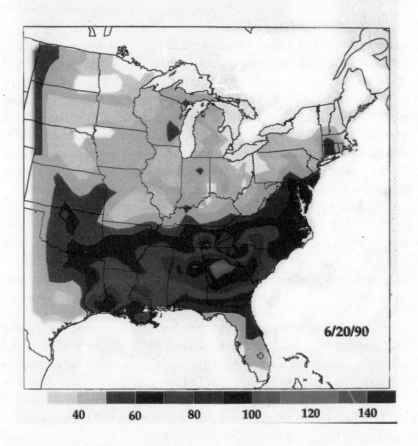

Figure 3.1: Ozone "lake" observed around Atlanta, Georgia, during the Southern Oxidants Study in 1990.

Most perplexing is the discovery that a significant component of the emissions that cause episodes such as depicted here arises from emissions of isoprene from vegetation found in the surroundings of the city. Strenuous efforts at solving this instance of regional photochemical smog have yielded little advance.

AEROSOLS AS AIR POLLUTANTS

Aerosols are liquid or solid particles suspended in the air. They occur naturally in the atmosphere (e.g., sea salt particles or windblown dust) or they can be produced by human activities (e.g., combustion processes). As with the gaseous pollutants discussed above, they can act as significant air pollutants. In fact, before the advent of the automobile and its explosive growth in usage in the 20th century, solid particles (including soot) produced from the burning of wood and coal for home heating and industrial processes were probably the most obvious source of pollution in urban areas. In the latter half of the 20th century a switch to alternate energy sources for home heating, together with increasing gaseous emissions from automobiles and industry, meant that gases such as ozone and sulphur dioxide supplanted aerosols as "priority" urban air pollutants. However, air pollution resulting from fine particulate matter (aerosols) has recently re-emerged as the pollutant of most concern, due to mounting evidence that very small particles may be ingested deep into the human respiratory system and cause significant negative health impacts (including even death for susceptible groups in the population). Such particles can also be responsible for significant visibility degradation not only in and around urban areas but also sometimes far from the particles' source.

Aerosols originate from a number of natural and anthropogenic sources and therefore vary considerably in chemical composition, size, and atmospheric lifetime. From an air pollution perspective, most interest lies in the smaller particles (so-called PM_{10} — particulate matter less than 10 millionths of a metre [μm] in diameter). These very small particles can be inhaled deep into the lungs, are sufficiently small that they can be transported long distances without settling out, and have light extinction characteristics that promote very poor visibility. The largest particles within the PM_{10} size range are formed primarily by the disintegration of larger particles, and include windblown material from soil surfaces and roadways, evaporation of salt spray, and biological material. The smallest particles ($PM_{2.5}$) are usually formed from gases and include material emitted during combustion processes, and secondary particles formed by gas-to-particle conversion in the atmosphere (some of the latter are derived from agricultural emissions of ammonia and nitrates). It is thought that fine-mode particles may in fact have a more deleterious impact on human health.

Ambient concentrations of aerosols vary greatly. It is important to note that some of the highest concentrations observed occur during natural events. For example, during duststorms, PM_{10} concentrations may exceed 1,000 $\mu g/m^3$ (with the bulk of particles residing in the supposedly more benign larger size ranges). At the opposite end of the spectrum, in relatively unpolluted environments such as rural Scandinavia, Switzerland or Canada, mean daily concentrations are generally less than 20 $\mu g/m^3$ and seldom exceed 100 $\mu g/m^3$ on an hourly basis. However, where significant industrial sources exist, or where coal and wood are used for space heating in areas where pollution dispersion is limited (e.g., valleys in wintertime), hourly concentrations of PM_{10} may reach 300-500 $\mu g/m^3$. A large component of particulate pollution from such sources includes small particles ($PM_{2.5}$) thought to be more damaging to human health.

In many cities around the world, concentrations of particulate matter are now dominated by the transportation sector. Approximately 75% of PM_{10} emitted within cities typically originates from road transport (this includes resuspended road dust and primary emissions from tailpipes). As a consequence, in large cities such as Los Angeles and Mexico City daily average concentrations of PM_{10} may frequently exceed 200 $\mu g/m^3$. Even at relatively low concentrations and depending on meteorological conditions and the types of particles involved, fine particulate matter in the atmosphere can have a significant impact on visibility. Particles in the $PM_{2.5}$ size range typically dominate visibility impairment (as a result of their ability to scatter and absorb light). Figure 3.2 shows the effect on atmospheric clarity (visibility) on clear and smoggy days in Santiago, Chile.

Figure 3.2: Two views of the city of Santiago, in Chile. Mobile sources, including old diesel buses, constitute the major source of PM_{10} levels in this city. Photographs by Dr. Bart Ostro of the Environmental Health Department of the State of California.

MEASUREMENT OF AIR POLLUTANTS

Air pollutants are routinely monitored in and around urban areas, as well as at more remote locations. As pollutants cannot be measured at all places at the same time, a network of surface monitors (pollution-measuring instruments) is usually installed across a region in an attempt to represent the actual distribution of pollutant concentrations over space and through time. Generally, a suite of pollutants is measured at a monitoring site. At some sites, supporting meteorological measurements are also made (e.g., wind speed and direction, temperature, and humidity). Sampling of air pollution concentrations serves a range of purposes. From a regulatory perspective, pollutant monitoring may be used as an indication of population exposure, and to identify those locations or regions in non-compliance with regulatory standards or guidelines. If concentrations are deemed to be of concern, then abatement strategies may be instituted. A long record of concentration data from a monitoring station may be used to assess trends in air quality and to assess the impact of abatement strategies. As mentioned above, due care must be taken in trend assessment, as climatic variations as well as changes in population density and distribution may significantly affect trends in concentrations. Observations from remote locations often provide an indication of "background" or "natural" pollutant levels, although in some cases they provide evidence of the long-range transport of pollutants.

Various methods are used to measure pollutant concentrations at monitoring stations. Generally a sample is drawn from the surrounding (or ambient) air into a monitoring instrument. In some cases pollutants are trapped on small filters and then weighed (either instantaneously or at some later time) to determine concentrations (this is used for particulate matter). They may also be subject to various chemical analyses (eg., to determine lead concentrations). For other pollutants (O_3, CO, SO_2, NO_2), principles of light absorption or light emission (when chemical reactions occur between the pollutant and some other species, light may be given off and measured) by the pollutant may be exploited within instruments. Generally such monitoring is conducted on the basis of strict protocols and standards, ensuring data quality and comparability.

Sampling of ambient (outdoor) pollutants at monitoring stations has limitations. Firstly, air pollution monitoring stations tend to be located in populated areas in order to meet the goal of addressing concerns related to population exposure and health impacts. However, the relationship between personal exposure (reflecting the combination of indoor, in-vehicle, and outdoor or ambient concentrations as measured at monitoring stations) is not well established. Consequently, considerable research is currently directed at methods by which personal exposures to pollutants can be more accurately quantified. Secondly, individual monitoring stations generally form part of a network of stations designed to capture and resolve spatial variations in pollutant concentrations across a region. However, networks seldom meet this goal. Monitoring stations tend to be biased toward areas of greatest population density, and for logistical reasons are sparsely distributed (networks are expensive to run and maintain). Consequently, they seldom adequately capture the true spatial gradients as well as maxima and minima in pollutant concentrations. Finally, surface observations reveal little about the vertical distribution of pollutants in a region. Often pollutants may be stored in layers above the ground and may subsequently be mixed to the surface. Routine monitoring networks tell us little about such patterns and processes.

SUMMARY

Air pollution, the state of the atmosphere in which harmful substances exist above their normal or background levels, has long been a consequence of human habitation. Historically, the nature and magnitude of pollutant emissions has changed considerably. What once tended to be a "local" problem now takes on a "regional" or even "global" scope. Today, primary and secondary pollutants arising from combustion processes (primarily from industry and transportation sources) are of most concern. To some degree, concentrations of these substances in the atmosphere are controlled by seasonal and daily patterns of emissions. However, of greater importance is the role that the state of the atmosphere plays in controlling dilution, transformation, and removal of pollutants. It is differences in meteorology that usually distinguish a day of good air quality from one with very poor air quality. Finally, it should be stressed that although the concepts of air pollution meteorology are universal, the nature of air pollution problems in any locality (and their solution) tend to be site-specific. Particular physiographic and meteorological settings, combined with local spatial distributions of sources and mixes of emissions, create unique air quality problems. Consequently, adopted in one locality may not necessarily translate well to others.

FURTHER READING

BOUBEL, R. W., D.L. FOX, D.B. TURNER & A.C. STERN. 1994. Fundamentals of Air Pollution, Academic Press, 574 pp.

COMMITTEE ON TROPOSPHERIC OZONE, 1991. Rethinking the Ozone Problem in Urban and Regional Air Pollution, National Research Council, National Academy Press, Washington, DC, 524 pp.

GRAEDEL, T.E. & P.J. CRUTZEN. 1995. Atmosphere, Climate and Change, Scientific American Library, W.H. Freeman & Co., New York. 196 pp. (A broad, general survey, illustrated)

SEINFELD, J.H. & S.N. PANDIS. 1998. Atmospheric Chemistry and Physics, from Air Pollution to Climate Change, John Wiley & Sons. 1,326 pp. (A complete, university-level text)

Chapter 4
Adverse Health Effects

David V. Bates and Sverre Vedal

INTRODUCTION

In this text, no detailed description is given of the physiology of the lung, or of disease states such as asthma that are important in relation to the effects of air pollution. Definitions of some of these aspects will be found in the Glossary. We make extensive reference to the primary literature in this chapter rather than to general review articles, since we found no satisfactory comprehensive review that took into account the most recent research findings. The details from the literature cited are not necessary to understanding the thrust of the presentation — they are presented for completeness for those who wish to follow up with more in-depth reading.

In the sections that follow, reference is made to a test of lung function known as the "forced expired volume in one second." This is an easily performed test of a single maximal forced expiration. It can be performed by children over the age of 7, and has been shown to be highly repeatable (with a coefficient of variation of less than 3%) and is now well standardized. It is abbreviated as "FEV_1." Another test commonly used is the peak expiratory flow rate (PEFR). Using a small portable meter, a maximal expiration is made after the lungs have been filled. The peak velocity of the subsequent fast expiration is measured. This device has proved very useful in studies of panels of asthmatics, who can keep the meter at home and use it to record their lung function in the morning and evening.

CONTROLLED ACUTE HUMAN EXPOSURES

Since the first edition of this book appeared in 1972, a striking major advance has been in the development of studies of the effects of controlled acute human exposures to air pollutants. These studies have had a substantial effect on the standards set for different air pollutants. In the following sections, these experiments are described in terms of the pollutant exposure. In the section "Linking Effects to Specific Pollutants," the attribution of effects, both acute and chronic, to specific pollutants is discussed.

Sulphur Dioxide (SO$_2$)

Non-asthmatic subjects may be capable of breathing SO$_2$ in concentrations as high as 8 parts per million (ppm) (2,290 micrograms/m^3) without any bronchoconstrictor response, though nose and throat irritation may be noticed. Recent data have suggested that airway inflammation may be induced in normal subjects by SO$_2$ inhalation at high concentrations, even though airflow limitation has not occurred. Studies of a randomly selected adult population in Hamburg Germany [114], showed that 3.4% of the population were hyper-responsive to SO$_2$.

It was first shown in 1980 that asthmatic subjects responded to inhaled SO$_2$ by developing airway narrowing, at far lower concentrations than affected non-asthmatic people. There are now a sufficient number of studies that the response to SO$_2$ in asthmatics [23] can be characterized, as shown in Table 4.1. Other studies have shown that the onset of the response may be rapid (within 2 minutes); that oral breathing accentuates the response because the removal of SO$_2$ in the nasal passages is reduced; that there does not appear to be any "late" reaction in the asthmatics; that the response may be increased by concomitant cold, dry air; and that there is a more or less linear decline in the FEV$_1$ in an asthmatic as the inhaled concentration of SO$_2$ is increased. It has been noted that a significant number of moderately severe asthmatics exposed to 0.6 ppm or 1.0 ppm of SO$_2$ during exercise had to have their exposure terminated or the level of exercise reduced, whereas with the same level of exercise but without SO$_2$, they could complete the exercise without difficulty.

Concentration of SO$_2$ (ppm)	Cumulative frequency of asthmatics affected (%)
0.25	0
0.5	20
0.75	40
1.0	60
2.0	80

Table 4.1: Response of asthmatic subjects to inhaled SO$_2$. The asthmatics were generally mild in degree, and were exposed to the indicated concentration of SO$_2$ for 5 minutes while performing moderate exercise (mean ventilation = 40 L/min). The outcome measured was a doubling of airway resistance. Data from reference [23].

A recent British Report [11] contains an interesting section on the potential mechanisms of sulphur-induced airway obstruction, from which the following notes have been derived:

- The increase in nasal airflow resistance when SO_2 is inhaled is due to distension of the vascular bed, together with some fluid extravasation.

- Obstruction in the airway may be caused in four ways: (1) by contraction of airway smooth muscle; (2) by vascular congestion in the small airways; (3) by edema of the mucosa of the airways; and (4) by causing increased secretions from the airways.

- SO_2 stimulates sensory nerves in the airway lining, leading to cough and a sense of irritation or tightness. Irritant receptors and fibres of the "C-fibre system" are both stimulated by SO_2.

- SO_2 causes neurogenic inflammation in the airways, and it is possible that the sequence of responses to this is responsible for further airway obstruction due to the release of mediators.

The response to SO_2 seems to be highly individual and does not appear to be closely related to the severity of the clinical asthma, although there are still too few studies of more severe asthmatics for this conclusion to be considered definite.

In all cases, the administration of beta-agonists, sodium cromoglycate, and histamine receptor antagonists inhibits the response. The airflow limitation induced by SO_2 can be quickly reversed by inhaling a beta-agonist, or metaproterenol. However, the effect of SO_2 is not changed by inhalation of ipratropium bromide.

Acid Aerosols

Sulphuric acid (H_2SO_4) aerosol has been studied in normal subjects and asthmatics. Normal subjects do not show any significant changes until the concentration has reached about 1,000 micrograms/m^3, even with a 1 hour exposure with exercise. Asthmatic subjects, on the other hand have shown in one series of studies significant decrements in lung function with exposure to 100 micrograms/m^3 H_2SO_4 for 40 minutes with 10 minutes of exercise. In these studies, it is important that the neutralizing effect of ammonia in the mouth be eliminated before the aerosol is administered. However, there must be great variability in the asthmatic response, because some other investigators could find no response at concentrations as high as 3,000 micrograms/m^3. It has been calculated that the total dose of acid delivered to the tracheo-bronchial region during exercise for a few hours in an ambient exposure episode (400 micrograms/m^3 H_2SO_4) is more than the delivered dose shown to affect lung function in one of the asthma studies.

Comparative studies of asthmatics inhaling sulphites (sodium sulphite, sodium bisulphite, acetic acid, and SO_2), which may be contained in wine or food for preservation purposes, have indicated that the response to sulphites is related to the production of SO_2, and is not a consequence of the alteration in pH (acidity) of the airway. Inhaled metabisulphite causes bronchoconstriction, an effect thought to be due to the release of SO_2, since there is a close relationship between the SO_2 response and the metabisulphite response in individual cases.

Patients with chronic obstructive lung disease did not show any response to inhalation of sulphuric acid aerosol at 75 micrograms/m^3 for 2 hours with intermittent exercise; hence, it may be inferred that this group is not an especially sensitive population.

Controlled exposures to particulate matter

With the introduction of a device to concentrate urban particles, it has been possible to study the effects of concentrated urban PM_{10} or $PM_{2.5}$. Recent human studies have found that these induce a mild inflammatory response in the lung and, in addition, cause changes in the blood of normal subjects. Ghio, Kim, and Devlin [203] have recently shown that concentrated $PM_{2.5}$ inhaled by young normal subjects causes an increase in blood fibrinogen. Changes in heart rate variability in elderly subjects were also documented [181]. Studies of experimental exposure of normal humans to diesel exhaust have shown that this also induces lung inflammation [198, 202], and a short-term exposure of asthmatic subjects in Sweden to PM_{10} in a road tunnel [197] was shown to result in an enhanced response to a subsequently delivered allergen.

Ozone (O₃) Exposure

The section on controlled human exposures to ozone in the recent Ozone Criteria Document of the US EPA [24] runs to 77 pages of text with many references.

A recent review of controlled human studies of ozone exposure was published in Sweden [109]. Studies of normal subjects have been conducted over the past 20 years in about eight different laboratories; there is a very satisfactory concordance between the results. This work has led to the following conclusions:

- There is a wide variation in response between normal subjects, but the results in one individual are highly reproducible if studies are replicated some weeks apart.

- The FEV_1 declines progressively as exposure is continued.

- The ability to take a full inspiration (the forced vital capacity) declines initially, and this is followed by reduced airflow. The initial response is thought to be due to stimulation of the "C-fibre" system of nerves in the airway.

- The FEV_1 begins to decline after 2 hours of exposure to 0.08 ppm of ozone with moderate exercise during the exposure. The greater the level of exercise, the greater the FEV_1 decline at a given ozone concentration; and the longer the exposure period, the greater the decline in FEV_1.

- A careful documentation of respiratory symptoms in over 400 young subjects exposed to ozone [159] showed the increasing incidence of cough, inability to take a deep breath, and general chest discomfort as the ozone concentration increased.

- The effect on the FEV_1 is greater if, over a period, the concentration starts at zero, rises to a peak, and then declines to zero, than it is when some concentration is breathed continuously, although the amount of delivered ozone is the same in both cases. Hence a "concentration * time" index cannot be universally used to predict the FEV_1 fall.

- Recovery is relatively slow, taking several hours to complete. There is evidence that ozone exerts a major effect on the small airways of the lung; it may be that it is in this region that inflammation is first induced.

- Ozone causes lung inflammation, as detected by changes in the fluid recovered from lung washings, which shows an increase in inflammatory cells, in protein content, and in mediators of the inflammatory response. This evidence is present 18 hours after exposure has ceased, but the peak response as judged by an increase in polymorphonuclear (inflammatory) cells is maximal 6 hours after exposure. It has also been shown that the inflammatory cells (polymorphonuclear neutrophils) are increased in lung tissue (and not just in washings from the lung) after ozone exposure.

  A number of investigators have found that there is not a close association between the magnitude of the decline in FEV_1 and the intensity of the inflammatory reaction. There is a general correlation between the magnitude of the FEV_1 decline and the severity of symptoms noted.

- There are no differences between Caucasians and African-Americans in their responses, and only slight differences between men and women and children. Older individuals appear to have a reduced ozone response. Smokers have a slightly reduced response compared with nonsmokers, and a six month abstinence from smoking led to an increase in the ozone response in 15 subjects in whom this was studied.

- On maximal exercise in athletes, ozone exposure reduces the maximal oxygen uptake of which they are capable.

- If ozone exposure occurs on consecutive days, the response may be enhanced on the second day but is reduced by the third day, and by the end of seven consecutive exposures, the FEV_1 decline may be almost zero. The original response is regained after about two weeks. However, the inflammatory response is not attenuated by consecutive exposures.

- Ozone exposure causes an increase in bronchial responsiveness (measured with methacholine or with histamine challenge) in normal subjects.

- Ozone exposure (0.2 ppm for 4 hours with moderate exercise) caused a similar FEV_1 decline in asthmatics as in normal subjects, but the inflammatory response 18 hours after exposure was greater in the asthmatics [46].

- Prior ozone exposure increases the response to a subsequent exposure to SO_2.

There are strong *a priori* reasons for suggesting that asthmatic subjects may be at increased risk from ozone inhalation. Ozone causes both inflammation in the lung and enhanced airway responsiveness, and both of these are hallmarks of asthma. Initial studies showed that the percentage decline in FEV_1 was not much different between normal subjects and asthmatics, and from this it was inferred that asthmatics were no more sensitive to ozone than normal subjects. However, the decline in function occurs in the asthmatic when function is usually already lowered, and is therefore of more significance. Furthermore, while a small increment of airway responsiveness in a normal subject may have little effect, an increase in responsiveness superimposed on an already abnormally responsive airway may be of much greater significance. Asthmatics may also have a greater inflammatory response than normal subjects. It is clear therefore, that asthmatics are at greater risk from ozone inhalation than are normal subjects. It has recently been shown that prior ozone exposure (to levels of 0.12 ppm in one study) may enhance the penetration, and hence the effect, of a subsequently administered allergen. This has been convincingly shown in detailed experiments on the nasal mucosa. This is an additional reason for concluding that ozone exposure constitutes an increased risk for asthmatic subjects.

The wide variation in response in normal subjects indicates that there must be a wide spectrum of risk from ozone exposure in the general population.

Nitrogen Dioxide (NO$_2$)

Studies of controlled exposure to nitrogen dioxide provide a striking contrast to the virtual unanimity of the results of ozone exposure, since the findings have often been contradictory, and in one instance a single laboratory was unable to reproduce their earlier results in later experiments.

Nevertheless some useful generalizations are possible:

- In normal subjects, NO$_2$ exposure can induce an increase in airway responsiveness. This has been documented at exposures to about 1,500 ppb of NO$_2$ for 3 hours with moderate exercise, and in one laboratory a change was seen after exposure to only 244 ppb. These levels do not induce a significant fall in lung function, which has been observed only at concentrations of 2,500 ppb or more.

- Variable results have been reported in asthmatics, with increases in non-specific airway responsiveness reported at concentrations as low as 100 ppb in one laboratory, but this result was not confirmed in another. Increases either in SO$_2$ responsiveness or in methacholine or histamine response have generally been reported after exposures to 200 ppb or greater for 2 hours, but one laboratory could not demonstrate this even after an exposure to 600 ppb for 2 hours with exercise.

- One study indicated that NO$_2$ did not induce an inflammatory response in the lung, but there is evidence from lung washings after exposures of normal subjects to NO$_2$ levels of 4,200 ppb on six occasions that reductions occurred in macrophages, B cells, and lymphocytes, indicating that some interference had occurred in the immune system. There was no increase in mast cells. This concentration is, however, nearly 10 times greater than would be encountered in the ambient atmosphere. A more recent study has found that inhalation of 2 ppm of NO$_2$ induces an inflammatory reaction — as evidenced by neutrophils in lung washings — that is maximal 6 hours after exposure has ended. From the analyses of lung washings, it was concluded that the site of the NO$_2$ effect was probably the small airways.

- Recent research has shown that the gas nitric oxide (NO) is an important neurotransmitter in the normal lung, being responsible for inhibition of non-adrenergic and non-cholinergic fibres. Inhalation of NO at a concentration of 40,000 ppb in air for two 5-minute periods has been shown to induce a significant fall in the vascular resistance of the lung in patients with a raised pulmonary arterial pressure.

- Studies on the response of asthmatic subjects to an inhaled allergen to which they were sensitive have indicated that prior NO_2 exposure may lead to an enhancement of the "late response" to the allergen.

- Exposure to NO_2 (60 ppb for 2 hours) enhances the response to subsequently inhaled ozone. This is an important observation, since it is probably common to encounter NO_2 in the city environment before ozone has had time to form, and therefore a prior NO_2 exposure may be commonly followed by exposure to ozone.

As was noted in Chapter 2, NO_2 is a relatively insoluble gas (with a high Henry's Law constant (see Table 2.2), and hence the maximal deposition will be in the smallest airways of the lung. In acute exposures to very high concentrations (which may occur in men welding inside boilers, or after explosives have been used underground, or in agricultural silos), it has long been known that there is usually a time interval between the acute exposure and the onset of severe symptoms. The symptoms are caused by the development of acute inflammation in the small airways and fluid extravasation (edema) in the lung. This fact makes it uncertain whether the acute exposure protocols that have been used in controlled exposures are likely to detect all the effects of NO_2 inhalation. It might also account for the variability in the results from different laboratories.

Hydrogen Sulphide (H₂S)

Some severe episodes of accidental exposure to high concentrations of this gas have been reported. In very high concentrations, H_2S leads to immediate unconsciousness and death. The odour may be detectable at levels as low as 0.13 ppm, and it is easily perceptible at 0.77 ppm. Most people find it very offensive at levels of 3-5 ppm.

The most serious episode of public exposure occurred in Poza Rica in Mexico, when 320 people required hospital treatment and 22 died. In another episode in Terre Haute, Indiana, the exposure was to 0.027-0.125 ppm for seven consecutive hours, and this led to symptoms of eye irritation, cough, headache, and nausea. Legator and his colleagues [235] compared self-reported symptoms in two exposed communities. Odessa, Texas, where contaminated ponds released H_2S (3-40 micrograms/m^3 or 7-27 ppb as an annual average, with an 8-hour maximum of 335-503 ppb or 500-750 micrograms/m^3); and Puna, Hawaii, where wells for geothermal power have been drilled. In Puna H_2S is in the low ppb range, though a single peak of 301 ppb was recorded and releases in the range of 200-500 ppb have been reported. These communities were compared with Hilo, Hawaii, Midlothian, Texas; and Waxachie, Texas. The numbers of individuals interviewed were: Odessa, 126; Puna, 97; Midlothian, 58; Waxachie, 54; and Hilo, 58.

Comparisons of self-reported symptoms revealed excess odds ratios (ORs) between clean and contaminated communities, as follows:

CNS symptoms = 12.7	Cardiovascular = 2.03
Ear/nose/ throat = 7.24	Digestive = 4.05
Respiratory = 11.92	Teeth/gums = 6.31
Muscle/bone = 3.06	Urinary system = 2.48
Skin = 3.6	Blood = 8.07
Immune system = 5.35	Endocrine = 1.06

Of CNS symptoms, fatigue, restlessness, depression, memory loss, balance, difficulty sleeping, anxiety, lethargy, headache, dizziness, and change in senses were noted in 30-50% of those in contaminated regions compared with 10-25% in clean regions.

Respiratory symptoms, wheezing, shortness of breath, persistent cough, and bronchitis were all between 20 and 30% in contaminated locations compared to about 5% in clean areas. Anemia and easy bruising were twice as common in contaminated locations. Although the difficulty of relying on self-reported symptoms is obvious, this study appears to be one of the first reputable attempts to establish the reality of chronic symptoms as a consequence of low-level H_2S exposure.

It is not known whether asthmatics are more sensitive than others. In one study, a group of 10 asthmatic subjects were exposed to 2 ppm of H_2S for 30 minutes at rest. This did not produce any changes in spirometric lung function tests, but there was a slight increase in airflow resistance. It was noted that three of the subjects complained of a headache following the exposure [26].

Volatile Organic Compounds

Most of the controlled exposure studies involving volatile organic compounds have been designed to throw light on which of these may have been responsible for the symptoms associated with the so-called "sick building" syndrome — an issue in indoor air quality [27] (see Chapter 10 for details).

The symptoms most commonly complained of are:

- Irritation of the eyes, nose, and throat
- Dry mucous membranes
- Erythema
- Mental fatigue and headache
- Airway infections and cough
- Hoarseness and wheezing
- Non-specific hypersensitivity reactions
- Nausea and dizziness

The exposure chamber studies carried out in Denmark involved a mixture of 22 different organic compounds in fixed concentration ratios, at levels of 0, 5, or 25 mg/m^3. The first of these levels corresponds to average concentrations measured in new houses, and the highest to the maxima found in new Danish houses. The experiments showed that irritative symptoms occurred in increasing percentages of normal people as the highest concentration was approached. Other experiments of this kind have shown that n-decane, a constituent of turpentine, induces subjective complaints of eye irritation, substantiated by objective measurements of changes in the surface tension of fluid over the eyes, at concentrations 500 times lower than the level deduced to have any effect on rats.

In the case of formaldehyde, the onset of eye irritation occurs with exposures to between 10 and 1,900 micrograms/m^3; irritant symptoms in the nose and throat are noted at higher levels with a range of from 100 to 3,700 micrograms/m^3. It is possible that long-term exposures can induce increased airway responsiveness, but the exposures and the risks of this are not precisely known. Styrene has been shown to induce asthma in one well-documented case. In controlled exposures with three normal subjects, toluene was shown to induce moderate fatigue and sleepiness at levels of 187 mg/m^3, with severe symptoms at three times that concentration. Eye irritation is said to occur at levels as low as 375 mg/m^3.

Studies of simultaneous or sequential exposure to pollutants

It is of course obvious that we do not breathe air pollutants one at a time; very often the citizen or the child playing out of doors will be exposed to complex mixtures, and will often encounter one pollutant after being exposed to another.

Early data indicating that ozone and SO_2 if breathed together might have a greater effect than either alone were not confirmed in later work on normal subjects. Ozone and nitric acid administered together have not been shown to lead to an enhanced response. However, simultaneous exposure of asthmatics to ozone and to sulphuric acid aerosol indicated that the ozone response had been enhanced. Significant increases in the response to one pollutant have been shown to occur if there was a preceding exposure to another. These experiments (noted above) indicate that:

- Prior exposure to ozone (0.12 ppm) enhanced the subsequent response to SO_2 (0.10 ppm) in 13 allergic adolescent asthmatic subjects.

- Prior exposure to NO_2 increases the response to ozone. In studies of 21 healthy women, pre-exposure for 2 hours to 0.6 ppm of NO_2 significantly increased the FEV_1 decline with a subsequent 2-hour exposure to 0.3 ppm of ozone. Airway responsiveness was increased.

There are no human data indicating the effect of simultaneous gas and particle exposures, though some animal work has suggested that when both are present, the effects may be greater than when each is inhaled separately.

EPIDEMIOLOGICAL STUDIES

There is a great variety of epidemiological studies attempting to assess the acute or long-term effects of air pollutants. In the following sections, the different types of study, with their results, are described. In the section "Linking Effects to Specific Pollutants," the problem of relating these observations to individual pollutants is addressed. Nyberg and Pershagen [110] have recently reviewed the epidemiological data relevant to ozone exposure.

Mortality time-series studies

In a "time-series" study, a day is the unit around which the observations are centred. The mortality on a particular day (usually after accidents and suicides have been excluded) is compared with pollutant levels in the same city or region, either on the same day or, more commonly, for the preceding day or the preceding three days. Corrections then have to be applied for the season of the year or separately for temperature or other weather variables. In some studies a Poisson distribution is assumed, which is used when erratic and relatively infrequent events are to be analyzed; or a regression relationship is plotted which enables the magnitude of the effect of changes in pollution on the daily mortality to be calculated.

Particulate Pollution

In 1979, the US EPA changed the indicator for particulate pollution from Total Suspended Particulate (TSP) to PM_{10} (particles with a mean aerodynamic diameter less than or equal to 10 microns, or millionths of a metre). Measurements of PM_{10} were made every sixth day in a number of locations, and later began to be measured every day. From 1987 onwards, studies began to be reported from a number of locations that indicated a significant association between daily mortality and PM_{10} levels on the day before. By the time of the first major review of these findings in 1994 [29], data had been published from Philadelphia, St. Louis, San Jose in California, Utah, Detroit, and New York. By 1996, to these centres had been added Chicago, Birmingham in Alabama, Cincinnati, Los Angeles and Toronto; and also London, Athens, Erfurt, Amsterdam, Milan, Santiago, Chile, and Sao Paulo, Brazil. A recent report [86] has confirmed the same association in Brisbane, Australia, and other cities have been added to the list, including Buffalo and Rochester, New York, and Phoenix, Arizona [200].

The recent draft criteria document on particulates circulated by the US EPA [232] contains an exhaustive review of the character, origin, concentrations, and adverse health effects of particulate matter. It is in two volumes, each of several hundred pages.

So great was the impact of this avalanche of data that the Health Effects Institute in Boston (jointly funded by the EPA and the automobile industry) commissioned a review by two independent biostatisticians/epidemiologists. They re-analyzed the original data from Detroit and Philadelphia, and confirmed the original findings, adding the observation that in the case of Philadelphia, they could not completely exclude SO_2 from a role in the mortality effect. Most of the studies reported a 3% to 9% increase in daily mortality for a 50 microgram/m^3 increase in PM_{10}. Cardiovascular mortality was affected, but the greatest percentage increase was in respiratory disease mortality, with the relative risk being up to four times larger than that for total mortality. As one would expect, the risk was higher in those over the age of 65. Vedal has recently contributed a valuable critical review of these data [83].

The Health Effects Institute has now completed a review of the PM_{10}/mortality relationship in 90 regions of the US [224], and this and other studies are well summarized in the current EPA criteria document [232]. The following generalizations appear valid:

- In some regions (30 of the 90 analyzed), the association was not demonstrable.

- Associations were higher, and generally more significant, in the northeast of the US and weaker in the central and southwestern regions.

- Associations were stronger when $PM_{2.5}$ could be used rather than PM_{10}.

- There was no significant confounding by weather.

- There was no evidence of a threshold (this has been recently re-studied with new methodology by Schwartz and Zanobetti [206]).

- There is no evidence that "harvesting" (advancing mortality by a few days only) plays a significant role in the data, though it may be occurring to some extent in the case of mortality from chronic obstructive pulmonary disease [172, 192].

There are at least three reasons why the association might be stronger in the northeast than in the south and west. It might be that the sulphate component of $PM_{2.5}$ is important; there might be higher exposures to diesel particles in the northeast; and data from the south and west might include regions where particles originating from the earth's crust (rather than combustion particles) are a more significant component of the measured PM_{10}. Analyses of data from Spokane, where both dust storms and traffic-generated particulate pollution occurs, have indicated that the crustal PM_{10} is not associated with increased mortality [160].

Samet and his colleagues [205] have analyzed the association between PM_{10} and daily mortality (lagged 24 hours) in 20 of the largest cities in the US. They concluded that overall mortality increases by 0.5% per 10 microgram/m^3 increase in PM_{10}, and that mortality from cardiovascular and respiratory disease increases by 0.68%. This study is important because the same statistical analytical methods were used in all cases, making the results comparable [219]; their findings are shown in Figure 4.1. They found no evidence of a threshold, and some differences between the cities, but their results generally confirm the conclusions of earlier analyses.

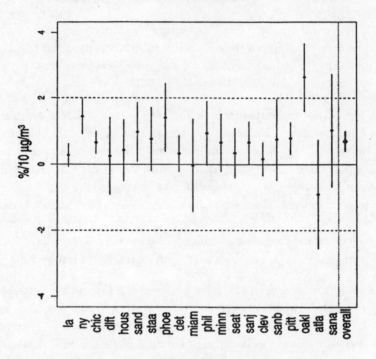

Figure 4.1: Association between daily mortality and PM_{10} in US cities. The ordinate shows the percentage increase in cardiac and respiratory mortality for a 10 micrograms/m^3 increase in PM_{10} in the 20 largest urban areas in the US. All the data were analyzed by the same standardized statistical technique. Note that all cities except Atlanta show an elevation above the zero line. From reference [219].

One way of overcoming the problem of confounding of the data by the effects of weather (rather than pollution levels) is to aggregate the data so that variations in temperature are reduced. This can usually be done only where there is a large bank of data, so that segments of the total data still have enough power to detect events. Figure 4.2 shows this technique used in a recalculation of data from London, England, in a study by Lippmann and Ito [32]. With results from the spring and fall each year collected together, extremes of temperature variation are excluded. The strength of the associations between daily mortality and SO_2, aerosol acidity, and black smoke in that city can be appreciated from this figure.

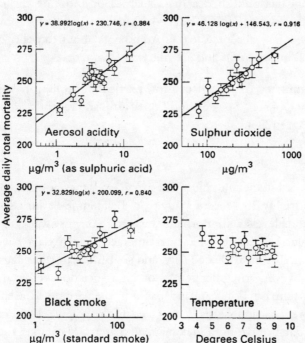

Figure 4.2: Association between daily mortality and SO$_2$, aerosol acidity, and black smoke in London, England, based on data for the period 1965-72, from reference [32]. By aggregating data from the spring and autumn months, the range of temperature change has been much reduced.

Routine daily measurements of PM$_{2.5}$ have recently become available as a coloured map of the United States on the EPA Web site (see figure 2.4). Observations were initiated in the six US cities included in a long-running air pollution study initiated by the Harvard School of Public Health [9]. A recent report on the time-series mortality data from these cities showed that PM$_{2.5}$ had a stronger association with mortality than PM$_{10}$, with a 10 microgram/m^3 increase in PM$_{2.5}$ being associated with a 1.5% increase in mortality (CI 1.1-1.9%). Pneumonia and chronic obstructive lung disease had the highest risk factors, but ischemic heart disease risk was also raised above the mean level. Different models for dealing with the effects of weather and seasonality were without effect on the association. Schwartz [35] has published a meta-analysis of most of the existing data. That the association of $PM_{2.5}$ with daily mortality is robust has now been generally accepted [6,83]. Arguments about causality depend on additional information and are noted in Chapter 5.

A useful summary of the effects of particulate pollution has been published by Dockery, Speizer, and Pope [176], and recently brought up to date by Pope [223].

Ozone

There are several studies indicating that ozone levels may be associated with increased mortality. In a recent study from Belgium [80], the association of raised ozone levels with mortality was strong on very warm days, and it is probable that these two factors interact. Similar data have been reported from Toronto, Mexico City, and six European cities aggregated together. However, an earlier report of an association between ozone and mortality in London England has not been found in a later and more comprehensive analysis. Samet and his colleagues [205] recently re-analyzed data for ozone, and concluded that in 20 US cities, there was evidence that it was influencing mortality in the summer, a 10 ppb increase in ozone being associated with a 1.1% increase in rate of death.

These studies raise a number of important issues regarding exposures, confounding of the studies by other pollutants, and statistical issues primarily involving the handling of weather and temperature variables [83]. These are discussed in Chapters 7 and 8.

Longitudinal Studies

Survival

Longitudinal survival studies are those in which a population is followed for a span of years. The results from such studies complement the time- series data in several ways. If "harvesting" was dominant, and lives were cut short by only a few days, the longitudinal survival data would show little effect of higher PM_{10} levels on survival. Also, longitudinal data would include any possible effect of PM_{10} in increasing the severity (or even the prevalence) of conditions such as myocardial disease, or in leading to death at a younger age.

Three longitudinal survival studies have been available for retrospective studies. A detailed analysis by Pope and his colleagues [31] of a study established six years before by the American Cancer Society, involving 552,138 adults who lived in 151 US metropolitan areas and whose cigarette smoking habits were known, recorded survival in relation to the levels of sulphate and fine particulate pollution in the areas in which they lived. Particulate air pollution was shown to be associated with cardiopulmonary and lung cancer mortality, after cigarette smoking had been allowed for, but not with mortality due to other causes. The data were adjusted for age, sex, race, cigarette smoking, exposure to passive cigarette smoke, and occupational exposures. Sulphate exposure was associated with a 36% increase in lung cancer and a 26% increase in other cardiopulmonary causes of death. Fine particle exposure was associated with cardiopulmonary deaths, but not with lung cancer. Higher pollution levels were clearly associated with a reduced survival, the difference in survival being about three years between the highest and lowest 5% of counties studied in terms of their air pollution.

An objection has been raised that some untested variables, associated by chance with pollution levels, might account for the observed relationship between pollutant levels and premature mortality. So far, no convincing evidence for this hypothesis has been presented. A 16-year follow-up of the populations in six US cities who had been the subjects of a continuing analysis of air pollution effects came to similar conclusions. The cohort was aged between 25 and 75 years when the study began, and included 8,111 adults. Occupational factors and, more particularly, a detailed smoking history were both known. The adjusted mortality ratio for the most polluted of the cities, a steel-making town in Ohio, compared with the least polluted (in rural Kansas) was 1.26, and air pollution was positively associated with deaths from lung cancer and from cardiopulmonary causes, but not with other diseases. Survival decreased monotonically with particulate pollution across the six cities, and the relationship was as strong for aerosol sulphates (which constituted a major fraction of the $PM_{2.5}$ component) as for PM_{10}. Figure 4.3 shows a plot of the data from these two longitudinal studies.

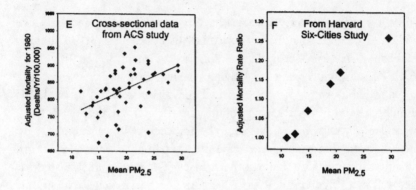

Figure 4.3: Association between mortality and $PM_{2.5}$ in two US studies, with data from reference [223]. The left-hand panel shows the relationship between adjusted mortality and $PM_{2.5}$ in the prospective American Cancer Society study. The right- hand panel is from the Harvard six-city study and shows the close association between the adjusted mortality rate ratio and mean $PM_{2.5}$. Both of these studies extended over more than 16 years of observation.

The Health Effects Institute undertook a comprehensive re-analysis of both of these studies. Their committee recently reported on their findings, which corroborated those of the original investigators [215]. The report noted:

The Risk Estimates reported by the original investigators were remarkably robust to alternative specifications of the underlying risk models, thereby strengthening confidence in the original findings. Specifically, the inclusion of additional individual-level covariates beyond those considered by the original investigators had little impact on the original risk estimates. Similar risk estimates also were obtained regardless of whether age or calendar year was used as the time axis.

The Reanalysis Team did find evidence of variation in risk among population subgroups: the most important was that the relative risk of mortality associated with fine particle air pollution decreased with increasing educational attainment.

We observed this modifying effect of education in both studies. Although the interpretation of this finding is unclear, it is possible that educational attainment is a marker for socioeconomic status, which in turn may be correlated with exposure to fine particle air pollution.

A third study, of well-characterized Seventh Day Adventists in California [211], a non-smoking cohort of 3,914 adults, also found increased risk of mortality related to residence in regions of increased particle pollution, and also with other pollutants. This study also showed that the relative risks of developing chronic respiratory symptoms (including asthma) were associated significantly with their computed lifetime PM_{10} exposure levels.

These studies have confirmed the importance and significance of the daily time-series studies of PM_{10} in relation to mortality. Although "harvesting" must occur to some extent, the impact of the effect of pollution exposure on survival and on symptom development has been confirmed. There is, however, still considerable controversy about the significance of these cross-sectional longitudinal studies. Vedal [83] has recently argued that the observed differences are probably attributable to the short-term daily mortality time-series effect — and this is certainly possible. However, the probability that living in regions of higher air pollution has a long-term effect on survival can also be argued. This hypothesis is supported by the studies done in Britain and in France [1] more than 30 years ago, which showed that when smoking had been accounted for, the FEV_1 of the population was lower in the more polluted regions. The same data have recently been found to be true of non-smoking women in China. The FEV_1 is known to be closely related to survival, and therefore such a diminution caused by long-term residence in more polluted regions is likely to lead to reduced survival, without the direct time-series daily mortality data being invoked [81].

Furthermore, longitudinal survival studies would take account of any effect of the pollutants on increasing the prevalence of a condition, or in causing more severe disease at an earlier age. Neither of these effects would be recorded by time-series analyses.

Lung Growth

The Southern California Children's study, involving 3,800 children in 12 different communities in the Los Angeles basin [127, 129], has recently reported an effect of higher exposure to vehicle pollutants (PM_{10}, $PM_{2.5}$, NO_2, and organic acids) on the rate of increase in lung function over a five-year period [195].

A second cohort followed for the same length of time has shown the same effect, namely, a reduced rate of growth of lung function in those with higher pollution exposure. Remarkably, Avol and his colleagues in the same study [183] were able to do repeat lung function tests on about 120 children who have moved from their original home to either cleaner or more polluted regions. They found that lung function improved in those who moved to a cleaner area, and declined in those in a more polluted region. This reinforced the conclusions drawn from the longitudinal data analysis.

Morbidity Time-Series Studies

Although studies of premature mortality in relation to air pollution are of great importance, it is likely that any significant pollution impact in relation to premature death would also cause changes in other indices. Hospital admissions for the relevant day should rise, and there may be a significant increase in hospital emergency department visits. The demonstration that these events are occurring in addition to an increase in mortality constitutes the fulfilment of the criterion of "coherence" in relation to a judgement of causality [42].

Hospital Admissions

When the first edition of this book was prepared, the only evidence that an increase in hospital admissions occurred in an episode of pollution that caused increased mortality was in the greatly increased demand for hospital beds that occurred in the London episode of December 1952. There have now been a large number of studies of hospital admissions independently of specific air pollution episodes. One of the earliest of these was of hospital admissions in southern Ontario. This analyzed hospital admissions data on a daily basis starting in 1975 and continuing for several years. There was a highly significant association (judged by the Pearson correlation coefficient) between hospital admissions for respiratory disease and pollutants in the summer, comparing each day with the mean admission values for that day of the week in the same season of the year [41]. This work has now been greatly extended, and the exposure data have been refined by Burnett and his colleagues [39], and most recently by Zidek and his colleagues [78]. Using data from 168 Ontario hospitals over a six-year period, there are highly significant associations between ozone and sulphate levels in the summer and hospital admissions in all age groups. Interestingly, in infants between the ages of 0 and 1 year, the diagnostic category of "acute infections" showed a strong association, and a model including both ozone and sulphate showed that the data accounted for 19% of summer admissions in infants in this diagnostic category (see Table 4.2). In older age groups, "asthma" and "pneumonia" were both significant. By devising different models for the regression analyses, the authors were able to exclude the effect of temperature.

Age (years)	Asthma	COPD	Infection	All
0-1	13.0*	–	19.1***	14.8***
2-34	5.5*	23.8*	4.4	5.5*
35-64	9.8***	8.6	3.1	7.2***
65+	7.0	6.0**	2.5	4.3*
All	7.1***	5.8**	4.3*	5.8***

Table 4.2: Percentage of acute respiratory hospital admissions associated with summer air pollutants in southern Ontario, calculated from a model which incorporated ozone lagged 1 and 3 days and sulphate lagged 1 day with added "potency" factors. Average number of daily respiratory admissions was 107.5, and the data extended over six years. Note that the diagnosis in infants under the age of 1 year was an infection (probably bronchiolitis) and that the air pollutants accounted for 19.1% of these admissions. Significance
* $p = <0.05$
** $p = <0.01$
*** $p = >0.001$
Data from reference [39].

The significant association of pollutants with "infections" in infants is noteworthy, and probably attributable to the fact that ozone causes lung inflammation at very low concentrations. In the older age groups, the association is strongest for the diagnostic category of asthma, but over the age of 65, the diagnostic category of COPD (chronic obstructive pulmonary disease) is principally affected.

Another study analyzed respiratory admissions to hospitals in Toronto [45] in three consecutive summers. This confirmed the strong associations between admissions and PM_{10}, ozone, sulphates, and acidic aerosols. What was interesting was that although total suspended particulate (TSP) was positively associated with admissions, as was PM_{10}, when TSP minus PM_{10} was studied, it showed no association with admissions, confirming that it was the PM_{10} particles that were important.

A recent analysis of data from Buffalo and Rochester by Thurston and his colleagues [167] showed that pollution levels were associated with daily mortality and increased hospital admissions in the same region, and also found that daily measurements of hydrogen ion (H^+) and sulphates (SO_4^{-2}) were strongly associated with the outcomes. However, a later study of the Detroit-Windsor area [218] failed to confirm the strong association with H^+; the hospital admission data were mainly associated with measures of particulate pollution.

Sulphates are an important constituent of $PM_{2.5}$ in Ontario and in the northeast generally. Schwartz [33, 36, 37] has shown that both PM_{10} and ozone are associated with increased hospital admissions. In view of the association between particulates and mortality, it is important to note that hospital admissions for cardiovascular disease have been noted to be associated with PM_{10} levels in Ontario and Detroit, and most recently in Tucson, Arizona [89], where climatic conditions are very different. The association between hospital admissions and air pollutants has also been studied in Sao Paulo [184] and Philadelphia [180].

A strong association between hospital admissions for asthma and ozone levels has been reported from Brisbane in Australia [229]. In that city, ozone levels are relatively similar in all seasons of the year. The study analyzed over 13,000 asthma admissions. Remarkable confirmation of the effect of ozone on hospital admissions was obtained from an analysis of data from Atlanta [231] comparing the 17 days of the 1996 Summer Olympic Games with other periods. During the games, car usage fell 20% and the ozone peak fell by about 30 ppb; hospital admissions for acute respiratory disease fell 38% and other indices changed similarly. Non-respiratory conditions were not affected. Burnett and his colleagues in Canada [227] have recently found a strong association between ambient ozone levels and hospital admissions for respiratory illness of infants under the age of 2 years. This is the first study to indicate that children of this age are at risk from ambient ozone.

These data, taken together, provide striking evidence that hospital admissions are regularly influenced by pollution levels. It seems likely that PM_{10} and ozone act independently. In Utah, where ozone was not present, the admission of children to hospital with acute respiratory infections was shown to be closely associated with levels of PM_{10} in the community. A local steel mill was the source of about half of the PM_{10}. Data have recently been presented that confirmed the greater toxicity of the PM_{10} particles when the steel mill was operating compared with when it was closed by a strike [154].

Hospital admissions also increased in the 1991 London episode in which NO_2 reached high levels and PM_{10} was also increased, although the exact levels of PM_{10} were not known [21]. A recent study in Holland has found that hospital admissions are related to ozone and other pollutants [43]. This is an important observation since there is no aerosol sulphuric acid in Holland associated with raised ozone levels, as occurs in southern Ontario [13]. Both ozone and particulate pollution have been shown to be associated with respiratory hospital admissions in different cities in Europe [103, 104, 106, 111].

PM_{10}, $PM_{2.5}$, aerosol sulphates and ozone are not the only pollutants with which increased hospital admissions have been found to be associated. Carbon monoxide (CO), the levels of which have been considerably reduced over the past 10 years, was shown to be associated with an increased risk of hospital admission for congestive heart failure in the elderly in a six-year study of seven large US cities. A risk ratio of 1.37 was reported for Los Angeles for a 10 ppm increase in CO; the other six cities were somewhat lower than this but all showed significant association. In Canada, Burnett and his colleagues also found significant associations between CO and hospital admissions [190].

Although there are sound physiological reasons why an increase in CO might adversely affect a subject with heart disease [222], it is also possible that the CO level is acting as a general indicator of exposure to vehicle emissions.

Since the first edition of this book, it has become clear that hospital admission data are valuable indicators of the adverse effects of air pollutants.

Hospital Emergency Visits

The first study of the relationship between hospital emergency visits and pollutants would appear to have been one conducted in Philadelphia in 1965 by Girsch and his colleagues [44]. Comparing 1,346 patient visits to the Emergency Department of the Children's Hospital, they concluded: "There was a threefold greater incidence of bronchial asthma during days of noteworthy high pollution." This was compared to the observation that very few asthma attacks occurred during the ragweed season. It is remarkable that very little attention seems to have been paid to these data. Other early studies of associations between pollutants and emergency room visits were conducted in Utah, in Steubenville, Ohio, and in Los Angeles.

More recent studies have led to the following conclusions:

- Asthma emergency visits of children to a children's hospital in Atlanta, Georgia, were strongly affected by ozone levels.

- Strong associations were demonstrated between asthma emergency visits and ozone in New Jersey over a five-year period. Similar data have recently been published from Houston, Texas [182].

- An association was shown between PM_{10} values and asthma emergency visits in Seattle. A similar strong association between asthma emergency visits and PM_{10} levels (or PM_{10} levels calculated from coefficient of haze data) has been shown to exist in Santa

Clara County, California, in the winter [82]. Three hospitals were used, with an average of 7.6 asthma emergency visits per day. Interestingly, the effect was greater at low ambient temperatures, and almost disappeared on the warmest days of the winter. In this region, 45% of the PM_{10} has been shown to be due to residential wood burning.

- No relationship could be found between SO_2 and emergency asthma visits in New York City. By contrast, SO_2 levels were associated with emergency visits for respiratory disease in Vancouver [19]. This may well have been due to a concomitant rise in particulate levels, but these were not being monitored at the time.

- An important study of emergency visits in London, England, covered 12 emergency departments over a three-year period [131]. Strong associations for all respiratory complaints were noted, such that there was a 2.8% increase in visits for an 18 microgram/m^3 increase in SO_2; a 3.0% increase for a 31 microgram/m^3 increase in PM_{10}; and significant associations between visits of children with asthma and NO_2 levels. Several other studies have found a weak association between SO_2 and emergency visits, including the one in Vancouver noted above, another in Barcelona, and a third in Helsinki. However in none of these were measurements of PM_{10} available, so it can be argued that SO_2 was acting as a surrogate for PM_{10}. These two pollutants are often closely correlated.

- A major study reported by Romieu and her colleagues, based on a children's hospital in Mexico City [47] serving 450,000 children, tabulated emergency visits for asthma for a six-month period. The authors calculated that "an increase of 50 ppb in the maximal one hour ozone level would lead to a 43% increase in the number of emergency visits for asthma on the following day." Exposure to high ozone levels (more than 110 ppb) for two consecutive days increased the number of asthma related visits by 68%. There was some evidence that SO_2 also affected the number of visits, though this might have been a surrogate for particulate levels.

- In Birmingham, England, it was shown that the risk of an asthma emergency visit by a child was associated with the proximity of the child's home to a major motorway. It was not known whether increased PM_{10} or NO_2 exposure (or both together) might be responsible for this observation. Another study from Britain, in north-west London, did not find a significant association [155].

- Emergency visits for respiratory disease in Montreal were associated with ozone levels [99].

These studies serve to reinforce the hospital admissions data. As noted later in Chapter 5, the effects of air pollution should be viewed as a "cascade" of phenomena, but the relationships between emergency visits and admissions to hospital, or both of these to mortality, may depend on a variety of local and other factors.

Other Indices of Morbidity

There are other indices of morbidity that are less direct than those already discussed, but which may reflect the impact of pollution on the community. These include the following:

- Doctor's house calls have been successfully used in a study conducted in Paris [116]; air pollution levels were shown to influence the number of such calls to the homes of asthmatic children. Similar data have been published from Switzerland [185] and London [149]. Increases in respiratory symptoms in schoolchildren have been documented in the steel-producing cities in New South Wales in Australia [220].

- Increased school absences have been found to be associated with both SO_2 and PM_{10}. These studies were reported from Helsinki and from Utah. A strong association between school absences for respiratory illness and ambient ozone has been reported from the Southern California children's study [212].

- "Reduced Activity Days" recorded in survey work were later shown to be associated with pollution levels. Work absences can be similarly studied.

- Particulate pollution has been shown to be associated with a worsening of the status of patients with chronic obstructive lung disease in New Zealand; London, England; and Spain.

- There have recently been an important series of studies of school children living adjacent to major motorways in Holland. These have shown that the risk of lower respiratory infections and a reduction in lung function are related to both the distance the child lives from the motorway and the diesel traffic travelling along it [85].

- A remarkable observation was recently made by Peters and her colleagues in Germany [96]. In Augsburg, a study of routinely collected blood samples was in progress in the general population. The investigators found that over the course of a week when there was an air pollution episode for 12 days, with raised levels of SO_2 and particulate pollution, there was a significant increase in the measured viscosity of the blood samples they had collected from individuals between the ages of 25 and 64. The odds ratio for plasma viscosity above the 95th percentile during the episode was 3.6 for men and 2.3 for women. Since an increased viscosity is a risk factor for a heart attack, the authors suggested that this change might be the intermediary between increases in particulate pollution and an increase in cardiovascular mortality.

- In the city of Le Havre, France [156], sales of respiratory drugs were shown to be related to air pollution levels.

- It has been very difficult to design epidemiological studies which might throw light on long-term consequences of continued air pollution exposure. One study of incoming students to the Berkeley campus of the University of California has been conducted by Kuenzli and his colleagues [77]. It involved about 130 non-smoking students aged about 18 coming from different parts of California. A very detailed questionnaire involving all places of residence since birth was completed, and spirometric tests were done on at least two occasions. Eight different indices of lifetime oxidant exposure were calculated; all of these were highly inter-correlated as one would expect. From these data, it was concluded that although FVC and FEV_1 levels did not show any differences in relation to lifetime oxidant exposure (however this was calculated), measurements of airflow did show differences. Statistically significant regressions between the calculated exposure and the maximal mid-expiratory flow rate (FEF_{25-75}), and with the flow velocity at 50% of expiration ($Vmax_{50}\%$) and at 75% of expiration ($Vmax_{75}\%$) were found. These changes might indicate chronic changes in the region of the terminal bronchiole. It is noted below that experimental long-term exposures of primates to ozone indicate that morphological changes in this region of the lung follow such ozone exposure. Recent work from the Primate Center at the University of California at Davis, in which infant rhesus monkeys were exposed to ozone in repeated episodes, showed clear evidence that this altered the postnatal development of the distal conducting airways [177].

- Studies of military service recruits by Lippmann and Kinney [60] also indicated that residence in more highly polluted regions had led to a chronic decrement in lung function in young army cadets.

- A recent analysis of 520 students entering Yale University showed the same decrement in lung function in those coming from regions of higher ozone pollution [228].

- Observations in England in the 1960s showed lower lung function in men living in regions with higher air pollution, with socioeconomic factors and cigarette smoking taken into account [1]. This also indicated a long-term effect of pollution (at that time largely from coal burning and heavy industry) on the population.

Studies of Specific Episodes

The episodes of industrial pollution in the valley of the Meuse in Belgium in 1930, and in Donora, Pennsylvania, in 1948, indicated that severe effects might occur in temperature inversions. The London episode in December 1952 was fully described in the first edition of this book; it was in fact the culmination of worsening ambient pollution due to uncontrolled coal burning [1]. Detailed statistical studies were hardly required after the London episode, in which mortality increased in all age groups, including children. As noted in Chapter 1, it is probable that at least 8,000 people, and possibly as many as 12,000, were victims of this disaster. Most of the victims were elderly, and there were reasons to believe that in the majority of cases, there was pre-existing heart or lung disease; but the mortality among children also increased.

Other specific episodes have been recorded. In one, Germany was affected by pollutants coming in from the east. Most indices of effects increased, and the use of ambulances in the affected area was one indicator that changed significantly during the episode. It was also shown that the blood carboxyhemoglobin level (COHb) in non-smokers increased in this episode (the first time that had been demonstrated).

In Barcelona, episodes of periodic increased morbidity and mortality from asthma were shown to be associated with windblown soy bean fragments from the harbour — those affected were shown to have a positive skin reaction to soy beans. It has now been shown that "New Orleans Asthma" was probably to be explained by soy dust blowing out of the storage facilities in the harbour [112]. This was an important study because it showed that the association between the occurrence of episodic asthma and unloading at the port could be made to disappear if certain statistical methods (which had previously been applied to the data) were used.

Remarkable "outbreaks" of acute asthma have occurred during thunderstorms in both Britain and in Melbourne, Australia. In these, more than 150 asthma cases have been seen in hospital emergency departments during and a few hours after the storm. In both instances, it has been shown that the rain interacted with spores in the air, causing them to break up and release fragments small enough to penetrate into the deep lung.

The recent London episode in December 1991, when NO_2 was above 400 ppb for 8 hours on two consecutive days [21], was studied in considerable detail. The highest level of black smoke was 228 micrograms/m^3, recorded in Essex. A maximum of 144 micrograms/m^3 (0.054 ppm) of SO_2 was also recorded, and levels of CO increased. Respiratory and cardiac mortality increased (to an extent approximately concordant with predictions from time-series data). Hospital admissions increased, with 14% increases for obstructive lung disease and asthma, 8% for asthma, and 4% for ischemic heart disease. All these risks were higher in those over the age of 65, and in this category, hospital admissions for obstructive lung disease were 43% above predicted. Small increases in family practice consultations were noted. It was concluded that it was not possible to differentiate between the effects of the raised NO_2 and the impact of the increased particulate pollution.

When a cohort of schoolchildren has been followed on a routine basis, it has been possible to show (in Holland) that there is a significant decline in lung function occasioned by an episode of increased air pollution (probably particulates) and continuing for about three weeks afterwards.

Cross-Sectional Comparisons

In a cross-sectional study, subjects living in one community are compared with similar samples in two or more communities with different levels of air pollution. Usually the subjects complete a detailed respiratory questionnaire, and often lung function tests are performed.

A recent study of 22 communities in the US and Canada [48, 49, 50] collected such information from 10,251 children between the ages of 7 and 12. Daily measurements of pollutants were made in the schoolyards of the schools the children were attending. The main conclusions of the study were:

- Asthma prevalence was not related to pollution levels.

- Bronchitic symptoms were more frequent in children in communities with higher acidic aerosol pollution: both ozone and acidic aerosol levels were related to a decrement in the forced vital capacity (FVC) such that a 52 nmol/m^3 difference in annual mean particle strong acidity was associated with a 3.5% decrement in the FVC. The FVC was also strongly related to daytime ozone.

The Southern California children's study, involving 3,800 children in 12 communities chosen for their different patterns of air pollution, did not find major differences in respiratory questionnaire data between the different locations; in particular, the prevalence of asthma was unrelated to pollution pattern [127]. Regions with higher vehicle pollution data were associated with slightly but significantly lower pulmonary function test results [129].

Several large Swiss cross-sectional studies of respiratory symptoms in schoolchildren have been published. With many thousands of children participating, it has been shown that ambient pollution levels, PM_{10}, SO_2, and NO_2 are associated with an increased prevalence of bronchitis and the associated symptoms. In these studies, large samples are required because corrections have to be applied for all known factors that might influence the results. Thus the percentage of asthmatics in each community must be known and allowed for, and domestic factors such as parental smoking, damp housing, and gas cooking must be noted. These corrections have the effect of reducing sample size, so a large initial sample is required if the study is to have sufficient statistical power to detect differences that might be attributable to differences in air pollution exposure.

The Swiss Research Group on Air Pollution [121] have recently reported that higher NO_2 exposure is associated with a lower FVC and FEV_1. The communities studied were 82 residential zones in eight different areas — Geneva, Basel, Lugano, Aarau, Payerne, Wald, Davos, and Montana. The range of estimated average home outdoor exposure to NO_2 was 9.9-62.4 micrograms/m^3. The range of estimated average personal exposure was 12.8-49.2 micrograms/m^3 (6.65-5.58 ppb). Five hundred sixty adult subjects made personal measurements of NO_2 exposure. The original total sample was 7,656, but 1,995 were later excluded. Smoking was taken into account. The authors concluded that a 10 microgram/m^3 increase in average home outdoor and personal exposure to NO_2 was associated with a change in FVC of -2.93% between communities, and of -0.68% between zones of residence in the same community. FEV_1 differences were -0.94% and -1.36%. NO_2 measurements were by passive samplers.

The authors of this study have recently argued that small differences in FVC between populations may indicate a serious impact of air pollution [175].

A study of 1,213 Dutch schoolchildren in six communities, noted earlier [85], showed that their exposure to particulate pollution, largely from diesel traffic on adjacent motorways, was strongly associated with a lowered level of lung function when all other factors had been taken into account. Measurements of black smoke and PM_{10} were made at the children's schools. All indices of lung function, particularly the measurements of terminal airflow velocity, showed an almost linear relationship to the density of truck traffic. The authors also found an association between the particle exposure and respiratory symptoms.

A comparison between two communities in Israel before and after the start-up of a power station did not show any differences in respiratory symptoms. Recent comparisons between communities around Beijing, China comparing areas with greater and less coal-burning pollution, found that the SO_2 level was significantly related to decrements in FEV_1 in non-smoking women. This conclusion was similar to the PAARC study conducted in France in 1970, which showed the same effect. In neither of these studies was PM_{10} being measured, and the possibility that differences in fine particulate pollution was the major factor cannot be excluded. A study in Hong Kong [233] compared the status of 848 children in a polluted area and 812 in a cleaner suburb. The children were aged 8-12 years, and respiratory questionnaires were completed and spirometry performed. Both boys and girls in the more polluted region had a higher prevalence of symptoms and significantly lower pulmonary function values. Particulate pollution, SO_2, and NO_2 levels were all higher in the polluted region.

Studies of regions where there have been substantial reductions in air pollution are important. In East Germany, the decline in ambient air pollution (largely from coal burning) has been followed by a decline in the prevalence of respiratory symptoms in children [196]; and in Finland, respiratory health has been shown to improve following the reduction in emissions of malodorous sulphur compounds from pulp mills [142].

Panel Studies

A panel study is one in which a selected group of individuals is followed on a continuing basis. They may record their symptoms and peak flow rate, daily activity patterns, medication use, etc., and simultaneously their exposure to pollutants is measured or calculated.

A considerable number of such studies have been conducted, and some of the important results are as follows:

- The peak expiratory flow rate (PEFR) in a panel of children in Utah was affected by changes in the PM_{10} level.

- Respiratory symptoms and PEFR measurements were related to levels of acidic aerosol in Uniontown, Pennsylvania. Exposure data from this study were noted in Chapter 2.

- A recent study reported orally at the American Thoracic Society meeting in Toronto in May 2000, but not yet published, involved over 500 infants in Santiago, Chile, and was conducted by Romieu and her colleagues. The infants were recruited at the age of 4 months, and followed closely for the next eight months. Lower respiratory illness episodes were strongly associated with ambient PM_{10}.

- There have been a number of panel studies of children in Mexico City. One involved 83 boys and 65 girls aged 7-9 years. Cough and decrements in forced vital capacity (FVC) were related to the maximal ozone level, which exceeded 120 ppb every week of the study. In another study, of 71 children aged 7-11 years, it was shown that PM_{10} levels were strongly related to PEFR decrements. Both ozone and PM_{10} levels affected respiratory symptoms, and a 50 ppb increase in ozone was related to an increase in lower respiratory illness in these children.

- In a panel study of non-atopic adult asthmatics in Denmark, the evening PEFR self-measured was shown to be related to SO_2 and NO_2 levels encountered that day. Medication use also increased as pollution levels were higher.

- In Denver, a study of a panel of adult asthmatics showed that as levels of acidic aerosols rose, their asthma worsened and symptoms of chest tightness and cough increased.

- One panel study of asthmatic children and adults has been reported from Erfurt and Weimar in Germany, and from Sokolov in the Czech Republic. Levels of SO_2 were associated with increased symptoms and with reductions in the evening Peak Expiratory Flow rate; the effects on adults were less marked.

- A recent report from Holland on a panel of 61 children [88], 77% of whom were taking medication for asthma, showed that levels of black smoke, and also PM_{10} and ozone, were associated with increased symptoms and medication need. The levels of the pollutants were relatively low, and did not exceed current standards. A similar study in Finland [92] showed that PM_{10} levels, black smoke, and NO_2 exposure were all related to a decline in function in symptomatic children.

- In a panel of 83 asthmatics in Los Angeles County, raised levels of ozone affected about 15% of the subjects enrolled, and a small subset of the whole sample showed significant declines in lung function.

- As noted above, in a panel of patients with chronic obstructive lung disease in New Zealand, their lung function status and symptoms were shown to be affected by increased levels of particulate pollution — in this case, attributable mostly to wood burning.

- In a unique study of schoolchildren in the Kanawha valley in West Virginia, which is the location of a concentration of chemical industries, a panel study of children in different regions involved detailed air sampling on a continuing basis. All the children were aged between 8 and 11 years. There were 1,566 children in the valley near the factories; 2,768 in the valley but more distant; 1,122 out of the valley but near factories; and 2,136 children out of the valley and distant from factories. The wide spectrum of organic chemicals emitted was associated with irritant symptoms in the eyes and throat, and evidence of airway irritation and increased bronchitis.

- There have been two studies of NO_2 exposure in Swiss children, one involving 625 children and the other 1,225 children living in four different regions. Personal NO_2 samplers were attached to their clothing. These studies indicated that increased lower respiratory symptoms were related to the highest levels of NO_2 exposure.

- A detailed study of schoolchildren in the US involving indoor NO_2 sampling also showed a relationship between the highest NO_2 levels and lower respiratory symptoms; however, a study involving households without smokers, and following all respiratory events from birth to the second year of life, found no association between NO_2 levels in the home and such respiratory episodes.

- An imaginative study in South Australia [234] used Palmes tubes to record weekly NO_2 exposure in 125 self-reported asthmatic adults and children. 76% of males and 81% of females lived in houses using gas cooking. In children only, worsening asthma (assessed by four criteria) was strongly associated with the recorded level of NO_2 exposure. In the age group 35-49, the only associated symptom was cough.

- An 18-month study of grade school children in British Columbia's Vancouver Island community of Port Alberni [198] showed that increases in symptoms (cough and phlegm) and reductions in evening peak flow followed increases in PM_{10}. The effects were restricted to a group of 54 children with doctor-diagnosed asthma, and did not occur in a control group of normal children over the same time period. The PM_{10} combustion particles were derived from wood smoke from residential areas, together with emissions from two pulp and paper mills in the community. No other pollutants were present, and there was no significant heavy diesel traffic.

- Delfino and his colleagues [136] reported on a detailed panel study of asthmatic children in the community of Alpine in southern California. A clear adverse effect of both ozone and PM_{10} was recorded. In this study, fungal spores were also measured and did not appear to be related to worsening symptoms or function.

- Schwartz and Neas [161] have noted that fine particles are more strongly associated with adverse effects in schoolchildren than are coarse particles.

- A number of panel studies of elderly subjects with chronic heart disease have been reported. These have noted an increase of symptoms in relation to particulate pollution [178]; changes in the electrocardiogram [179]; and reductions in heart rate variability [181]. In a remarkable study of a panel of elderly people in Provo, Utah, Pope and his colleagues observed that PM_{10} levels were associated with an increase in resting pulse rate [174].

- A study of PM_{10} exposures in a traffic tunnel in Sweden showed that in a panel of adult asthmatic subjects, the exposure enhanced the response to a subsequently administered allergen [125].

Field Studies:

Field studies have contributed important information on air pollution effects. Most of these have involved studies of children at summer camps. Spirometry may be carried out twice a day as part of the camp routine, and air monitoring equipment is usually run at the camp. There are at least a dozen of these studies, and the important conclusions they have yielded are as follows:

- Decrements in the forced vital capacity (FVC) and forced expired volume in 1 second (FEV_1) are related to ambient ozone levels. The magnitude of the decrement is similar to or slightly greater than that observed in controlled chamber exposures, probably because the duration of exposure and the level of exercise may be greater in the camp studies. In one of these studies, regression slopes for FVC of -1.03 mL/ppb O_3; for FEV_1 of -1.42 mL/ppb O_3; for PEFR of -6.78 mL/sec/ppb O_3; and for FEF_{25-75} of -2.48 mL/sec/ppb O_3 were documented.

- Decrements in peak flow rate (PEFR) may persist for 36 hours or so.

- In a study of 30 healthy office workers exercising during their lunch break, in which they could choose their exercise intensity and duration, voluntary ventilation levels as high as 150 L/min were recorded. Spirometry was performed immediately before and after their exercise. The ozone level varied between 21 and 124 ppb. All measured indices showed a significant correlation with O_3, and the decrements were similar to those recorded from camp studies. The responses were somewhat higher than would be predicted from chamber exposures, however, and the authors suggested that pure chamber experiments might substantially underestimate the O_3-associated responses that can occur among populations engaged in normal outdoor recreational pursuits.

- In one recent study of asthmatic children at such a camp, the children had access to their medications only by going to a tent, where there were a nurse and a physician. It was found that requests for medication were strongly associated with the ozone level on that day. This study confirmed the highly significant association between daily ozone levels and decrements in respiratory function [100].

- In studies of farm workers in the Fraser Valley in British Columbia, picking fruit for more than 10 hours a day, decrements in FVC and FEV_1 were related to peak ozone levels during the day, although the ozone concentrations were not more than 66 ppb (within the Canadian objective of 82 ppb for 1 hour). It was also noted that the mean FEV_1 level of the workers fell progressively over the 60 days of observation, indicating that a long-term decrement in lung function was being caused by the daily exposure [64]. Follow-up observations during a second year have confirmed these results; associations between decrements of lung function and ozone level were also found to be present the morning after the exposure, suggesting a persistent air pollution effect [204].

- In one remarkable study in Mexico City, a tarpaulin was set up to cover an exercise treadmill in the schoolyard. Twenty-two boys and 18 girls aged 7-11 exercised eight times each on different days with two cycles of treadmill exercise. Twenty-one of the children had chronic respiratory symptoms. Decrements in FVC and FEV_1 and in mid-expiratory flow rate (FEF_{25-75}) were noted to be related to ozone level, which reached 229 ppb. The authors observed that despite repeated exposures to oxidants, these children responded acutely to ozone at levels above 150 ppb much as did children exposed under controlled conditions who did not live in a high-ozone region.

- Observations were made during the summers of 1991 and 1992 on 530 non-smoking hikers on Mount Washington in New Hampshire. The average ozone exposures varied between 21 and 74 ppb. There was a 2.6% decline in FEV_1 (106 mL) and a 2.2% (113 mL) decline in FVC per 50 ppb of ozone. Decrements in FVC and PEFR with $PM_{2.5}$ were also observed, and in PEFR with strong aerosol acidity. Forty of the hikers with asthma or a history of wheeze had a fourfold greater responsiveness to ozone than others. Two hundred sixty-five hiked for 8-12 hours, and the same number hiked for 2-8 hours.

These studies in the field are important because they have shown clearly the adverse effects of current ambient levels of air pollutants in interfering with the normal activities of those exercising out of doors.

Special Topics

Effects of Low Levels of Lead

Epidemiological studies of children involving the measurement of the lead content of their deciduous teeth, their measured IQ, and records of their school behaviour and performance were first reported over 20 years ago. By 1990, there had been 24 studies from many different countries, and the regression coefficients for lead levels (variously measured) and IQ were negative in 11 of the 12 studies in which it could be calculated [1], indicating an association between their blood lead levels and IQ. There was determined opposition from the lead tetra-ethyl industry, which argued that this evidence was not substantive, and that unaccounted variables, such as socioeconomic status, were probably responsible for the associations. It therefore took a relatively long time for the importance of the epidemiological observations to be accepted. It is mainly because of the evidence relating lead levels to brain development and behaviour in children that permissible blood lead levels in children have been progressively reduced. In the US, average blood lead levels in children 5 years old and under dropped from 16.5 micrograms per decilitre between 1976 and 1980, to 3.6 micrograms per decilitre between 1992 and 1994 [217]. In adults, there is an association between lead levels and the incidence of strokes and hypertension. All of this evidence was reviewed by Schwartz in 1994 [62], in a very thorough review of the societal benefits that would follow reductions in lead exposure.

Use of MMT in Gasoline

Methylcyclopentadienyl manganese tricarbonyl (MMT) is added to gasoline to increase the octane value. In Ontario, it has been added to gasoline for 15 years. The inhalation of manganese with a particle size of about 0.2 microns cannot be viewed with equanimity because the inhaled compound reaches the brain without a passing through the liver, which clears 98% of manganese entering the body via the digestive system in one pass. The target organ is the limbic system of the brain; occupational poisoning with manganese shows that it can result in a syndrome with some of the features of Parkinson's disease and some of Alzheimer's syndrome. It has been shown that higher exposures lead to higher blood levels [188], and it is disquieting that the only epidemiological study of the effect of low exposures to manganese found evidence of neuropsychiatric disturbances in men over the age of 60 in association with higher blood levels [128, 138].

The "precautionary principle" (the current phrase for common sense) would indicate that the use of MMT in gasoline should have been prohibited until its possible toxicity was better understood, especially with the experience of leaded gasoline additive in hand.

Effects on Fetal and Neonatal Development

There have been reports of an association between pollutant exposure and lower birthweight [168, 214], and from the Czech Republic, of an effect on infant mortality specifically from respiratory causes [153]. Late fetal losses and neonatal mortality appear to be associated with air pollutants in Sao Paulo, Brazil [186].

The mechanisms underlying these effects are not understood. However, the higher post-neonatal (first year of life) mortality documented in the Czech Republic in regions of high coal-burning pollution [168] can almost certainly be attributed to the effect of high particulate and acidic atmospheres on pneumonia.

Effects of Air Pollution on Disease Prevalence

There are very considerable variations in the prevalence of asthma worldwide. Scandinavia and China have relatively low rates, while countries in the southern hemisphere, particularly Australia, have the highest rates. In epidemiological studies, asthma is usually defined as a positive answer to the question "Does the child have doctor-diagnosed asthma?" One of the difficulties in studying prevalence is the probability that in different countries, many factors might affect the answer to this question, including language differences, educational level, and even the availability of a medical opinion.

Comparisons between East and West Germany (where there was linguistic comparability) showed that asthma prevalence was generally lower in the East, where there were high levels of coal-burning pollution, than in the West. Other studies supported the conclusion that asthma prevalence was unaffected by air pollution.

Such a conclusion might have been premature. Studies in France [152] showed that asthma prevalence was related to pollution level — both industrial and vehicle-related pollutants being present. Furthermore, detailed studies of asthma prevalence in large cohorts of children in Taiwan indicated that the higher the exposure to traffic-generated pollutants, the higher the prevalence of asthma when all other factors had been taken into account [158, 169]. This question cannot be completely resolved on the basis of present data; nevertheless it is important since the economic consequence of any factor that affects the prevalence of such a common disease as asthma is quite evident.

The question of whether exposure to higher levels of particulate pollution might cause heart disease to be more severe at a younger age is also very difficult to address. So many factors have been identified that affect the prevalence of myocardial disease that the task of determining whether exposure to air pollutants adds to the risk is difficult. Nevertheless, as the Harvard Institute of Risk Analysis [207] has pointed out, the economic implications of such an influence would be major.

Effects of Wood Smoke and Fires

Domestic wood smoke has been shown to have adverse effects on asthmatic children [210]. Long and his colleagues in Winnipeg, Manitoba [144], were already following a cohort of adult asthmatics when smoke pollution from slash burning occurred over a wide area. They documented the adverse effects on lung function that occurred; this confirmed earlier work on controlled exposure of asthmatics to open leaf burning [146]. Emergency room visits increased in California during the 1997 forest fire disaster [147], but residents in Australia did not seem to be affected by the extensive bush fires around Sydney and Melbourne.

The Asian fires in Indonesia in 1998 affected Singapore, where PM_{10} levels rose to over 160 micrograms/m^3 for days at a time. Tan and her colleagues in Vancouver showed that this affected the percentage of banded neutrophils in the peripheral blood of a cohort of exposed young army cadets [193]. The same group of workers had previously shown experimentally that particulate (PM_{10}) instillation into the lung in rabbits led to a mobilization of newly formed neutrophils from the bone marrow.

Air Pollution and Lung Cancer

Cigarette smoking is such a strong risk factor for the development of lung cancer that it is not easy to quantity any effect that air pollution might have on its incidence. Cohen and Pope [93] have summarized recent data on this question; it seems appropriate to conclude that air pollution might be responsible for between a 10% and 30% increase in the risk of lung cancer. Such a conclusion is supported by a recent analysis of data from Stockholm [208].

Summary of Epidemiological Data

It should be apparent from the reviewed data that the epidemiological evidence of the adverse effects of different air pollutants is extraordinarily rich. Although it is easy to raise objections to one particular type of study design, it is difficult to deny the impact of the studies considered as a whole. Furthermore, in significant instances, the epidemiological data confirm the relevance of controlled exposure studies. The confidence with which specific effects can be ascribed to specific pollutants is discussed in the following section.

LINKING EFFECTS TO SPECIFIC POLLUTANTS

Different air pollutants are usually intercorrelated; this comes about either because the emission sources are common to different compounds — vehicles emit particles, oxides of nitrogen, and CO, for example — or because there are atmospheric interactions which lead to intercorrelations, as is true in the case of ozone and secondary aerosols which are a component of $PM_{2.5}$. Meteorology plays a more general role in the sense that airshed ventilation, dispersion, and atmospheric mixing that control ultimate concentrations of pollutants act on all pollutants simultaneously.

This leads to difficulty in the interpretation of epidemiological data. Correct interpretation of the results of studies comes to depend on comparing results from different locations or using the results of acute human or animal exposures as indicators of the primary pollutant.

In Table 4.3 an attempt has been made to link effects with individual pollutants, and the information there should be taken as a general guide rather than a hard and fast differentiation. Currently, there are areas of particular uncertainty; for guidance these are enumerated below.

Role of SO_2

Sulphur dioxide has been associated with adverse health outcomes in many studies. The intitial re-analysis of Philadelphia mortality data indicated that both SO_2 and PM_{10} were associated with daily mortality. However, Schwartz [187] used the large bank of data from that city, and the fact that SO_2 levels had declined substantially, whereas the particulate pollution had changed little, to show that SO_2 was not playing any part in affecting the association in time-series data between PM_{10} and mortality. Other associations between SO_2 and health outcomes, such as that between emergency hospital visits and air pollution [19], are generally interpreted to indicate that unmeasured particulate pollution might be responsible for the association. It has been suggested that in some environments, such as in China, SO_2 might be a better indicator of $PM_{2.5}$ pollution than the TSP measurements that might be affected by crustal dust.

Role of Sulphate (SO_4)

SO_4 is an important constituent of $PM_{2.5}$ in the northeastern sector of North America. The question of whether this constituent plays an independent role in determining adverse health effects is currently not resolved. Certainly the associations between SO_4 and health outcomes have been shown to be strong in many regions, but it is unclear if SO_4 should be considered to be playing a primary role. The associations between $PM_{2.5}$ and adverse health outcomes in western regions of the continent, where SO_4 levels are generally very low, has suggested that SO_4 does not have an individual primary effect apart from its indicator of $PM_{2.5}$ level.

Ultrafine Particles

As noted below, there is abundant experimental evidence that particle toxicity may be more closely related to the surface area of the particles than to their mass. Whether the toxicity of urban $PM_{2.5}$ depends on the number of ultrafine particles inhaled is less clear, and work has been published with both negative and positive answers to this question. The close intercorrelation of urban air pollutants is indicated by the recent observation that in Los Angeles, CO levels are very closely correlated with the numbers of ultrafine particles; this may account for the associations observed between CO at very low levels and some health outcomes.

Role of Hydrogen Ion (H+) and Acidity

When air pollution was caused by massive uncontrolled coal burning, high levels of sulphuric acid were recorded in pollution episodes; there was little doubt that this contributed to mortality and morbidity.

Hydrogen ion levels are still elevated in modern urban environments, and some studies indicated that these were associated with some adverse health outcomes, such as hospital admissions for respiratory disease. More recent observations [218] have indicated that the H^+ associations are weaker than those for $PM_{2.5}$ and this makes it unlikely that H^+ is now a primary contributor to the adverse health effects.

Pollutant	Definite effects	Probable effects	Possible effects
Fine particles (PM_{10}, $PM_{2.5}$)	Time-series association with daily respiratory and cardiac mortality Aggravation of asthma Increased hospital admissions for respiratory and cardiac conditions Depressed lung function in schoolchildren (acute and chronic) Increased prevalence of bronchitis Increased risk of lung cancer School absences increased Increased blood fibrinogen; increase in banded neutrophils; tachycardia in the elderly; reduced heart rate variability	Aggravation of acute respiratory infections Increased risk of wheezy bronchitis in infants 4-12 months Decreased rate of lung growth in children	
Diesel emissions (in addition to particle effects)	Increased response to allergens	Increased risk of lung cancer	
Ozone	Increased hospital admissions for acute respiratory diseases Aggravation of asthma Increased bronchial responsiveness Increased response to SO_2 Reduced activity days are increased Increased school absences for respiratory illness Reduced lung function Reduced crop yields	Effect on mortality Effects on forest productivity	Aggravation of acute respiratory infections Chronic bronchiolitis with repetitive exposure

Pollutant	Definite effects	Probable effects	Possible effects
Acid aerosols	Increased prevalence of bronchitis Aggravation of asthma Effects on forests		May increase all effects of concomitant ozone
Aerosol sulphates and nitrates	Reduced visibility	May be partly responsible for effects of $PM_{2.5}$	May increase all effects of concomitant ozone
Sulphur dioxide	Acute bronchoconstriction in asthmatics	Increased prevalence of lung cancer	Interaction with particles in relation to mortality and morbidity effects Increased prevalence of chronic bronchitis
Nitrogen dioxide	Increased respiratory morbidity Aggravation of asthma in children Lowered FVC and FEV_1 Increased response to ozone Reduced rate of lung growth		
Carbon monoxide	Increased cardiac ischaemia	Increased hospital cardiac admissions	Increased cardiac mortality
Hydrogen sulphide	Central nervous system and respiratory symptoms Eye irritation	Chronic sinusitis	

Table 4.3: Summary of definite, probable, and possible health effects of individual air pollutants.

Effects of CO

The pathophysiology of CO is very well understood [222], and there is every reason to expect that elevated levels might be associated with some cardiovascular outcomes. However, CO does not exert any effect on the lung; hence its association with respiratory outcomes must indicate that in that case, it is acting as a surrogate for vehicle emission exposure.

Earlier as noted, CO is closely correlated with the numbers of ultrafine particles in the modern urban environment, and this may well explain its role as an indicator of exposure.

Effects of NO_2

It has been difficult to define the role of NO_2 as a pollutant in health studies. It is often strongly associated with specific outcomes, and some studies of respiratory illness in homes with and without gas heating (which about doubles NO_2 exposure) have indicated an association with an increased risk for lower respiratory illness. These associations have also been observed in some environments where SO_2 and O_3 are absent. The episode in London, England, in December 1991, when NO_2 levels exceeded 400 ppb for 8 hours on two consecutive days [21, 221], was not accompanied by any very large scale effects on either morbidity or mortality, although increased hospital admissions of people with chronic lung disease did occur. However, these might have been due to the concomitant elevation of PM_{10}.

SENSITIVE POPULATIONS

A review of the extensive data on adverse health effects indicates that the following groups should be considered at increased risk from the effects of air pollutants:

Asthmatic Subjects

It has been shown that asthmatic subjects, both adults and children, are at increased risk from the effects of SO_2, PM_{10}, O_3, and probably NO_2.

Children

Because children are physically active out of doors, particularly in the summer, they may receive a higher dose of air pollutants than adults. It is probable that their exposure to lead particles emitted from vehicles may have been higher than that in adults, not only from the direct emissions but also from entrained particles in road dust.

Subjects with Cardiac Conditions

It is clear that cardiovascular mortality and hospital admissions are affected by PM_{10} levels. It has been shown that both heart rate and heart rate variability are affected by PM_{10}; there are also concomitant changes in the blood (increased fibrinogen and banded neutrophils). A recent major prospective study conducted in Quebec [216] has indicated that people with congestive heart failure are at special risk, but it is not known whether other myocardial conditions also increase the risk from PM_{10} exposure.

The Elderly

PM_{10} is associated with increased hospital admissions for pneumonia in the elderly. If the effector particles are small (less than 1 micron, for example), indoor concentrations might be much the same as outdoor, making those confined to their homes as much at risk as those who can be physically active out of doors. More exact data on the toxicology of urban particles and on the mechanism of their effect are required before this question can be more precisely answered.

ANIMAL EXPOSURE DATA

There is a voluminous literature on the effects of exposing animals to single pollutants or to combinations of them. Biochemical effects at the cellular level, as well as changes in structure (morphology) and even in pulmonary function have all been reported in most species. A detailed description of these findings is beyond the scope of this volume. Nevertheless, the data are important because they throw light on possible effects of long-term exposures (which cannot be studied in controlled exposure chambers), and because they provide an important background for the consideration of the significance of epidemiological data. In the case of ozone, a very detailed account of the animal exposure data is found in the EPA criteria document [24] and in a recent Swedish review [107]. Some of the most important findings are the following:

- Tyler and his colleagues at the University of California at Davis Primate Center showed that morphological changes occur in the lungs of monkeys exposed to 0.64 ppm ozone for 8 hours a day for 12 months [52]. Their descriptive paper summarizing their work is excellently illustrated. The terminal airway region shows structural changes, and there are changes in the numbers of individual cell types. As noted above, recent work from this centre in which infant rhesus monkeys were exposed to ozone in repeated episodes showed clear evidence that this altered the postnatal development of the distal conducting airways [177].

Similar changes are found in rat lungs, and these have been studied in detail using electron microscopy. In both species, the changes persist after exposure has stopped. The molecular basis of ozone toxicity has been well reviewed by Cotgreave [107].

• There are many experiments showing that ozone and NO_2 (at higher concentrations) interfere with the capability of the lung to defend itself against inhaled bacteria. This is thought to be due to interference with the functioning capability of the cells which are in the alveoli (small air sacs) of the lung. These cells are called macrophages, and they normally ingest bacteria and other foreign material which has penetrated into the lung. Prior exposure of the animals to these two gases increases the lethality of a subsequent exposure to a bacterial aerosol.

• Ultrafine particles of teflon (<0.01 micron) have been shown to be very toxic to rats, and induce an acute inflammatory response. A general conclusion from a large body of work is that the level of toxicity is determined more by the total surface area of the particles than by such measurements as the gravimetric weight.

• Recent experiments using concentrated urban PM_{10} (from Boston) have not yet been described in full. However, Godleski and his colleagues [55] have reported the results shown in Table 4.4. It will be seen that in the group of rats pretreated with the drug monocrataline, which produces a pulmonary vessel change, there was a dose-response relationship, with increasing mortality at higher levels of exposure to concentrated Boston air particles (e.g., 228 and 588 micrograms/m^3). Similarly, at the lower exposure level in rats pre-exposed to SO_2 to produce a chronic bronchitis, there was also an excess mortality of 37% over that seen in normal rats exposed to the same level of PM_{10}.

Factor	Control	MC	MC	ChB
CAP ($\mu g/m^3$)	245	228	580	288
% Mortality	0	19	42	37
Inflammation	0	+++	+++	+++
Bronchoconstriction	0	+	+	+++
Edema	0	-	-	++
Pulmonary vascular congestion	0	-	-	++

Table 4.4: Results of exposing rats to concentrated urban (Boston) PM_{10}. CAP = concentrated air particles, PM_{10}. MC = monocrataline-treated rats; ChB = rats pre-treated with SO_2 to induce chronic bronchitis. Data from reference [55].

These data indicate that there is a dose-response in monocrataline-treated rats, in that the mortality increased from 19% to 42% when PM_{10} increased from 228 micrograms/m^3 to 580. At the lower exposure, the mortality in the rats pre-exposed to SO_2 was twice as great as it was in the monocrataline-treated group.

- Saldiva and his colleagues in Sao Paulo [53, 54] exposed 60 rats to the ambient pollutants of the city by keeping them in a church tower for 3 months or 6 months. These were compared with similar rats kept in a clean country area. Not only were there morphological changes in the lungs of city rats, but their airways had become significantly more responsive to methacholine.

- There is some evidence that simultaneous exposure of rats to ozone and to carbon particle inhalation induces a greater inflammatory response than exposures to either alone. Animal data also provide some support for the hypothesis that concurrent ozone and acid aerosol exposure may be more damaging than either alone [81].

- No changes have been reported in the lungs of animals exposed to concentrations of SO_2 encountered in the ambient atmosphere. At higher concentrations (200-300 ppm), SO_2 induces an inflammatory reaction. Long-term exposures to somewhat lower levels induces an increase in the number of cells that secrete mucus into the airway. Acid aerosols produce greater changes in airway resistance than SO_2 for a given concentration of sulphur.

Sulphuric acid aerosol seems to enhance the removal of tracer particles in the airways of rabbits at low concentrations, and inhibit such removal at higher concentrations.

- Rats exposed to 25 ppm of NO_2 for 6 hours per day for up to 21 days showed evidence of selective damage to some of the airway lining cells, and to the cells lining the alveoli. No effects have been demonstrable at concentrations encountered in the ambient environment.

This is a small sample of the very large volume of animal exposure work that has been reported.

REFERENCES

[1]   BATES, D.V., Environmental Health Risks & Public Policy, University of Washington Press, Seattle & London. 1994. Pp 117.

[2]   BRIMBLECOMBE, P., The Big Smoke: A history of air pollution in London since medieval times, Methuen, London & New York 1987. Pp 185.

[3]   SEIBERLING, G., Monet in London, High Museum of Art; University of Washington Press, Seattle & London. 1988. Pp 103.

[4]   FREUND, P. & MARTIN, G. The Ecology of the Automobile, Black Rose Books, Montreal, New York & London. 1993. Pp 213.

[5]   NATIONAL RESEARCH COUNCIL, USA, Rethinking the Ozone Problem in Urban and Regional Air Pollution, National Academy Press, Washington, DC. 1991. Pp 489.

[6]   REVIEW OF THE NATIONAL AMBIENT AIR QUALITY STANDARDS FOR PARTICULATE MATTER: OAQPS STAFF PAPER,. Office of Air Quality Planning and Standards, US Environmental Protection Agency, Research Triangle Park, NC 27711. April 1996.

[7]   THE UNITED KINGDOM NATIONAL AIR QUALITY STRATEGY, Department of the Environment, London, UK. August 1996.

[8]   OSTRO, B., SANCHEZ, J.M., ARANDA, C., & ESKELAND, G.S., Air Pollution and Mortality: Results from a study of Santiago, Chile, J Exposure Analysis & Environmental Epidemiology 6, 97-114, 1996.

[9]   SCHWARTZ, J., DOCKERY, D.W., & NEAS, L., Is Daily Mortality Associated Specifically with Fine Particles? J Air & Waste Manage. Assoc. 46, 927-39, 1996.

[10]   COMMITTEE ON THE MEDICAL EFFECTS OF AIR POLLUTANTS, DEPARTMENT OF HEALTH, Non-Biological Particles and Health, Her Majesty's Stationery Office, London. 1995. Pp 141.

[11]   ADVISORY GROUP ON THE MEDICAL ASPECTS OF AIR POLLUTION EPISODES, DEPARTMENT OF HEALTH, Sulphur Dioxide, Acid Aerosoles and Particulates, Her Majesty's Stationery Office, London. 1992. Pp 157.

[12]   REVIEW OF THE NATIONAL AMBIENT AIR QUALITY STANDARDS FOR SULFUR OXIDES: Updated assessment of scientific and technical information, Office of Air Quality Planning and Standards, US Environmental Protection Agency. March 1994.

[13]   KEELER, G.J., SPENGLER, J.D., KOUTRAKIS, P., ALLEN, G.A., RAIZENNE, M., & STERN, B., Transported Acid Aerosols Measured in Southern Ontario, Atmospheric Environment 24A, 2935-50, 1990.

[14]   STUDNICKA, M.J., FRISCHER, T., MEINERT, R., STUDNIC KA-BENKE, A., HAJEK, K., SPENGLER, J.D., & NEUMANN, M.G., Acidic Particles and Lung Function in Children: A summer camp study in the Austrian Alps, Am J Respir Crit Care Med 151, 423-30, 1995.

[15]   OZKAYNAK, H., XUE, J., ZHOU, H., SPENGLER, J.D., & THURSTON, G.D., Intercommunity Differences in Acid Aerosol (H^+)/Sulfate (SO_4) ratios, J Exposure Analysis & Environmental Epidemiology 6, 35-55, 1996.

[16]   THURSTON, G.D., GORCZYNSKI, J.E. Jr., CURRIE, J.H., HE, D., ITO, K., HIPFNER, J., WALDMAN, J., LIOY, P.J., & LIPPMANN, M., The Nature and Origins of Acid Summer Haze Air Pollution in Metropolitan Toronto, Ontario, Environ Research 65, 254-70, 1994.

[17]   NEAS, L.M., DOCKERY, D.W., KOUTRAKIS, P., TOLLERUD, D.J., & SPEIZER, F.E., The Association of Ambient Air Pollution with Twice Daily Peak Expiratory Flow Rate Measurements in Children, Am J Epidemiol 141, 111-122, 1995.

[18]   Oxides of Nitrogen, ADVISORY GROUP ON THE MEDICAL ASPECTS OF AIR POLLUTION EPISODES, DEPART-MENT OF HEALTH. Her Majesty's Stationery Office, London. 1993. Pp 137.

[19]   BATES, D.V., BAKER-ANDERSON, M., & SIZTO, R., Asthma Attack Periodicity: A study of hospital emergency visits in Vancouver, Environ Research 51, 51-70, 1990.

[20]   ROMIEU, I., MENESES, F., RUIZ, S., SIENRA, J.J., HUERTA, J., WHITE, M.C., & ETZEL, R.A., Effects of Air Pollution on the Respiratory Health of Asthmatic Children Living in Mexico City, Am J Respir Crit Care Med 154, 300-7, 1996.

[21]   THE HEALTH EFFECTS OF AN AIR POLLUTION EPISODE IN LONDON, DECEMBER 1991, Report commissioned by the Department of Health, London. 1995.

[22]   STEER, K., & HEISKANEN, L., Australian Air Quality Goals for Oxides of Sulphur, Health & Environment Policy Section, Department of Health, Housing, Local Government and Community Services, Canberra, Australia. November 1993. Pp 170.

[23]   SUPPLEMENT TO THE SECOND ADDENDUM (1986) TO AIR QUALITY CRITERIA FOR PARTICULATE MATTER AND SULFUR OXIDES (1982), US EPA/600/AP-93/002. March 1994.

[24]   AIR QUALITY CRITERIA FOR OZONE AND RELATED PHOTOCHEMICAL OXIDANTS, 3 Volumes, Office of Research & Development, US Environmental Protection Agency, Research Triangle Park, NC 27711, USA. EPA/600/P-93/004cF. July 1996.

[25]   SPENGLER, J.D., KOUTRAKIS, P., DOCKERY, D.W., RAIZENNE, M., & SPEIZER, F.E., Health Effects of Acid Aerosols on North American Children: Air pollution exposures, Environ Health Perspect 194, 492-99, 1996.

[26]   GLASS, D.C., A Review of the Health Effects of Hydrogen Sulphide Exposure, Ann Occup Hyg 34, 323-27, 1990.

[27]   MØLHAVE, L., Volatile organic compounds as indoor air pollutants, In: Indoor Air & Human Health, edited by R.B. Gammage & S.V. Kaye, Lewis Publishers Inc., Chelsea, Michigan. 1985.

[28]   BATES, D.V., Particulate Air Pollution, Thorax, 51 (Suppl 2), 53-58, 1996.

[29]   DOCKERY, D.W., & POPE, C.A. III, Acute Respiratory Effects of Particulate Air Pollution, Annu Rev Public Health 15, 107-32, 1994.

[30]   DOCKERY, D.W., POPE, C.A. III, XU, X., SPENGLER, J.D., WARE, J.H., FAY, M.E., FERRIS, B.G. Jr., & SPEIZER, F.E., An Association between Air pollution and Mortality in Six US Cities, New Engl J Med 329, 1753-59, 1993.

[31]   POPE, C.A. III, THUN, M.J., NAMBOODIRI, M.M., DOCKERY, D.W., EVANS, J.S., SPEIZER, F.E., & HEATH, C.W. Jr., Particulate Air Pollution as a Predictor of Mortality in a Prospective Study of US Adults, Am J Respir Crit Care Med 151, 669-74, 1995.

[32]   LIPPMANN, M., & ITO, K., Separating the Effects of Temperature and Season on Daily Mortality from those of Air Pollution in London: 1965-1972, Inhalation Toxicology 7, 85-97, 1995.

[33]   SCHWARTZ, J., Air Pollution and Hospital Admissions for Respiratory Disease, Epidemiology 7, 20-28, 1996.

[34]   SCHWARTZ, J., What Are People Dying of on High Air Pollution Days? Environ Research 64, 26-35, 1994.

[35]   SCHWARTZ, J., Air Pollution and Daily Mortality: A review and meta analysis, Environ Research 64, 36-52, 1994.

[36]   SCHWARTZ, J., Air Pollution and Hospital Admissions for the Elderly in Birmingham, Alabama, Am J Epidemiol 139, 589-98, 1994.

[37]   SCHWARTZ, J., Air Pollution and Hospital Admissions for the Elderly in Detroit, Michigan, Am J Respir Crit Care Med 150, 648-55, 1994.

[38]   SCHWARTZ, J., Particulate Air Pollution and Chronic Respiratory Disease, Environ Research 62, 7-13, 1993.

[39]   BURNETT, R.T., DALES, R.E., RAIZENNE, M.E., KREWSKI, D., SUMMERS, P.W., ROBERTS, G.R., RAAD-YOUNG, M., DANN, T., & BROOK, J., Effects of Low Ambient Levels of Ozone and Sulphates on the Frequency of Respiratory Admissions to Ontario Hospitals, Environ Research 65, 172-94, 1994.

[40]   BURNETT, R.T., DALES, R.E., KREWSKI, D., VINCENT, R., DANN, T., & BROOK, J.R., Associations between Ambient Particulate Sulfate and Admissions to Ontario Hospitals for Cardiac and Respiratory Disease, Am J Epidemiol 142, 15-22, 1995.

[41]   BATES, D.V., & SIZTO, R., Hospital Admissions and Air Pollutants in Southern Ontario: The acid summer haze effect, Environ Research 43, 317-31, 1987.

[42]   BATES, D.V., Health Indices of the Adverse Effects of Air Pollution: The question of coherence, Environ Research 59, 336-49, 1992.

[43]   VONK, J.M., DE GRAAF, A., & SCHOUTEN, J.P., Short-term Effects of Air Pollution on Emergency Hospital Admissions for Respiratory and Cardiovascular Disease in the Netherlands 1977-1989, Am J Respir Crit Care Med 153, Abstract 479, 1996.

[44]   GIRSCH, L.S., SHUBIN, E., DICK, C., & SCHULANER, F.A., A Study on the Epidemiology of Asthma in Children in Philadelphia, J Allergy 39, 347-57, 1967.

[45]   THURSTON, G.D., ITO, K., HAYES, C.G., BATES, D.V., & LIPPMANN, M., Respiratory Hospital Admissions and Summertime Haze Air Pollution in Toronto, Ontario: Consideration of the role of acid aerosols, Environ Research 65, 271-90, 1994.

[46]   SCANNELL, C., CHEN, L., ARIS, R.M., TAGER, I., CHRISTIAN, D., FERRANDO, R., WELCH, B., KELLY, T., & BALMES, J.R., Greater Ozone-induced Inflammatory Responses in Subjects with Asthma, Am J Respir Crit Care Med 154, 24-29, 1996.

[47]   ROMIEU, I., MENESES, F., SIENRA-MONGE, J.J.L., HUERTA, J., VELASCO, S.R., WHITE, M.C., ETZEL, R.A., & HERNANDEZ-AVILA, M., Effects of Urban Air Pollutants on Emergency Visits for Childhood Asthma in Mexico City, Am J Epidemiol 141, 546-53, 1995.

[48]   SPENGLER, J.D., KOUTRAKIS, P., DOCKERY, D.W., RAIZENNE, M., & SPEIZER, F.E., Health Effects of Acid Aerosols on North American Children: Air pollution exposures, Environ Health Perspect 194, 492-99, 1996.

[49]   DOCKERY, D.W., CUNNINGHAM, J., DAMOKOSH, A.I., NEAS, L.M., SPENGLER, J.D., KOUTRAKIS, P., WARE, J.H., RAIZENNE, M., & SPEIZER, F.E., Health Effects of Acid Aerosols on North American Children: Respiratory symptoms, Environ Health Perspect 104, 500-5, 1996.

[50]   RAIZENNE, M., NEAS, L.M., DAMOKOSH, A.I., DOCKERY, D.W., SPENGLER, J.D., KOUTRAKIS, P., WARE, J.H., & SPEIZER, F.E., Health Effects of Acid Aerosols on North American Children: Pulmonary Function, Environ Health Perspect 104, 506-14, 1996.

[51]   EDGERTON, S.A., HOLDREN, M.W., SMITH, D.L., & SHAH, J.J., Inter-urban Comparison of Ambient Volatile Organic Compound concentrations in US cities, J Air & Waste Manage. Assoc. 39, 729-32, 1989.

[52] TYLER, W.S., JULIAN, M.D., & HYDE, D.M., Respiratory Bronchiolitis Following Exposures to Photochemical Air Pollutants, Seminars in Resp Med 13, 94-113, 1992.

[53] SALDIVA, P.H.N., KING, M., DELMONTE, V.L.C., MACCHIONE, M., PARADA, M.A.C., DALIBERTO, M.L., SAKAE, R.S., CRIADO, P.M.P., SILVEIRA, P.L.P., ZIN, W.A., & BOHM, G.M., Respiratory Alterations Due to Urban Air Pollution: An experimental study in rats. Environ Research 57, 19-33, 1992.

[54] PEREIRA, P.M., SALDIVA, P.H.N., SAKAE, R.S., BOHM, G.M., & MARTINS, M.A., Urban Levels of Air Pollution Increase Lung Responsiveness in Rats. Environ Research 69, 96-101, 1995.

[55] GODLESKI, J., SIOUTAS, C., KATLER, M., & KOUTRAKIS, P., Death from Inhalation of Concentrated Ambient Air Particles in Animal Models of Pulmonary Disease. Abstract (11.4) at Second Colloquium on Particulate Pollution and Health, Park City, Utah May 1-3, 1996.

[56] McKEE, D.J., ed., Troopospheric Ozone: Human health and agricultural impacts. Lewis Publishers, Boca Raton, FL. 1994. Pp 333.

[57] AIR QUALITY GUIDELINES FOR EUROPE, World Health Organization; Regional Office for Europe, Copenhagen. 1987. Pp 426.

[58] HILL, Sir Austin Bradford, The Environment and Disease: Association or causation? Proc Roy Soc Med 58, 295-300, 1965.

[59] LANES, S.F., Error and uncertainty in causal inference, In: Causal Inferenc; edited by Kenneth J. Rothman. Epidemiology Resources Inc., Chestnut Hill, MA. 02167. Pp 173-88, 1988.

[60]   KINNEY, P.L., & LIPPMANN, M., Respiratory Effects of Seasonal Exposures to Ozone and Particles. Arch Environ Health 55; 210-16; 2000.

[61]   UPDATE AND REVISION OF THE AIR QUALITY GUIDELINES FOR EUROPE, Meeting of the Working Group on "Classical" Air Pollutants, Bilthoven, Netherlands, October 11-14, 1994. WHO Regional Office for Europe, Copenhagen. 1995.

[62]   SCHWARTZ, J., Societal Benefits of Reducing Lead Exposure. Environ Res 66, 105-24, 1994.

[63]   BATES, D.V., Standard-setting as an integrative exercise: Alchemy, juggling, or science? In: Inhalation Toxicology, edited by U. Mohr. Springer-Verlag, New York & Heidelberg. 1988. See p 1-9.

[64]   BRAUER, M., BLAIR, J., & VEDAL, S., Effect of Ambient Ozone Exposure on Lung Function in Farm Workers. Am J Respir Crit Care Med 154, 981-87, 1996.

[65]   KRAHN, M.D., BERKA, C., LANGLOIS, P., & DETSKY, A.S., Direct and Indirect Costs of Asthma in Canada, 1990. Can Med Assoc J 154, 821-31, 1996.

[66]   SMALL, K.A., & KAZIMI, C., On the Costs of Air pollution from Motor Vehicles. J Transport Economics & Policy 29, 7-32, 1995.

[67]   ROWE, R.D., LANG, C.M., CHESTNUT, L.G., LATIMER, D.A., RAE, D.A., BERNOW, S.M., & WHITE, D.E., The New York Electricity Externality Study Volume I: Introduction & Methods, p 835. Volume II: Appendices, p 720. Oceana Publications Inc. December 1995. No address given.

[68]   CHESTNUT, L.G., Human Health Benefits Assessment of the Acid Rain Provisions of the 1990 Clean Air Act Amendments. EPA Contract No. 68-D3-0005. November 1995. (Hagler-Baily Consulting, Inc., P.O. Drawer O, Boulder, CO 80306-1906)

[69]   HALL, J.V., Economic Assessment of the Health Benefits from Improvements in Air Quality in the South Coast Air Basin, Final Report to South Coast Air Quality Management District, Contract No. 5685. June 1989. California State University Fullerton Foundation.

[70]   HALL, J.V., WINER, A.M., KLEINMAN, M.T., LURMANN, F.W., BRAJER, V., & COLOME, S.D., Valuing the Health Benefits of Clean Air. Science 255, 812-17, 1992.

[71]   HALL, J., BRAJER, V., & KLEINMAN, M., The Economic Value of Quantifiable Ozone and PM_{10}-related Health Effects in the San Francisco Bay Area. Final Report to the Bay Area Air Quality management District. October 1995.

[72]   BOVAR-CONCORD ENVIRONMENTAL Economic Analysis of Air Quality Improvement in the Lower Fraser Valley, Report Prepared for the BC Ministry of Environment, Lands & Parks, Environmental Policy Branch; BCE 42149687. Bovar-Concord Environmental, November 1995.

[73]   US ENVIRONMENTAL PROTECTION AGENGY, The Benefits and Costs of the Clean Air Act, 1970 to 1990, Prepared for the US Congress, October 1997.

[74]   PORTER, M.E., America's Green Strategy, Scientific American 264, 168, April 1991.

[75]   MURRAY, A.B., FERGUSON, A.C., & MORRISON, B., The Seasonal Variation of Allergic Respiratory Symptoms Induced by House Dust Mites, Ann Allergy 45, 347-50, 1980.

[76]   PANDEY, M.R., SMITH, K.R., BOLEIJ, J.S.M., & WAFULA, E.M., Indoor Air Pollution in Developing Countries and Acute Respiratory Infection in Children. Lancet 427-29, February 25, 1989.

[77]   KUNZLI, N., LURMANN, F., SEGAL, M., NGO, L., BALMES, J., & TAGER, I.B., Association between Lifetime Ambient Ozone Exposure and Pulmonary Function in College Freshmen — results of a pilot study. Environ Research 72, 8-23, 1997.

[78]   ZIDEK, J.V., WHITE, R., LE, N.D., SUN, W., & BURNETT, R.T., Imputing Unmeasured Explanatory Variables in Environmental Epidemiology with Application to Health Impact Analysis of Air Pollution. Biostatistics Research Report No. 11, University of British Columbia Department of Statistics. December 1996.

[79]   KARL, T.R., NICHOLLS, N., & GREGORY, J., The Coming Climate. Scientific American 276, 79-83, May 1997.

[80]   SARTOR, F., DEMUTH, C., SNACKEN, R., & WALCKIERS, D., Mortality in the Elderly and Ambient Ozone Concentration During the Hot Summer, 1994, in Belgium. Environ Research 72, 109-17, 1997.

[81]   WILSON, R., & SPENCER, J.D., eds., Particles in Our Air Concentrations and Health Effects, Harvard University Press, Boston, MA. 1996. Pp 259.

[82]   LIPSETT, M., HURLEY, S., & OSTRO, B. Air Pollution and Emergency Room Visits for Asthma in Santa Clara County, California, Environ Health Perspect 105, 216-22, 1997.

[83]   VEDAL, S. Ambient Particles and Health: Lines that divide, Air & Waste Manage. Assoc. 47, 551-81, 1997.

[84]   HARRISON, K. Passing the Buck: Federalism and Canadian environmental policy, UBC Press, Vancouver. 1996. Pp 238.

[85]   BRUNEKREEF, B., JANSSEN, N.A.H., DE HARTOG, J., HARSSEMA, H., KNAPE, M., & VAN VLIET, P. Air Pollution from Truck Traffic and Lung Function in Children Living Near Motorways, Epidemiology 8, 298-303, 1997.

[86]   SIMPSON, R.W., WILLIAMS, G., PETROESCHEVSKY, A., MORGAN, G., & RUTHERFORD, S. The Association Between Outdoor Air Pollution and Daily Mortality in Brisbane, Australia Arch. Environ. Health 52:442-454; 1998.

[87]   CHURG, A., & BRAUER, M.., Human Lung Parenchyma Retains $PM_{2.5}$, Am J Respir Crit Care Med 155 2109-11, 1997.

[88]   GIELEN, M.H., VAN DER ZEE, S.C., VAN WIJNEN, J.H., VAN STEEN, C.J., & BRUNEKREEF, B. Acute Effects of Summer Air Pollution on Respiratory Health of Asthmatic Children, Am J Respir Crit Care Med 155, 2105-08, 1997.

[89]   SCHWARTZ, J, Air Pollution and Hospital Admissions for Cardiovascular Disease in Tucson, Epidemiology 8, 371-77, 1997.

[90]   GAMBLE, J.F., & LEWIS, R.J. Health and Respirable Particulate (PM_{10}) Air Pollution: A causal or statistical association? Environ Health Perspect 104, 838-50, 1996.

[91]   ENVIRONMENTAL EPIDEMIOLOGY, Use of the Gray Literature and Other Data in Environmental Epidemiology, Volume 2, National Academy Press, Washington, DC. 1997. Pp 189.

[92]   TIMONEN, K.L., & PEKKANEN, J., Air Pollution and Respiratory Health Among Children with Asthmatic or Cough symptoms, Am J Respir Crit Care Med 156, 546-52, 1997.

[93]   COHEN, A.J., & POPE, C.A. III, Lung Cancer and Air Pollution, Environ Health Perspect 103(Suppl 8), 219-24, 1995.

[94]   CONTINENTAL POLLUTANT PATHWAYS, Commission for Environmental Cooperation, Montreal. 1997 Pp44.

[95]   STEYN, D.G., BOTTENHEIM, J.W., & THOMSON, R.B., Overview of Tropospheric Ozone in the Lower Fraser Valley, and the Pacific '93 Field Study, Atmospheric Environment 31, 2025-35, 1997.

[96]   PETERS, A., DORING, A., WICHMANN, H-E., & KOENIG, W., Increased Plasma Viscosity During an Air Pollution Episode: A link to mortality? Lancet 349, 1582-87, 1997.

[97]   LONG-RANGE TRANSPORT OF GROUND-LEVEL OZONE AND ITS PRECURSORS, Commission For Environmental Cooperation, Montreal. 1997. Pp 108.

[98]   RAASCHOU-NIELSEN, O., SKOV, H., LOHSE, C., THOMSEN, B.L., & OLSEN, J.H. Front-door Concentrations and Personal Exposures of Danish Children to Nitrogen Dioxide, Environ Health Perspect 105, 964-70, 1997.

[99]   DELFINO, R.J., MURPHY-MOULTON, A.M., & BECKLAKE, M.R., Emergency Room Visits for Respiratory Illnesses Among the elderly in Montreal: Association with low level ozone exposure, Environ Research, Section A, 76, 67-77, 1998.

[100]   THURSTON, G.D., LIPPMANN, M., SCOTT, M.B., & FINE, J.M., Summertime Haze Air Pollution and Children with Asthma, Am J Respir Crit Care Med, 155, 654-60, 1997.

[101]   GIELEN, M.H., VAN DER ZEE, S.C., VAN WIJNEN, J.H., VAN STEEN, C.J., & BRUNEKREEF, B., Acute Effects of Summer Air Pollution on Respiratory Health of Asthmatic Children, Am J Respir Crit Care Med 155, 2105-08, 1997.

[102]   ROMIEU, I., MENESES, F., RUIZ, S., HUERTA, J., SIENRA, J.J., WHITE, M., ETZEL, R., & HERNANDEZ, M., Effects of Intermittent Ozone Exposure on Peak Expiratory Flow and Respiratory Symptoms Among Asthmatic Children in Mexico City, Arch Environ Health 52, 368-76, 1997.

[103]   SPIX, C., ANDERSON, H.R., SCHWARTZ, J., VIGOTTI, M.A., LE TETRE, A., VONK, V.J.M., TOULOUMI, G., BALDUCCI, F., PIEKARSKI, T., BACHAROVA, L., TOBIAS, A., PONKA, A., & KATSOUYANNI, K., Short-term Effects of Air Pollution on Hospital Admissions of Respiratory Diseases in Europe: A quantitative summary of APHEA study results, Arch Environ Health 53, 54-60, 1998.

[104]   PONCE DE LEON, A., ANDERSON, H.R., BLAND, J.M., STRACHAN, D.P., & BOWER, J., Effects of Air Pollution on Daily Hospital Admissions for Respiratory Disease in London between 1987-88 and 1991-92, J Epidemiol Comm Health, Suppl. 1, S63-S70, 1996

[105]   SCHOUTEN, J.P., VONK, J.M., & DE GRAAF, A., Short-term Effects of Air pollution on Emergency Hospital Admissions for Respiratory Disease: Results of the APHEA project in two major cities in the Netherlands, 1977-1989, J Epidemiol Comm Health 50 (Suppl. 1), S22-S29, 1996.

[106]   ANDERSON, H.R., SPIX, C., MEDINA, S., SCHOUTEN, J.P., CASTELLSAGUE, J., ROSSI, G., ZMIROU, D., TOULOUMI, G., WOJTYNIAK, B., PONKA, A., BACHAROVA, L., SCHWARTZ, J., & KATSOUYANNI, K., Air Pollution and Daily Admissions for Chronic Obstructive Pulmonary Disease in 6 European Cities: Results from the APHEA project, Eur Respir J. 10, 1064-71, 1997.

[107]   COTGREAVE, I.A., Absorption and Metabolic Fate of Ozone — the molecular basis of ozone-induced toxicity, Scand J Work Environ Health 22 (Suppl. 3), 15-26, 1996.

[108]   SUNDELL, J., & ZUBER, A., Ozone and Other Photochemical Oxidants in Ambient and Indoor Air — Properties, Sources and Concentrations, Scand J Work Environ Health 22 (Suppl. 3), 5-14, 1996.

[109]   BYLIN, G., Controlled Human Studies of Ozone Exposure, Scand J Work Environ Health 22 (Suppl. 3), 52-71, 1996.

[110]   NYBERG, F., & PERSHAGEN, G., Epidemiologic Studies on Ozone, Scand J Work Environ Health 22 (Suppl. 3), 72-98, 1996.

[111]   WORDLEY, J., WALTERS, S., & AYRES, J.G., Short-term Variations in Hospital Admissions and Mortality and Particulate Air Pollution, Occup Environ Med 54, 108-16, 1997.

[112]   WHITE, M.C., ETZEL, R.A., OLSON, D.R., & GOLDSTEIN, I.F., Reexamination of Epidemic Asthma in New Orleans, Louisiana, in Relation to the Presence of Soy at the Harbor, Am J Epidemiol 145, 432-38, 1997.

[113]   BURNETT, R.T., CAKMAK, S., BROOK, J.R., & KREWSKI, D., The Role of Particulate Size and Chemistry in the Association Between Summertime Ambient Air Pollution and Hospitalization for Cardiorespiratory Disease, Environ Health Perspect 105, 614-20, 1997.

[114]   NOWAK, D., JORRES, R., BERGER, J., CLAUSSEN, M., & MAGNUSSEN, H., Airway Responsiveness to Sulfur Dioxide in an Adult Population Sample, Am J Respir Crit Care Med 156, 1151-56, 1997.

[115]   ELLEGARD, A., Tears while Cooking: An indicator of indoor air pollution and related health effects in developing countries, Environ Research 75, 12-22, 1997.

[116]   MEDINA, S., LE TETRE, A., QUENEL, P., LE MOULLEC, Y., LAMELOISE, P., GUZZO, J.C., FESTY, B., FERRY, R., & DAB, W., Air Pollution and Doctor's House Calls: Results from the ERPURS system for monitoring the effects of air pollution on public health in Greater Paris, France, 1991-1995, Environ Research 75, 73-84, 1997.

[117]   SAMET, J., ZEGER, S., KELSALL, J., XU, J., & KALKSTEIN, L., Does Weather Confound or Modify the Association of Particulate Air Pollution with Mortality? Environ Research, Section A 77, 9-19, 1998.

[118]   NATIONAL RESEARCH COUNCIL, Research Priorities for Airborne Particulate Matter, I: Immediate Priorities and a Long-Range Research Portfolio, National Academy Press, Washington DC. 1998. Pp 195.

[119]   HARRISON, R.M., DEACON, A.R., & JONES, M.R., Sources and Processes Affecting Concentrations of PM_{10} and $PM_{2.5}$ Particulate Matter in Birmingham (UK), Atmospheric Environment 31, 4103-17, 1997.

[120]   BROOK, J.R., WIEBE, A.H., WOODHOUSE, S.A., AUDETTE, C.V., DANN, T.F., CALLAGHAN, S., PIECHOWSKI, M., DABEK-ZLOTORZYNSKA, E., & DLOUGHY, J.F., Temporal and Spatial Relationships in Fine Particle Strong Acidity, Sulphate, PM_{10} and $PM_{2.5}$ across Multiple Canadian Locations, Atmospheric Environment 31, 4223-36, 1997.

[121]   CHINDLER, C., ACKERMAN-LIEBRICH, U., LEUEN-BERGER, P. and 14 others plus the SAPALDIA TEAM, Associations between Lung Function and Estimated Average Exposure to NO_2 in Eight areas of Switzerland, Epidemiology 9, 405-11, 1998.

[122]   BRAUER, M., & VEDAL, S., Health Effects of Photochemical Smog: Seasonal and acute lung function change in outdoor workers, J Environ. Med 1, 163-70, 1999.

[123]   MAR, T.F., NORRIS, G.A., KOENIG, J.Q., & LARSON, T.V., Associations between Air Pollution and Mortality in Phoenix, 1995-1997, Environ Health Perspect 108, 347-53, 2000.

[124]   NORDENHALL, C., POURAZAR, J., BLOMBERG, A., LEVIN, J-O., SANDSTROM, T., & ADELROTH, E., Airway Inflammation Following Exposure to Diesel Exhaust: a Study of time kinetics using induced sputum, Eur Respir J 15, 1046-51, 2000.

[125]   SVARTENGREN, M., STRAND, V., BYLIN, G., JARUP, L., & PERSHAGEN, G., Short-term Exposure to Air Pollution in a Road Tunnel Enhances the Asthmatic Response to Allergen, Eur Respir J 15, 716-24, 2000.

[126]   HEINRICH, J., HOELSCHER, B., & WICHMANN, H.E., Decline of Ambient Air Pollution and Respiratory Symptoms in Children, Am J Respir Crit Care Med 161, 1930-36, 2000.

[127]   PETERS, J.M., AVOL, E., NAVIDI, W., LONDON, S.J., GAUDERMAN, W.J., LURMANN, F., LINN, W.S., MARGOLIS, H., RAPPAPORT, E., GONG, H. Jr., & THOMAS, D.C., A Study of Twelve Southern California Communities with Differing Levels and Types of Air Pollution, Am J Respir Crit Care Med 159, 760-67, 1999.

[128]   MERGLER, D., Neurotoxic Effects of Low Level Exposure to Manganese in Human Populations, Environ Research Section A 80, 99-102, 1999.

[129]   PETERS, J.M., AVOL, E., GAUDERMAN, W.J., LINN, W.S., NAVIDI, W., LONDON, S.J., MARGOLIS, H., RAPPAPORT, E., VORA, H., GONG, H. Jr., & THOMAS, D.C., A Study of Twelve Southern California Communities with Differing Levels and Types of Air Pollution. II. Effects on Pulmonary Function, Am J Respir Crit Care Med 159, 768-75, 1999.

[130]   SALVI, S., BLOMBERG, A., RUDELL, B., KELLY, F., SANDSTROM, T., HOLGATE, S.T., & FREW, A., Acute Inflammatory Responses in the Airways and Peripheral Blood After short-term Exposure to Diesel Exhaust in Healthy Human Volunteers, Am J Respir Crit Care Med 159, 702-9, 1999.

[131]   ATKINSON, R.W., ANDERSON, H.R., STRACHAN, D.P., BLAND, J.M., BREMNER, S.A., & DE LEON, P., Short-term associations between Outdoor Air Pollution and Visits to Accident and Emergency Departments in London for Respiratory Complaints, Eur Respir J 13, 257-65, 1999.

[132]   BERUBE, K.A., JONES, T.P., WILLIAMSON, B.J., WINTERS, C., MORGAN, A.J., & RICHARDS, R.J., Physicochemical Characterisation of Diesel Exhaust Particles: Factors for assessing biological activity, Atmospheric Environment 33, 1599-1614, 1999.

[133]   ANUSZEWSKI, J., LARSON, T.V., & KOENIG, J.Q., Simultaneous Indoor and Outdoor Particle Light-scattering Measurements at Nine Homes using a Portable Nephelometer, J, Exp Analysis Environ Epidemiol 8, 483-88, 1998.

[134]   BREMNER, S.A., ANDERSON, H.R., ATKINSON, R.W., McMICHAEL, A.J., STRACHAN, D.P., BLAND, & BOWER, J.S., Short Term Associations between Outdoor Air Pollution and Mortality in London 1992-4, Occup Environ Med, 56, 237-44, 1999.

[135]   DONOGUE, A.M., & THOMAS, M., Point Source Sulphur Dioxide Peaks and Hospital Presentations for Asthma, Occup Environ Med 56, 232-36, 1999.

[136]   DELFINO, R.J., ZEIGER, R.S., SELTZER, J.M., & STREET, D.H., Symptoms in Pediatric Asthmatics and Air Pollution: Differences in effects by symptom severity, anti-inflammatory medication use and particulate averaging time, Environ Health Perspect 106, 751-61; 1998.

[137]   CHESTNUT, L.G., OSTRO, B.D., & VICHIT-VADAKAN, N., Transferability of Air Pollution Control Health benefits from the United States to Developing Countries: Evidence from the Bangkok Study, Amer J. Agr. Econ. 79, 1630-35, 1997.

[138]   MERGLER, D., BALDWIN, M., BELANGER, S., LARRIBE, F., BEUTER, A., BOWLER, R., PANISSET, M., EDWARDS, E., DE GEOFFROY, A., SASSINE, M-P., & HUDNELL, K., Manganese Neurotoxicity, a Continuum of Dysfunction: Results from a community based study, NeuroToxicology 20, 327-42, 1999.

[139]   MOORE, C., The Impracticality and Immorality of Cost-Benefit Analysis in Setting Health-related Standards, Tulane Environmental Law Journal 11, 187-216, 1998.

[140]   ROSSI, G., VIGOTTI, M.A., ZANOBETTI, A., REPETTO, F., GIANELLE, V., & SCHWARTZ, J., Air Pollution and Cause-Specific Mortality in Milan, Italy, 1980-1989, Arch Environ Health 54, 158-64, 1999.

[141]   JAMMES, Y., DELPIERRE, S., DELVOLGO, M.J., HUMBERT-TENA, C., & BURNET, H., Long Term Exposure of Adults to Outdoor Air Pollution Is Associated with Increased Airway Obstruction and Higher Prevalence of Bronchial Hyperresponsiveness, Arch Environ Health 53, 372-77, 1998.

[142]   JAAKKOLA, J.J.K., PARTTI-PELLINEN, K., MARTTILA, O., MIETTINEN, P., VILKKA, V., & MAAHTELA, T., The South Karelia Air Pollution Study: Changes in respiratory health in relation to emission reduction of malodorous sulfur compounds from pulp mills, Arch Environ Health 54, 254-63, 1999.

[143]   FRISCHER, T., STUDNICKA, M., GARTNER, C., TAUBER, E., HORAK, F., VEITER, A., SPENGLER, J., KUHR, J., & URBANEK, R., Lung Function Growth and Ambient Ozone: A three-year population study in school children, Am J Respir Crit Care Med 160, 390-96, 1999.

[144]   LONG, W., TATE, R.B., NEWMAN, W., MANFREDA, J., BECKER, A.B., & ANTHONISEN, N.R., Respiratory Symptoms in a Susceptible Population due to Burning of Agricultural Residue, Chest 113, 351-57, 1998.

[145]   SORENSEN, B., FUSS, M., BIGLER, W., WIERSMA, S., HOPKINS, R., Surveillance of Morbidity During Wildfires — Central Florida, 1998, MMWR 48 (04), 78-79, 1999.

[146]   FROM, L.J., BERGEN, L.G., & HUMLIE, C.J., The Effects of Open Leaf Burning on Spirometric Measurements in Asthma, Chest 101, 1236-39, 1992.

[147]   DUCLOS, P., SANDERSON, L.M., & LIPSETT, M., The 1987 Forest Fire Disaster in California: Assessment of emergency room visits, Arch Environ Health 45, 53-58, 1990.

[148]   NEAS, L.M., DOCKERY, D.W., KOUTRAKIS, P., & SPEIZER, F.E., Fine Particles and Peak Flow in Children: Acidity versus mass, Epidemiology 10, 550-53, 1999.

[149]   HAJAT, S., HAINES, A., GOUBET, S.A., ATKINSON, R.W., & ANDERSON, H.R., Association of Air Pollution with Daily GP Consultations for Asthma and Other Lower Respiratory Conditions in London, Thorax 54, 597-605, 1999.

[150]   SEATON, A., SOUTAR, A., CRAWFORD, V., ELTON, R., McNERLAN, S., CHERRIE, J., WATT, M., AGIUS, R., & STOUT, R., Particulate Air Pollution and the Blood, Thorax 54, 1027-32, 1999.

[151]   NORTHRIDGE, M.E., YANKURA, J., KINNEY, P.L., SANTELLA, R.M., SHEPARD, P., RIOJAS, Y., AGGARWAL, M., & THE EARTH CREW, Diesel Exhaust Exposure Among Adolescents in Harlem: A community-driven study, Am J Public Health 89, 998-1002, 1999.

[152]   BALDI, I., TESSIER, J.F., KAUFFMANN, F., JACQMIN-GADDA, H., NEJJARI, C., & SALAMON, R., Prevalence of Asthma and Mean levels of Air Pollution: Results from the French PAARC survey, Eur Respir J 14, 132-38, 1999

[153]   BOBAK, M., & LEON, D.A., The Effect of Air Pollution on Infant Mortality Appears Specific for Respiratory Causes in the Postnatal Period, Epidemiology 10, 666-670, 1999.

[154]   BATES, D.V., Lines that Connect: Assessing the causality inference in the case of particulate pollution, Environ Health Perspect 108, 91-92, 2000.

[155]   WILKINSON, P., ELLIOTT, P., GRUNDY, C., SHADDICK, G., THAKRAR, B., WALLS, P., & FALCONER, S., Case-Control Study of Hospital Admission with Asthma in Children Aged 5-14 Years: Relation with road traffic in north west London, Thorax 54, 1070-74, 1999.

[156]   ZEGHNOUN, A., BEAUEAU, P., CARRAT, F., DELMAS, V., BOUDHABHAY, O., GAYON, F., GUINCETRE, D., & CZERNICHOW, P., Air Pollution and Respiratory Drug Sales in the City of Le Havre, France, 1993-1996, Environ Research Section A, 81,224-30, 1999.

[157]   OSTRO, B.D., HURLEY, S., & LIPSETT, M.J., Air Pollution and Daily Mortality in the Coachella Valley, California: A study of PM_{10} dominated by coarse particles, Environ Research Section A, 81, 231-38; 1999.

[158]   WANG, T-N., KO, Y-C., CHAO, Y-Y., HUANG, C-C., & LIN, R.-S., Association between Indoor and Outdoor Air Pollution and Adolescent Asthma from 1995 to 1996 in Taiwan, Environ Research Section A, 81, 239-47, 1999.

[159]   MCDONNELL, W.F., STEWART, P.W., SMITH, M.V., PAN, W.K., & PAN, J., Ozone-induced Respiratory Symptoms: Exposure-Response Models and Association with Lung Function, Eur Respir J 14, 845-53, 1999.

[160]   SCHWARTZ, J., NORRIS, G., LARSON, T., SHEPPARD, L., CLAIBORNE, C., & KOENIG, J., Episodes of High Coarse Particle Concentrations Are Not Associated with Increased Mortality, Environ Health Perspect 107, 339-42, 1999.

[161]   SCHWARTZ, J., & NEAS, L.M., Fine Particles Are More Strongly Associated than Coarse Particles with Acute Respiratory Health Effects in Schoolchildren, Epidemiology 11, 6-10, 2000.

[162] PETERS, A., LIU, E., VERRIER, R.L., SCHWARTZ, J., GOLD, D.R., MITTELMAN, M., BALIFF, J., OH, J.A., ALLEN, G., MONAHAN, K., & DOCKERY, D.W., Air Pollution and Incidence of Cardiac Arrhythmia, Epidemiology 11, 11-17, 2000.

[163] VAN DER ZEE, S.C., HOEK, G., BOEZEN, H.M., SCHOUTEN, J.P., VAN WIJNEN, J.H., & BRUNEKREEF, B., Acute Effects of Urban Air Pollution on Respiratory Health of Children with and without Chronic Respiratory Symptoms, Occup Environ Med 56, 802-13, 1999.

[164] ELLIOTT, S.J., COLE, D.C., KRUEGER, P., VOORBERG, N., & WAKEFIELD, S., The Power of Perception: Health risk attributed to air pollution in an urban industrial neighbourhood Risk Analysis 19, 621-34, 1999.

[165] MENESES, F., ROMIEU, I., RAMIREZ, M., COLOME, S., FUNG, K., ASHLEY, D., & HERNANDEZ-AVILA, M., A Survey of Personal Exposures to Benzene in Mexico City, Arch Environ Health 54, 359-63, 1999.

[166] LEVY, J.I., HAMMITT, J.K., & SPENGLER, J.D., Estimating the Mortality Impacts of Particulate Matter: What can be learned from between-study variability? Environ Health Perspect 108, 109-17, 2000.

[167] GWYNN, R.C., BURNETT, R.T., & THURSTON, G.D., A Time-Series Analysis of Acidic Particulate Matter and Daily Mortality and Morbidity in the Buffalo, New York, Region, Environ Health Perspect 108, 125-33, 2000.

[168] BOBAK, M., Outdoor Air Pollution, Low Birth Weight, and Prematurity, Environ Health Perspect 108, 173-76, 2000.

[169] GUO, Y.L., LIN, Y-C., SUNG, F-C., HUANG, S-L., KO, Y-C., LAI, J-S., SU, H-J., SHAW, C-K., LIN, R-S., & DOCKERY, D.W., Climate, Traffic-Related Air Pollutants, and Asthma Prevalence in Middle-School Children in Taiwan, Environ Health Perspect 107, 1001-06, 1999.

[170] SUNYER, J., SCHWARTZ, J., TOBIAS, A., MACFARLANE, D., GARCIA, J., & ANTO, J.M., Patients with Chronic Obstructive Pulmonary Disease Are at Increased Risk of Death Associated with Urban Particle Air Pollution; a CaseCrossover Analysis, Am J Epidemiol 151, 50-56, 2000.

[171] SCHWARTZ, J., & ZANOBETTI, A., Using Meta-Smoothing to Estimate Dose-Response Trends across Multiple Studies, with Application to Air Pollution and Daily Death, Epidemiology 11, 666-72, 2000.

[172] SCHWARTZ, J., Harvesting and Long Term Exposure Effects in the Relationship Between Air Pollution and Mortality, Am J Epidemiol 151, 440-48, 2000.

[173] SAMET, J.M., DOMINICI, F., CURRIERO, F.C., COURSAC, I., & ZEGER, S.L., Fine Particulate Air Pollution and Mortality in 20 US cities, 1987-1994, New Engl J Med 343, 1742-49, 2000.

[174] POPE, C.A. III., DOCKERY, D.W., KANNER, R.E., VILLEGAS, G.M., & SCHWARTZ, J., Oxygen Saturation, Pulse Rate, and Particulate Air Pollution, Am J Respir Crit Care Med 159, 365-72, 1999.

[175] KUNZLI, N., ACKERMANN-LIEBRICH, U., BRANDLI, O., TSCHOPP, J.M., SCHINDLER, C., LEUENBERGER, P., & SAPALDIA TEAM, Clinically "Small" Effects of Air Pollution on FVC Have a Large Public Health Impact, Eur Respir J 15, 131-36, 2000.

[176] DOCKERY, D.W., SPEIZER, F.E., & POPE, C.A. III, Effects of particulate air pollution exposures, In: Particle-Lung Interactions, edited by Peter Gehr and Joachim Heyder, Marcel Dekker, Inc., New York & Basel. 2000. Pp 671-703.

[177]   FANUCCHI, M.V., WONG, V., HINDS, D., TARKINGTON, B., VAN WINKLE, L.S., EVANS, M.J., & PLOPPER, C.G., Repeated Episodes of Exposure to Ozone Alters Postnatal Development of Distal Conducting Airways in Infant Rhesus Monkeys, Am J Respir Crit Care Med 161, A615, 2000.

[178]   PETERS, A., IBALD-MULLI, A., STADELER, S., WOELKE, G., TUCH, T., KREYLING, W.G., WICHMANN, H.E., PEKKANEN, J., & HEINRICH, J., Symptoms Increase in Association with Fine and Ultrafine Particles in Patients with Coronary Heart Disease, Am J Respir Crit Care Med 161, A24, 2000.

[179]   PEKKANEN, J., TIMONEN, K.L., TITTANEN, P., MIRME, A., RUUSKANEN, J., & VANNINEN, E., Daily Variations of Particulate Air Pollution and ST-T Depressions in Subjects with Stable Coronary Heart Disease. The Finnish ULTRA Study, Am J Respir Crit Care Med 161, A24, 2000.

[180]   THURSTON, G.D., ITO, K., LALL, R., & WILSON, W., Influence of PM Components in Associations with Philadelphia, PA Mortality and Hospital Admissions, Am J Respir Crit Care Med 161, A25, 2000.

[181]   DEVLIN, R.B., CASCIO, W., KEHRL, H., & GHIO, A., Changes in Heart Rate Variability in Young and Elderly Humans Exposed to Concentrated Ambient Air Particles, Am J Respir Crit Care Med 161, A239, 2000.

[182]   BAG, R., FROLOV, A.Q., KEYS, J., ZIMMERMAN, J.L., & HANANIA, N.A., Association between Ambient Ozone Levels and Emergency Department (ED) Visits for Asthma in Houston, TX, USA, Am J Respir Crit Care Med 161, A308, 2000.

[183]   AVOL, E.L., TAN, S.M., GAUDERMAN, W.J., VORA, H., LONDON, S.J., & PETERS, J.M., Follow-up of "Lost" Subjects in a Longitudinal Air Pollution Health Study, Am J Respir Crit Care Med 161, A308, 2000.

[184] BRAGA, A.L.F., SALDIVA, P.H.N., PEREIRA, L.A.A., CONCEICAO, G.M.S., LIN, C.A., KISHI, H.S., SCHWARTZ, J., ZANOBETTI, A., & DOCKERY, D.W., Time-Series Study of Children's Respiratory Hospital Admission versus Air Pollution in Sao Paulo, Brazil, Am J Respir Crit Care Med 161, A309, 2000.

[185] KUNZLI, N., SCHINDLER, C., KARRER, W., PERRU-CHOUD, A.P., ACKERMAN-LIEBRICH, U., BRANDLI, O., ZELLWEGER, J.P., LEUENBERGER, P., & SAPALDIA TEAM, Air Pollution Is Associated with Doctor's Visits (Swiss Study on Air Pollution and Lung Disease in Adults — Sapaldia), Am J Respir Crit Care Med 161, A309, 2000.

[186] PEREIRA, L.A.A., BRAGA, A.L.F., CONCEICAO, G.M.S., NISHIOKA, D.C., COURA, F.L.B., LIN, C.A., & SALDIVA, P.H.N., Association between Air Pollution and Late Fetal Losses and Neonatal Mortality in Sao Paulo, Brazil. Am J Respir Crit Care Med 161, A310, 2000.

[187] SCHWARTZ, J., Particles and Not SO_2 Are Responsible for the Air Pollution Associated Deaths in Philadelphia, Am J Respir Crit Care Med 161, A311, 2000.

[188] ZAYED, J., MIKHAIL, M., LORANGER, S., KENNEDY, G., & L'ESPERANCE, G., Exposure of Taxi Drivers and Office Workers to Total and Respirable Manganese in an Urban Environment, Am Indust Hygiene Ass J 57, 376-80, 1996.

[189] JANSSEN, N.A.H., HOEK, G., HARSSEMA, H., & BRUNEKREEF, B., Personal Exposure to Fine Particles in Children Correlates Closely with Ambient Fine Particles. Arch Environ Health 54, 95-101, 1999.

[190] BURNETT, R.T., SMITH-DOIRON, M., STIEB, D., CAKMAK, S., & BROOK, J.R., Effects of Particulate and Gaseous Air Pollution on Cardiorespiratory Hospitalizations, Arch Environ Health 54, 130-39, 1999.

[191]   BURINGH, E., FISCHER, P., & HOEK, G., Is SO_2 a Causative Factor for the PM-associated Mortality Risks in the Netherlands? Inhalation Toxicology 12 (Suppl 1), 55-60, 2000.

[192]   SCHWARTZ, J., The Distributed Lag between Air Pollution and Daily Deaths, Epidemiology 11, 320-26, 2000.

[193]   TAN, W.C., QIU, D., LIAM, B.L., NG, T.P., LEE, S.H., VAN EEDEN, S.F., D'YACHKOVA, Y., & HOGG, J.C., The Human Bone Marrow Response to Acute Air Pollution Caused by Forest Fires, Am J Respir Crit Care Med 161, 1213-17, 2000.

[194]   WYZGA, R.E., & LIPFERT, F.W., Commentary: Some Summary Comments on the Third Colloquium, Inhalation Toxicology 12 (Suppl 2), 1-2, 2000.

[195]   GAUDERMAN, W.J., McCONNELL, R., GILLILAND, F., LONDON, S., THOMAS, D., AVOL, E., VORA, H., BERHANE, K., RAPPAPORT, E., LURMANN, F., MARGOLIS, H., & PETERS, J., Association between Air Pollution and Lung Function Growth in Southern California, Am J Respir Crit Care Med 162, 1-8, 2000.

[196]   HEINRICH, J., HOELSCHER, B., & WICHMANN, H.E., Decline of Ambient Air Pollution and Respiratory Symptoms in Children, Am J Respir Crit Care Med 161, 1930-36, 2000.

[197]   SVARTENGREN, M., STRAND, V., BYLIN, G., JARUP, L., & PERSHAGEN, G., Short-term Exposure to Air Pollution in a Road Tunnel Enhances the Asthmatic Response to Allergen, Eur Respir J 15, 716-24, 2000.

[198]   VEDAL, S., PETKAU, J., WHITE, R., & BLAIR, J., Acute Effects of Ambient Inhalable Particles in Asthmatic and Nonasthmatic Children, Am J Respir Crit Care Med 157, 1034-43, 1998.

[199]   NORDENHALL, C., POURAZAR, J., BLOMBERG, A., LEVIN, J.-O., SANDSTROM, T., & ADELROTH, E., Airway Inflammation Following Exposure to Diesel Exhaust: A study of time kinetics using induced sputum, Eur Respir J 15, 1046-51, 2000.

[200]   MAR, T.F., NORRIS, G.A., KOENIG, J.Q., & LARSON, T.V., Associations between Air Pollution and Mortality in Phoenix, 1995-1997, Environ Health Perspect 108, 347-53, 2000.

[201]   KUNZLI, N., KAISER, R., MEDINA, S., STUDNICKA, M., CHANEL, O., FILLIGER, P., HERRY, M., HORAK, F .Jr., PUYBONNIEUX-TEXIER. V., QUENEL, P., SCHNEIDER, J., SEETHALER, R., VERGNAUD, J.-C., & SOMMER, H., Public-Health Impact of Outdoor and Traffic-Related Air Pollution: A European assessment, Lancet 356, 795-801, 2000.

[202]   NIGHTINGALE, J.A., MAGGS, R., CULLINAN, P., DONNELLY, L.E., ROGERS, D.F., KINNERSLEY, R., CHUNG, K.F., BARNES, P.J., ASHMORE, M., & NEWMAN-TAYLOR, A., Airway Inflammation after Controlled Exposure to Diesel Exhaust Particulates, Am J Respir Crit Care Med 162, 161-66, 2000.

[203]   GHIO, A.J., KIM, C., & DEVLIN, R.B., Concentrated Ambient Air Particles Induce Mild Pulmonary Inflammation in Healthy Human Volunteers, Am J Respir Crit Care Med 162, 981-88, 2000.

[204]   BRAUER, M., & VEDAL,S., Health Effects of Photochemical Smog: Seasonal and acute lung function change in outdoor workers, J Environ. Med 1, 163-70, 1999.

[205]   SAMET, J.M., DOMINICI, F., CURRIERO, F.C., COURSAC, I., & ZEGER, S.L., Fine Particulate Air Pollution and Mortality in 20 US Cities, 1987-1994, New Engl J Med 343 1742-49, 2000.

[206] SCHWARTZ, J., & ZANOBETTI, A., Using Meta-Smoothing to Estimate Dose-Response Trends across Multiple Studies, with Application to Air Pollution and Daily Death, Epidemiology 11, 666-72, 2000.

[207] RISK IN PERSPECTIVE, VALUING THE HEALTH EFFECTS OF AIR POLLUTION, Harvard Center for Risk Analysis Newsletter, Vol. 7, issue 5, July 1999, (Harvard School of Public Health, 718 Huntington Ave., Boston, MA 02115-5924)

[208] NYBERG, F., GUSTAVSSON, P., JARUP, L., BELLANDER, T., BERGLIND, N., JAKOBSSON, R., & PERSHAGEN, G., Urban Air Pollution and Lung Cancer in Stockholm, Epidemiology 11, 487-95, 2000.

[209] VEDAL, S., PETKAU, J., WHITE, R., & BLAIR, J., Acute Effects of Ambient Inhalable Particles in Asthmatic and Nonasthmatic Children, Am J Respir Crit Care Med 157, 1034-43, 1998.

[210] KOENIG, J.Q., COVERT, D.S., LARSON, T.V., MAYKUT, N., JENKINS, P., & PIERSON, W.E., Wood Smoke: Health effects and legislation, Northwest Environmental Journal 4, 41-54, 1988.

[211] ABBEY, D.E., NISHINO, N., McDONNELL, W.F., BURCHETTE, R.J., KNUTSEN, S.F., BEESON, W.L., & YANG, J.X., Long-term Inhalable Particles and Other Air Pollutants Related to Mortality in Nonsmokers, Am J Respir Crit Care Med 159, 373-82, 1999.

[212] GILLILAND, F.D., BERHANE, K., RAPPAPORT, E., THOMAS, D.C., AVOL, E., GAUDERMAN, W. J., LONDON, S.J., MARGOLIS, H.G., McCONNELL, R., ISLAM, K.T., & PETERS, J.M., The Effects of Ambient Air Pollution on School Absenteeism due to Respiratory Illness, Epidemiology 12, 43-54, 2001.

[213]   KORRICK, S.A., NEAS, L.M., DOCKERY, D.W., GOLD, D.R., ALLEN, G.A., HILL, L.B., KIMBALL, K.D., ROSNER, B.A., & SPEIZER, F.E., Effects of Ozone and Other Pollutants on the Pulmonary Function of Adult Hikers, Environ Health Perspect 106, 93-99, 1998.

[214]   ROGERS, J.F., THOMPSON, S.J., ADDY, C.L., McKEOWN, R.E., COWEN, D.J., & DECOUFLE, P., Association of Very Low Birth Weight with Exposures to Environmental Sulfur Dioxide and Total Suspended Particulates, Am J Epidemiol 151, 602-13, 2000.

[215]   REANALYSIS OF THE HARVARD SIX CITIES STUDY AND THE AMERICAN CANCER SOCIETY STUDY OF PARTICULATE AIR POLLUTION AND MORTALITY, Special Report, Health Effects Institute, Cambridge, MA 02139, USA, July 2000.

[216]   GOLDBERG, M.S., BAILAR, J.C. III., BURNETT, R.T., BROOK, J.R., TAMBLYN, R., BONVALOT, Y., ERNST, P., FLEGEL, K.M., SINGH, R.K., & VALOIS, M.-F., Identifying Subgroups of the General Population that May Be Susceptible to Short-term Increases in Particulate Air Pollution: A time-series study in Montreal, Quebec, Health Effects Institute, Research Report No. 97, October 2000.

[217]   OFFICE OF CHILDREN'S HEALTH PROTECTION, NATIONAL CENTER FOR ENVIRONMENTAL ECONOMICS, America's Children And the Environment, EPA 240-R-00-006, December 2000. Pp 86.

[218]   LIPPMANN, M., ITO, K., NADAS, A., & BURNETT, R.T., Association of Particulate Matter Components with Daily Mortality and Morbidity in Urban Populations, Health Effects Institute, Research Report No. 95, August 2000. Pp 82.

[219]   DANIELS, M.J., DOMENICI, F., SAMET, J.M., & ZEGER, S.L., Estimating Particulate Matter-Mortality Dose-Response Curves and Threshold Levels: An analysis of daily time-series for the 20 largest US cities, Am J Epidemiol 152, 397-406, 2000.

[220]   LEWIS, P.R., HENSLEY, M.J., WLODARCZYK, J., TONEGUZZI, R.C., WESTLEY-WISE, V.J., DUNN, T., & CALVERT, D., Outdoor Air Pollution and Children's Respiratory Symptoms in the Steel Cities of New South Wales, Med J Australia 169, 459-63(6b), 1998.

[221]   ANDERSON, H.R., LIMB, E.S., BLAND, J.M., PONCE DE LEON, A., STRACHAN, D.P., & BOWER, J.S., The Health Effects of an Air Pollution Episode in London, December 1991, Report commissioned by the Department of Health, England. July 1994.

[222]   HAZUCHA, M.J., Effect of carbon monoxide on work and exercise capacity in humans, In: Carbon Monoxide Toxicity, edited by D. Penney, CRC Press, Chapter 5, 101-134. 2000.

[223]   POPE, C.A. III, Invited Commentary: Particulate Matter-Mortality Exposure-Response Relations and Threshold, Am J Epidemiol 152, 407-12, 2000.

[224]   SAMET, J.M., ZEGER, S.L., DOMINICI, F., CURRIERO, F., COURSAC, I., DOCKERY, D.W., SCHWARTZ, J., & ZANOBETTI, A., The National Morbidity, Mortality, and Air Pollution Study: Part II, Morbidity and Mortality From Air Pollution in the United States, Health Effects Institute, Research Report No. 94, Part II, June 2000. Pp 82.

[225]   GAUDERMAN, W.J., McCONNELL, R., GILLILAND, F., LONDON, S., THOMAS, D., AVOL, E., VORA, H., BERHANE, K., RAPPAPORT, E., LURMANN, F., MARGOLIS, H., & PETERS, J., Association between Air Pollution and Lung Function Growth in Southern California, Am J Respir Crit Care Med 162, 1-8, 2000.

[226]   FRISCHER, T., STUDNICKA, M., GARTNER, C., TAUBER, E., HORAK, F., VEITER, A., SPENGLER, J., KUHR, J., & URBANEK, R., Lung Function Growth and Ambient Ozone: A three-year population study in school children, Am J Respir Crit Care Med 160, 390-96, 1999.

[227]   BURNETT, R.T., SMITH-DORION, M., STIEB, D., RAIZENNE, M.E., BROOK, J.R., DALES, R.E., LEECH, J.A., CAKMAK, S., & KREWSKI, D., Association between Ozone and Hospitalization for Acute Respiratory Diseases in Children Less than 2 years of Age, Am J Epidemiol 153, 444-52, 2001

[228]   GALIZIA, A., & KINNEY, P.L., Long-term Residence in Areas of High Oozone: Associations with Respiratory Health in a Nationwide Sample of Nonsmoking Young Adults, Environ Health Perspect 107, 675-79, 1999.

[229]   PETROESCHEVSKY, A., SIMPSON, R.W., THALIB, L., & RUTHERFORD, S., Associations between Outdoor Air Pollution and hospital admissions in Brisbane, Australia, Arch Environ Health 56, 37-52, 2001.

[230]   JALALUDIN, B.B., CHEY, T., O'TOOLE, B.I., SMITH, W.T., CAPON, A.G., & LEEDER, S.R., Acute Effects of Low Levels of Ambient Ozone on Peak Expiratory Flow Rate in a Cohort of Australian Children, Int J Epidemiol 29, 549-57, 2000.

[231]   FRIEDMAN, M.S., POWELL, K.E., HUTWAGNER, L., GRAHAM, L.M., & TEAGUE, W.G., Impact of Changes in Transportation and Commuting Behaviors During the 1996 Summer Olympic Games in Atlanta on Air Quality and Childhood Asthma, JAMA 285, 897-905, 2001.

[232]   AIR QUALITY CRITERIA FOR PARTICULATE MATTER, 2 volumes, March 2001, Second External Review Draft, US Environmental Protection Agency, EPA 600/P-99/002aB.

[233]   YU, T.-S., I., WONG, T.W., WANG, X.R., SONG, H., WONG, S.L., & TANG, J.L., Adverse Effects of Low-Level Air Pollution on the Respiratory Health of Schoolchildren in Hong Kong, J Occup Env Med 43, 310-16, 2001.

[234] SMITH, B.J., NITSCHKE, M., PILOTTO, L.S., RUFFIN, R.E., PISANIELLO, D.L., & WILSON, K.J., Health Effects of Daily Indoor Nitrogen Dioxide Exposure in People with Asthma, Eur Respir J 16, 879-85, 2000.

[235] LEGATOR, M.S., SINGLETON, C.R., MORRIS, D.L., & PHILIPS, D.L., Health Effects from Chronic Low-Level Exposure to Hydrogen Sulfide, Arch Environ Health 56, 123-31, 2001.

Chapter 5
Statistical Issues and Causality

James Zidek and David V. Bates

Studies in the epidemiology of air pollution and their implementation in formulating public policy raise a number of recondite statistical issues. While their technical roots lie outside the general reader's expertise and realm of interest, the conceptual issues can be described here. Knowledge of these issues seems essential to understanding the current debate about environmental policy. We begin with a motivating example.

Charlier compared the annual count of storks in Oslo with the number of babies born in that city over a number of years. He found these two variables to be closely associated as measured by a Pearson's correlation between these two series of $r = 0.91$ [9, p. 262]. That value is considered large since r must always lie between -1 and 1. Indeed, it suggested that nearly three-fourths (the square of r) of the variation in the baby counts could be associated with the variation in the stork counts. Moreover, since r measures the degree of linear association, the result naively suggests that doubling the number of storks in Oslo would cause the baby counts to double. That conclusion is reached by fallaciously interpreting association as causation.

Correlations like that are called spurious since the apparent association comes from a masked variable, in this case, Oslo's annual population count. The latter had increased steadily over the years, leading to natural increases in the annual baby count and the amount of garbage. Since storks are scavengers, the latter in turn caused the population of storks to grow at the same time.

Variables like this masked variable are often called *confounders* and are said to be confounded with the variables studied. Their existence is an ever-present possibility in a statistical investigation, yet they may not always be so easy to discover as in this simple example.

That example serves as a paradigm for much more complicated studies like those in environmental epidemiology inasmuch as they are all observational studies; the level of exposure of subjects in the experiment is not controlled (in particular, assigned at random) by the experimenter. Associations established in such studies cannot be interpreted as causal since those associations could derive from confounders, recognized or unrecognized. However, these studies can strongly support the hypothesis of causation in an observational study, as discussed next.

MAKING CAUSAL INFERENCES IN OBSERVATIONAL STUDIES

Statistical methods used in epidemiological research sometimes show a significant association between two variables, for example, a health outcome and a measure of pollution. The Scottish philosopher David Hume considered the question of when causality might be inferred from such an association. However, Sir Austin Bradford Hill, in a lecture at the Royal Society of Medicine in 1965 [23], was the first eminent epidemiologist to address this question in detail. At the time of his address, some biostatisticians [24] (a few distinguished) argued that the association between cigarette smoking and lung cancer need not demonstrate a causal relationship. Bradford Hill described criteria he had found useful in making a judgement about causality; he stressed that these were in no sense "laws", but simply aspects of the association that were of assistance in deciding the tenability of the causality hypothesis. These were:

- **Strength of the Association**

- **Consistency**: Observed by different people, in different places, circumstances and times?

- **Specificity**: As in occupational exposures

- **Temporality**: Exposure predates the outcome

- **Biologic Gradient**: Dose-response curve

- **Biological Plausibility**: "This is a feature I am convinced we cannot demand" (Bradford Hill)

- **Coherence**: Histopathological evidence (from smokers)

- **Experiment**: Effect of preventive action?

- **Analogy**: Argument from known effects from another agent

Not all of these criteria are directly relevant to epidemiological associations. The "coherence" criterion should now be expanded to include observations of morbidity effects when a mortality relationship has been found [25]. In further discussion of these criteria, Bradford Hill warned against armchair objections being advanced to deny causality. Although the strength of an association is important, we now recognize a number of factors that can weaken it. Dominant among these is the uncertainty of exposure to pollutants measured on ambient monitors. A weak association may therefore not be interpreted as necessarily indicating that the effect of the pollutant is "weak."

In a useful volume on causal inferences, Lanes [26] set out three rules, as follows:

Rule 1: "We cannot infer that an association is noncausal merely because error is possible. For an error to be considered as a potential explanation of an association, there needs to be some way of evaluating whether or not an error did in fact occur."

Rule 2: "We cannot infer that an association is noncausal because a source of error is identified. We must determine the direction of bias, if any, that the error produced. A bias that diminishes an association cannot be considered an adequate explanation for an observed association."

Rule 3: "We cannot infer that an association is noncausal because a source of error exists that would exert a bias in the direction of creating an association. To explain an association, the bias must be of sufficient magnitude to create the association that was observed."

There have been other attempts to codify what is often seen as a very uncertain process. The unfolding work on particulate pollution brought all of these considerations to the fore. The steps were the following:

- After the mortality relationship had been shown in two or three places, the consistency of the observation was demonstrated by the fact that wherever the measurements existed to study the relationship, a significant association between daily mortality and particulate pollution was found.

- Objections raised that weather changes were confounders not properly considered in the studies were met by showing that the association remained robust when different weather models were used. Taking into account specific environments could refute the importance of co-existent pollutants where the PM_{10} effect was present but SO_2 and O_3 were absent.

• The coherence criterion was met by showing that PM_{10} was responsible for a cascade of morbidity effects in addition to mortality, including increased hospital admissions for cardiac and respiratory disease.

• Finally, it was objected that no causal inference could be drawn unless the biological mechanism was known (this is directly contrary to what Bradford Hill had said about biological plausibility). Certainly the epidemiological data ran far ahead of the search for a biological mechanism, but the recent data presented by Godleski [27] (see Table 13) indicates that evidence of effects in animals at realistic concentrations of urban PM_{10} may well provide this last link in the chain. Furthermore, the finding by a group of researchers in Augsburg in Bavaria that a pollution episode there was associated with an increase in plasma viscosity [28] in randomly sampled normal residents might confirm a biological mechanism for the association of cardiac mortality and morbidity with exposure to particulate pollution.

Vedal has recently summarized the general problem of assigning causality to the associations between particulate pollution and health outcomes [29]. Gamble and Lewis [30] have argued that there is, at present, an insufficient basis for reaching a conclusion that the association between particulate pollution and different outcomes indicates a causal relationship.

That "causality" should be inferred is a judgement. As such it is prone to many influences, including, of course, those attributable to financial incentives. Sometimes one hears an individual talking about "proving" that an association is causal, which is really a misuse of the concept of "proof." Admittedly when the epidemiological data are overwhelming in volume, and biological plausibility is strong, one might say that the causal relationship had been proved to exist — as between cigarettes and lung cancer for instance; but even in that instance it is probably better to say that no reasonable man, looking at all the evidence, could believe that no causal relationship existed.

In the case of particulate pollution, the recent British Ministry of Health report [31], advised the Minister "that it would be imprudent not to conclude" that the association was causal, which was an interesting use of a double negative. However, skeptics will inevitably find grounds for arguing that any conclusion of causation derived from an observational study is merely a hypothesis that must be tested. Experimental designs for testing such hypotheses are considered next.

EXPERIMENTAL DESIGNS

Controlled Experiments:

Sir Ronald Fisher proposed the use of the (randomized) controlled experiment. In such an experiment the sample of experimental units to receive the treatment would be determined by the experimenter and chosen at random from the population under study. For example, adults might be chosen at random by the experimenter to spend a period of time exercising in an ozone-enriched chamber (the treatment). To infer the effect of the ozone on the lung functions of members of the treatment group, a control group would similarly be selected and treated in exactly the same manner except that the atmosphere in their chamber would consist of ordinary air. If the two groups were quite large, the random assignment of subjects to the two groups would ensure that the two samples would be alike in every respect save for the treatment difference. Hence, a significant difference in measured response between the two groups could be attributed solely to the (ozone) treatment.

When the samples are not large, random allocation to treatment like this would not suffice to ensure balance against all possible confounders. Indeed the treatment group could well possess by chance alone a characteristic that made it different from the control group. Then the observed difference between the two groups could be due to that characteristic rather than the treatment itself.

In this variation of the basic design, both the treatment and control groups would be selected from a group of population units that were considered to be homogeneous with respect to all relevant characteristics. For example, they might have the same gender, age, educational level, and so on. The experiment could in fact involve several such homogeneous blocks, with both treatment and control samples being taken in each block. Fisher showed how data from such a multi-block experiment could be analyzed to factor out the block effect and the null hypothesis of no treatment effect tested against the alternative that the treatment caused a change.

This idea can be extended to include several different treatments. In the example, several different levels of ozone could be used in different chambers so that the degree of the ozone effect on lung function (or more precisely dose-response curve) could be established quite precisely.

Although the value of the (randomized) controlled experiment seems obvious today, its use was strongly opposed when it was first proposed (1, pp. 149-50). In fact, opposition was seen as late as the 1950's, when its use in the Salk polio vaccine trials was initially questioned. However, by now its use has become standard and even demanded, for example, in the clinical trials of a new medical treatment.

Could such an experiment be used to prove the hypothesis of cause suggested by an epidemiological study of the effects of air pollution? Unfortunately the answer is "no" by and large, for both pragmatic and ethical reasons. People cannot be forced to undergo tests of the effect on their lungs of breathing fine particulates, for example.

Instead, animals are commonly used in controlled tests of such effects as noted above. However, this alternative does not prove altogether satisfactory since any conclusions drawn need not apply to human populations. Moreover, to see detectable responses in reasonably short time spans, the treatments are often made at extremely high relative dosages. Extrapolation to more realistic levels commensurate with those experienced by humans is required, but then the results become tenuous.

Thus controlled experiments cannot be used effectively to establish causal relationships in human health impact analysis. Most studies conducted today on the effects of air pollution on human health therefore continue to be of the observational type. However, some of the concepts underlying the randomized experiment can be used to enhance the design of such studies.

Design Strategies in Observational Studies:

Although the experimenter in air pollution effect analyses cannot generally control the assignment of treatments, experimenters can choose the experimental units (subjects) they observe. This advantage enables subjects to be chosen using design principles referred to above, to maximize the amount of information obtained.

Those principles suggest using controls (or, more properly, quasi-controls). An investigator interested in the health effects of ozone might select a sample of "cases" from an area known to have high ozone pollution levels. For contrast, a sample of quasi-controls might be chosen from an area of low pollution levels. The health responses of interest, for example, of acute asthma attacks in the two groups of subjects, might then be compared. Significantly higher levels in the group of cases would point to adverse effects of ozone. (However, problems with this approach remain and they will be discussed below.)

Although the use of such controls seems clearly desirable, the need for them quite commonly goes unrecognized. That design shortcoming is called the "physician's fallacy." To illustrate this fallacy in a non-medical context: the director of a law enforcement agency sought to determine the cause of juvenile male delinquent behaviour. To that end, a sample of juvenile prisoners was randomly selected and they were found to have typically possessed pornography when they were young. He concluded that possessing pornography caused the delinquency!

The fallacy in this example stems from the failure to sample a group of quasi-controls, men who were not juvenile delinquents. If subjects in this group were found not to have possessed pornography, a case for causation might at least then be entertained.

Classical design theory also points to the desirability of using homogeneous blocks of units from which to draw the cases and controls to be observed. For example, schoolchildren in a fixed age range would be a natural block from which to find samples of subjects in high-and-low exposure areas. In this way, the degree of extraneous variation can be controlled to some extent, as it is in randomized experiments. By extending these ideas in a natural way, the goal of developing a dose-response model can even be addressed.

The basic ideas described above have been elaborated upon to produce very sophisticated designs such as those reviewed by Tager [16]. To give one example, we describe the case cross-over design that Tager attributes to MacClure [13] where subjects serve both as case and control. If mortality were the study outcome, the air pollution exposure levels of the subjects in the period, say, two days, immediately prior to their deaths (the treatment) would be compared with their earlier exposure levels. With respect to time-invariant confounders at least, this case and control are perfectly matched. Thus, if members of the treatment group sustained higher exposure levels than those in the control group, one might infer with some confidence that air pollution was the cause of the mortality.

No matter how far the ideas of design are pushed in this way, however, causality cannot be established beyond doubt in an observational study. Indeed, that has been the complaint about so-called cross-sectional studies, where subjects were selected at random from a variety of subregions with different levels of the risk factor under consideration [6]. Although a significant association between level and response may be established, cause cannot be claimed because a confounder could well be present (like population count in the stork example above).

Statistical Strategies in Observational Studies:

Whether or not design strategies are used in non-randomized studies, statistical methods can be used to further improve their interpretability. One such method is sometimes called post-stratification. Here the sample is subdivided for response comparison after the data are obtained. For example, it could be broken into "gender"or "city." Well-known statistical methods can then be employed for analysis. Between-block differences can be assessed. However, such methods cannot achieve the analytical power with post-stratification that they achieve with pre-stratification. Good design always pays off.

A natural extension of post-stratification is the measurement of covariates. These (often quantitative) variables, like "age," for example, vary naturally in concert with the response. They differ from "design variables" that are fixed by the experimenter prior to identifying the subjects (with those fixed characteristics). If the relationship between the response and a covariate can be specified correctly, immense gains in the precision of the analysis of block response differences can be had by "factoring out" the effect of that covariate. The regression method has proven to be a powerful tool for addressing the problem of confounders. In fact, if all confounders could be included as covariates in the regression model their effect could be completely eliminated from the analysis! Any significant association could be interpreted as causal.

Of course, that ideal is unattainable. So while regression methods can greatly enhance the plausibility of a causality hypothesis the existence of a masked confounder cannot be ruled out. The problem with cross-sectional analysis will persist.

An ingenious modern alternative to the cross-sectional study is the longitudinal study [12, 18]. The idea embraces Bradford Hill's "temporality" criterion, particularly for assessing the risk of an acute health impact analysis.

The longitudinal approach avoids the need for a direct comparison of different experimental units. Instead health responses are compared before and after each of a set of episodes in the time series of an environmental risk factor. If the level of an adverse health response proves to be consistently higher after the episode than before, that factor would be implicated as a potential cause of that adverse effect. If the same result is seen consistently across all units, the strength of that implication increases. Very sophisticated and computationally intensive statistical methods are now available to make such comparisons, and they are commonly used. Nevertheless, the possibility of temporal confounders that ally themselves with these episodes remains. Thus cause cannot be conclusively demonstrated by these methods.

It should be noted that these longitudinal methods can also be used in the much more complex problem of assessing the chronic effect of an environmental risk factor. One such (prospective) study is being conducted by Dr. Duncan Thomas and his colleagues at the University of Southern California. In their study, the lung function and respiratory health of cohorts of randomly sampled children are being examined over time, along with their associated exposure to air pollution to seek the long-term effects of such pollution. These children are selected from a specified set more or less homogeneous urban environments of with varying levels of pollution, in keeping with the valuable design principles espoused above [32].

Alternatively such a study may be retrospective in nature. Dr. Nhu Le and his co-investigators at British Columbia's Cancer Control Agency are conducting a study of the association of between exposure to ozone and the risk of cancer. In this case the exposure history must be inferred by backcasting. Clearly, exposure estimates will be susceptible to substantial measurement errors. Subjects will have difficulty recalling their residential history over the long latency period of cancer. Moreover, ozone will not have been measured precisely in the various locales in which these subjects were located at some time in the past.

PERVASIVE PROBLEMS IN ENVIRONMENTAL HEALTH RISK ANALYSIS

Aggregated Data:

Commonly, data cannot be obtained about individuals, for either practical or ethical reasons. For example, daily mortality data may be available at the level of census subdivision but not by the residential address of the deceased. Thus, much of environmental epidemiology concerns itself with data that have been aggregated either across time or across space or both.

Such data invite a variety of unjustified or even fallacious conclusions. An early example of the difficulties that may arrive is offered by "Simpson's paradox." Suppose a fictitious experimenter classifies for each of 1,370 days the number of deaths as either "low" or "high," and likewise for the level of air pollution. The following hypothetical data are obtained. They point to an inverse relationship between pollution and mortality.

Death Counts	Pollution Level	
	Low	High
High	210	508
Low	150	502

Table 5.1: Results of a fictitious experiment that seem to show quite conclusively that high levels of pollution reduce mortality

In fact, these data were obtained by aggregating data from the two different urban regions in which the original study took place. The original data are shown in the following two tables.

Death Counts	Pollution Level	
	Low	High
High	200	8
Low	100	2

Table 5.2: Fictitious results for urban region A. The conclusion that would be drawn from these results contradict those from Table 5.1.

Death Counts	Pollution Level	
	Low	High
High	10	500
Low	50	500

Table 5.3: Fictitious results from urban region B. The conclusion that would be drawn from these results also contradict those from Table 5.1.

The reader can easily verify that the counts in Table 5.1 are just the sum of the corresponding entries for Tables 5.2 and 5.3. Yet paradoxically the latter suggest precisely the opposite conclusion from that which would be drawn from Table 5.1. This anomaly could be explained by a hypothetical confounder, say the overall health status of the community.

Region A has attracted residents who seem to have a poor health status because of its relatively small number of high-pollution days. However, relatively high mortality levels are seen even on low-pollution days because of that low health status. In the other region, health status is much better on the whole and people are well able to contend with the relatively large number of high-pollution days. This simple example demonstrates the logical pitfalls inherent in the use of aggregated data.

The so-called ecological fallacy takes Simpson's paradox into the realm of regression analysis. That fallacy is illustrated graphically with another fictitious example. First, look at the results depicted in Figure 5.1.

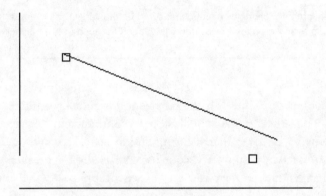

Figure 5.1: Mortality counts, measured on the vertical axis, versus pollution levels, measured on the horizontal axis.

In this figure we see increased levels of pollution yielding lower(!) mortality levels. Moreover, a perfect linear fit to the data is achieved, making the correlation between pollution and mortality highly significant, $r = -1$!

However, this conclusion proves to be fallacious because the points plotted were found by aggregating the data. The disaggregated data are shown in Figure 5.2.

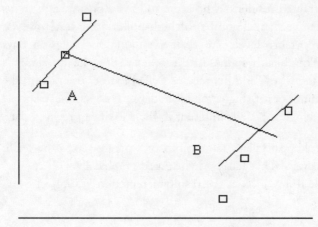

Figure 5.2: Disaggregated mortality counts, measured on the vertical axis versus pollution levels, measured on the horizontal axis, plotted for each of two distinct regions, A and B.

Notice that in each of the two clusters of data that were aggregated to produce the points in Figure 5.1, the correlation is actually positive (in fact $r = 1$). Thus the original conclusion is contradicted. The exact opposite seems to be true; increasing pollution levels seem to cause increases in mortality. In summary, conclusions based on aggregates of experimental units can be very misleading when applied to the units themselves.

For a very detailed recent assessment and critique of ecological studies, the reader may consult Wakefield [17], who notes that the risk factors in environmental pollution studies are far less predictive of health outcomes than, say, diet and smoking are for cancer. He notes therefore that the potential for confounding in the former case is much greater than in the latter.

Measurement Error and Collinearity.

Of all the pervasive problems faced by the environmental epidemiologists, undoubtedly none is more pernicious, yet more ignored, than measurement error. This may seem surprising given the inevitability of measurement error in practice. A simple result for the classical error model may help explain the apparent equanimity of analysts in the face of it.

The model applied to variables representing potential causes of a given response — sometimes called explanatory variables — says the measured value of that variable is its true value plus a random error not associated with that true value. That simple result can be seen quite easily. First, consider the plot in Figure 5.3, which depicts hypothetical data with values of the explanatory variable measured without error plotted on the horizontal axis.

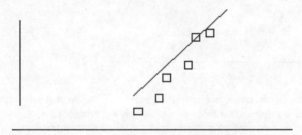

Figure 5.3: Strong association between a response, plotted on the vertical axis, and an explanatory variable measured without error plotted on the horizontal axis.

Note the strong association between the response and explanatory variable. Changes in that explanatory variable produce pronounced changes in the response.

In contrast, we see the same response values in Figure 5.4 plotted against values of the explanatory variable measured with error. That error causes much more scatter on the horizontal axis. Now big changes in the measured explanatory variables seem to produce rather little change in the response. In fact, in the limit the slope of the line relating the two values would be zero. Changes in the explanatory variable would then be seen as leading to no change in response. In other words, there would be no perceived association between the two variables.

Why the equanimity? It may well derive from a common view suggested by these figures that if anything, measurement error attenuates the estimated slope of the regression line relating the two variables. Thus if a significant association is actually found by the investigator when error is present, one can be assured that the real slope is even more significant. That is, the finding is actually conservative.

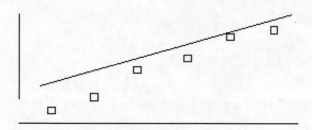

Figure 5.4: Strong association between a response, plotted on the vertical axis, and an explanatory variable measured with error, plotted on the horizontal axis.

Unfortunately, this view is not generally justified. For example, it does not obtain for the Berkson error model, where the true value is the sum of the measured value plus error. Such an error structure would obtain, for instance, when the epidemiologist measures the concentration of a pollutant at a distant monitoring station and uses it as a surrogate for the "true" subregional value. In this case, little if any attenuation will occur in the case of simple linear regression depicted in the figures.

Zidek [22] shows that the effect of measurement error can become almost entirely unpredictable when non-linear regression models are appropriate. For such models the size of the error comes to play a prominent part as the curvature in the model seems to pick up the effect of that error. In any case, it cannot be ignored.

The most satisfactory general approach of dealing with measurement error is called *regression calibration* [3, 15]. The idea is that the true value should be predicted from the observed value with the help of a regression model relating the true and measured value. Then that predicted value rather than the observed value, should be entered into the health impact analysis. That is in fact the approach advocated by Zidek et al. [20, 21] for such analysis.

Measurement error can have extraordinary and quite unforeseen consequences. For example, Greenland [8] proves the surprising result for case-controlled studies where case and control are matched that measurement error (or more precisely misclassification by level of exposure), can have more detrimental effects than when they are not so matched. In fact, the size of the detriment can be larger when the match is closer. Such findings mean that measurement error can thwart the search for a cause by reducing its apparent impact or by spuriously pointing to the wrong factors.

Collinearity can also thwart the search for cause. The problem arises because investigators wishing to eliminate confounders will naturally include a large number of covariates as potentially explanatory variables in their analysis. They do so in the hope of trapping the confounders amongst them. However, that creates another problem. Since these covariates will inevitably vary together to some extent, the investigator will not be able to single out the causative factor even if its covariate happens to be in the pack.

Moreover it makes implausible the quasi-causal interpretation of significant effects, ostensibly for the benefit of a user community not conversant with the arcane language of mathematical statistics. Often such effects will be explained by the assertion that if all other effects were held constant while levels of this one effect alone increased to some specified degree, the impact level would increase by such-and-such a degree. Such an interpretation presumes, of course, in the first instance that changing the explanatory effect would change the health response, that is, it presumes a causal connection. But secondly, collinearity means that the other effect cannot actually be held constant as supposed. In other words, whatever its superficial appeal, that explanation could be very misleading.

The anticipation of this difficulty can suggest more effective experimental designs to help mitigate the problem. Experimental units can be selected from regions where collinearity is likely to be minimized, perhaps from localities where emissions from sources of the environmental hazard are physically disassociated.

Although individually collinearity and measurement error can pose challenging obstacles to the discovery of cause, together they can prove an extraordinary team. Zidek et al. [19] demonstrate the known phenomenon that a standard statistical analysis can lead to the misattribution of cause to a surrogate. This occurs when the covariate associated with the true cause is measured with large error relative to another covariate that varies collinearly with the causative factor. Cause has been capriciously transferred so to speak, from the real cause to its surrogate. Fung and Krewski [33] demonstrate this phenomenon in greater generality, and, at the same time, the importance of regression calibration to mitigate the effect of measurement error.

Contending with Collinearity and Measurement Error:

Obviously measurement error can be reduced through such things as improved instrumentation, data quality measurement programs, and experimental design. However, the effect of measurement error can also be mitigated through the use of statistical models and methods such as:

• The imputation of ambient environmental hazard fields as required in regression calibration. Statistical methods can be used to predict unmeasured values over a region, thereby reducing reliance on the levels recorded at remote ambient monitoring stations [11]. Moreover, such models automatically associate prediction error intervals with the imputed values, thereby indicating the uncertainty in the prediction and allowing that uncertainty to be incorporated into any inferences made from the resulting imputations. In particular, the incorporation of such uncertainty will usually reduce the propensity to declare a false positive association with an imputed explanatory variable. The same methodology can be used to backcast data series for the purpose of reconstructing exposure histories for the challenging problem of inferring the chronic health impacts of environmental hazards.

• Accounting for human behaviour patterns and micro-environmental emission sources in models of human exposure. The US Environmental Protection Agency has developed a computer model (pNEM) that simulates population-level exposures for a variety of pollutants while accounting for such influences. A fast Internet-based alternative that incorporates pNEM's primary conceptual elements has been developed at the University of British Columbia.

In general to be credible the results of a statistical analysis must reflect the analyst's uncertainty about every element of that analysis including both the models and the data that went into that analysis. At the same time, modern statistical software, user-friendly as it might be, does not automatically reflect that uncertainty.

Filtering can be used as another post-design method for reducing collinearity. This can work when collinearity between factors derives from the influence of masked factors like that in the stork-versus-baby count example presented at the beginning of this chapter. Of course, this can be done only when it makes sense from a substantive point.

Air pollutants, for example, are commonly collinear because they share broad temporal patterns associated with such things as daily temperature levels that in turn are associated with seasonality or trends in population size. By filtering out these broad patterns and leaving just the short-term blips in the individual pollutant series collinearity is reduced. Indeed, the blips will represent pollution episodes that tend to occur at somewhat different times for different pollutants.

But justification for doing so involves profound questions beyond current medical knowledge. Moreover, it would challenge current regulatory policy in many countries. Suppose acute health impacts (blips) such as surges in the counts of individuals presenting themselves in emergency rooms with asthma attacks actually result from blips in the associated pollution series, ozone, for example. Then filtering makes good substantive and statistical sense. But it would require acceptance of the hypothesis that an ozone blip in spring (when the baseline ozone levels removed by filtering are low) has the same impact as a blip of the same size in mid summer (when the baseline level is high). Moreover, finding that ozone blips rather than ozone levels were the real causes of health impact blips would have serious implications for policymakers who currently regulate on the basis of levels fixed throughout the year rather than varying with the seasonal baseline. Finally, medical science has not yet determined if baseline levels affect the severity of acute asthma attacks.

CAN CAUSALITY BE ESTABLISHED:

In this chapter we have discussed a variety of statistical problems that may thwart efforts to establish the causality of an environmental hazard found to be associated with a negative health outcome. As well, we have discussed the many strategies for design and analysis of observational studies like those used in environmental epidemiology to mitigate the deleterious effects of those problems. However, without use of a randomized controlled experiment, causality can never be conclusively established. So what might be done as a basis for action?

What would seem to be needed is a different paradigm within which to address problems of this nature. The repeated sampling paradigm of classical statistics serves to operationalize the replicated experiment enshrined in the scientific notion of objectivity. But the latter is completely inappropriate for the large fraction of modern science like environmental epidemiology that must of necessity be based upon inherently non-replicable experiments.

One possibility that reflects the introductory discussion of this chapter may be found in Popper's notion of intersubjectivity. Superficially the idea is that if given all available knowledge, a conclusion is consensually reached by the community possessing that knowledge, then that conclusion would have the status of a fact relative to the knowledge available and the community formulating the conclusion. (Weerahandi and Zidek [34] operationalize this idea in a normative alternative to the repeated sampling paradigm.)

For now it seems unrealistic to expect that such an alternative would be adopted as a normative solution to the problem of interpreting observational data even if the principle of intersubjectivity were widely accepted. Nevertheless, in practice the idea is very much used. For example, that smoking is a cause of lung cancer is now regarded as a fact even though cause has not been demonstrated by a replicated scientific experiment. More generally, intersubjective truth about the causes of adverse health impacts, as in this example, has been embraced descriptively as a basis for action. We believe the process of reaching the truth defined in this way will be much assisted by invoking the criteria of Bradford Hill and using the statistical strategies discussed in this chapter.

REFERENCES

[1] BOX, J., RA Fisher: The life of a scientist, Wiley, New York. 1978.

[2] BROWN, P.J., LE, N.D., & ZIDEK, J.V. Multivariate Spatial Interpolation and Exposure to Air Pollutants, Can Jour Statist 22, 489-510, 1994.

[3] CARROLL, R.J., RUPPERT, D. & STEFANSKI, L.A. Measurement Error in Nonlinear Models, Chapman and Hall, London. 1995.

[4] DELFINO, R.J., BECKLAKE, M.R., HANLEY, J.A., & SINGH, B., Estimation of Unmeasured Particulatee Air Pollution Data for an Epidemiological Study of Daily Respiratory Morbidity, Environ Research 67, 20-38, 1994.

[5] DELFINO, R.J., BECKLAKE, M.R., & HANLEY, J.A., The Relationship of Urgent Hospital Admissions for Respiratory Illnesses to Photochemical Air Pollution Levels in Montreal, Environ Research, 67, 1-19, 1994.

[6] EVANS, J.S., TOSTESON, T., & KINNEY, P.L., Cross Sectional Mortality Studies and Air Pollution Risk Assessment, Environment International 10, 55-83, 1984.

[7] FULLER, W., Measurement Error Models, Wiley, New York. 1987.

[8] GREENLAND, S., The Effect of Misclassification in Matched-Pair Case-Control Studies, Amer Jour of Epidemiology 116, 402-6, 1982.

[9]   KEEPING, E.S., Mathematics of Statistics, Part One, 3rd edition, D. Van Nostrand Co., New York. 1954.

[10]   LE, N.D., & ZIDEK, J.V., Interpolation with Uncertain Spatial Covariances: A Bayesian alternative to kriging, Journal of Multivariate Analysis, 43, 351-74, 1992.

[11]   LE, N.D., SUN, W., & ZIDEK, J.V., Bayesian Multivariate Spatial Interpolation with Data Missing-By-Design, Jour Roy Statist Soc, Series B, 59, 501-10, 1995.

[12]   LIANG, K.Y., & ZEGER, S.L., Longitudinal Data Analysis Using Generalized Linear Models, Biometrika 73, 13-22, 1986.

[13]   MacCLURE, M., The Case-Crossover Design: A method for studying transient effects on the risk of acute events, Amer Jour. of Epidemiology 133, 144-53, 1991.

[14]   NAVIDI, W., Bi-directional Case-Crossover Designs for Exposures with Time Trends. MCS-97-03, Department of Mathematical and Computer Sciences, Colorado School of Mines. 1997.

[15]   PIERCE, D.A., STRAM, D.O., VAETH, M., & SCHAFER, D.W., The Errors-in-Variables Problem: Considerations provided by radiation dose-response analyses of the a-bomb survivor data, Jour Amer Statist Assoc. 87, 351-59, 1992.

[16]   TAGER, I.B., Current View of Epidemiologic Study Designs for Occupational and Environmental Lung Diseases, Environ Health Perspect 108 (Suppl A), 615-23, 2000.

[17]   WAKEFIELD, J., A Critique of Ecological Studies, Biostatistics 1, 1-18, 2001.

[18]   ZEGER, S.L., LIANG, K.Y., & ALBERT, P.S., Models for Longitudinal Data: A generalised estimating equation approach, Biometrics 44, 1049-60, 1988.

[19]   ZIDEK, J.V., WONG, H., LE, N.D., & BURNETT, R.T., Causality, Measurement Error and Multicollinearity in Epidemiology, Environmetrics 7, 441-51, 1996.

[20]   ZIDEK, J.V., LE, N.D., WONG, H., & BURNETT, R.T., Including Structural Measurement Errors in the Nonlinear Regression Analysis of Clustered Data, Can Jour Stat 26, 537-48, 1998.

[21]   ZIDEK, J.V., WHITE, R., LE, N.D., SUN, W., & BURNETT, R.T., Imputing Unmeasured Explanatory Variables in Environmental Epidemiology with Application to Health Impact Analysis of Air Pollution, Environmental and Ecological Statistics 5, 1998.

[22]   ZIDEK, J.V., Interpolating Air Pollution for Health Impact Assessment. In: Statistics for the Environment 3: Pollution Assessment and Control, edited by V. Barnett and K. Feridun Turkman, Wiley, New York. 1997. Pp 251-68.

[23]   HILL, Sir Austin Bradford, The Environment and Disease: Association or causation? Proc Roy Soc Med 58, 295-300, 1965.

[24]   BATES, D.V., Environmental Health Risks & Public Policy, University of Washington Press, Seattle & London. 1994. Pp 117.

[25]   BATES, D.V., Health Indices of the Adverse Effects of Air Pollution: The question of coherence, Environ Research 59, 336-49, 1992.

[26]   LANES, S.F., Error and uncertainty in causal inference, In: Causal Inferenc; edited by Kenneth J. Rothman. Epidemiology Resources Inc., Chestnut Hill, MA. 02167. Pp 173-88, 1988.

[27]   GODLESKI, J., SIOUTAS, C., KATLER, M., & KOUTRAKIS, P., Death from Inhalation of Concentrated Ambient Air Particles in Animal Models of Pulmonary Disease. Abstract (11.4) at Second Colloquium on Particulate Pollution and Health, Park City, Utah May 1-3, 1996.

[28]   PETERS, A., DORING, A., WICHMANN, H-E., & KOENIG, W., Increased Plasma Viscosity During an Air Pollution Episode: A link to mortality? Lancet 349, 1582-87, 1997.

[29]   VEDAL, S. Ambient Particles and Health: Lines that divide, Air & Waste Manage. Assoc. 47, 551-81, 1997.

[30]   GAMBLE, J.F., & LEWIS, R.J. Health and Respirable Particulate (PM_{10}) Air Pollution: A causal or statistical association? Environ Health Perspect 104, 838-50, 1996.

[31]   COMMITTEE ON THE MEDICAL EFFECTS OF AIR POLLUTANTS, DEPARTMENT OF HEALTH, Non-Biological Particles and Health, Her Majesty's Stationery Office, London. 1995. Pp 141.

[32]   GAUDERMAN, W.J., McCONNELL, R., GILLILAND, F., LONDON, S., THOMAS, D., AVOL, E., VORA, H., BERHANE, K., RAPPAPORT, E., LURMANN, F., MARGOLIS, H., & PETERS, J., Association between Air Pollution and Lung Function Growth in Southern California, Am J Respir Crit Care Med 162, 1-8, 2000.

[33]   FUNG, K., & KREWSKI, D. On measurement error adjustment methods in poisson regression. Environmetrics, 10:213-214., 1999.

[34]   WEERAHANDI, S., & ZIDEK, J.V. Elements of multi-Bayesian decision theory. Annals of Statistics, 11:1032-1046. 1983.

Chapter 6

Effects on Vegetation and Ecosystems

Victor Runeckles

PREAMBLE

The main focus of this book is on air pollution and human health, which is appropriate, given that air pollution is, for the most part, a man-made problem. But man is not the only species on earth, and just as air pollution can have undesirable effects on human health, so, too, it can adversely affect other terrestrial species, including the crops and livestock that provide man's food, and the wealth of plant and animal species that populate the ecosystems of our forests and wildlands. This chapter specifically focuses on plant life, because it is plant productivity based on the process of photosynthesis that supports almost all life on earth — without plants, none of us would be here to worry about pollution!

No plant species are completely resistant to the effects of air pollutants, from the most majestic trees such as the California redwoods down to the lowly mosses and lichens. However, species vary widely in their sensitivity to air pollutants as a result of genetic differences, and their susceptibility in a given location can be influenced by environmental factors, especially drought and mineral nutrition. Many plant species are much more sensitive to pollutants than humans, a feature which has been exploited in their utilization as bioindicators of polluted air, as discussed in a later section. But plants are sedentary, and without the opportunities for avoidance that are available to animals and man through their mobility, any resistance that plants may have is dependent upon their physiology and biochemistry. In fact, at the biochemical and molecular levels, there are many similarities in the responses of plants, animals, and man.

EXPOSURE AND DOSE

In humans, the breathing of polluted air leads to deposition in the respiratory tract and lungs. If the air taken into the lungs contains a pollutant, it is convenient to think of the "dose" of pollutant received simply as the product of its concentration (c) in the ambient air and the length of time (t) this polluted air is being inhaled, i.e., dose = c * t.

However, plants do not breathe and the uptake of gaseous pollutants into the leaves, the principal sites of deposition, is passive and dependent on the purely physical process of gaseous diffusion from a region of higher concentration to one with a lower concentration. If the air passing over the leaves is polluted, some of the pollutant gases may diffuse into the leaves. However, the sites at which toxic effects occur are in many cases deep-seated within the structure of the leaf and its cells, and, as discussed in the next section, there are many obstacles along the pathway a pollutant must follow to reach these sites. The greatest of these is the actual entry into the leaf interior air space. Hence, "dose" in terms of plant effects is a difficult concept since it is inappropriate to base its definition solely on ambient concentration and time; a high ambient concentration will not necessarily lead to a correspondingly high internal concentration at sites of action. Although ambient concentrations are readily measurable, the actual internal concentrations at such sites are impossible to determine accurately, if at all; hence, the actual dose is unknown. Plant scientists therefore use the term "exposure" rather than "dose" when describing the concentration of a pollutant that elicits a response. Some further ramifications of the concepts of exposure and dose are discussed in the following section.

In spite of these differences between plants and humans, much of the terminology is the same. For example, exposure to a high concentration is likely to produce an acute response. In plants, this is usually manifested by the rapid onset of visible symptoms of injury to the leaves, involving the necrosis of discrete areas of tissue. On the other hand, prolonged exposures to lower concentrations of pollutant may lead to chronic injury responses. In plants, these may take the form of less dramatic and more diffuse visual symptoms such as discolorations, with or without the necrosis of leaf cells. However, it must be borne in mind that any permanent loss of functioning leaf tissue will impair photosynthetic output and hence reduce the growth of the plant. So-called hidden injury may occur as a result of low exposures, with few if any outwardly visible signs other than adverse effects on growth itself.

GAS EXCHANGE AND POLLUTANT UPTAKE

Since pollutant uptake is a prerequisite to any effects, we first need to understand how gases enter the leaves. For plant growth, the most important gas to be taken up is carbon dioxide, CO_2, which is needed for photosynthetic combination with water to produce sugars (as a form of energy storage), with oxygen, O_2, being released back into the atmosphere. The energy needed to drive the process is obtained from light, and in the dark, the reverse process, respiration, occurs. In this, O_2 is taken into the leaf, CO_2 is released, and the energy stored in the sugars is used to drive the processes of growth and development. Since this exchange of gases is dependent upon diffusion, the typical leaf with its thin cross-section and large surface area (and hence a large surface area/volume ratio) is the evolutionary answer to the difficulty of getting CO_2 and O_2 into and out of the leaf as efficiently as possible. The process is all the more efficient since the actual cell surface area exposed to the air within the leaf may be as much as two orders of magnitude greater than the surface area of the leaf itself. However, this efficiency also carries a price tag: it also facilitates the entry of gaseous air pollutants into the leaf.

The first obstacle for any gas to overcome in passing from the atmosphere into the leaf is the leaf boundary layer, the layer of air in contact with the leaf surfaces. The thickness of the boundary layer is an inverse function of the turbulence of the surrounding air: thick in still air, thin in turbulent or windy conditions. Diffusion is dependent upon a spatial difference in concentration and the distance separating two concentrations, i.e., a thin boundary layer has a steep gradient while a thicker layer has a more gentle slope, which reduces the rate at which a gas can reach the leaf surface.

The surfaces of leaves are typically covered with a relatively impermeable cuticle that reduces water loss and also restricts the movement of gases. However, leaves also have small pores, stomata, through which gases can diffuse into and out of the interior air space. Stomata may occur on both leaf surfaces but in most species they are more abundant on the lower surface. The principal gas exchange routes into and out of the interior air space via the stomata are shown in the diagrammatic sections of part of a typical leaf in Figure 6.1.

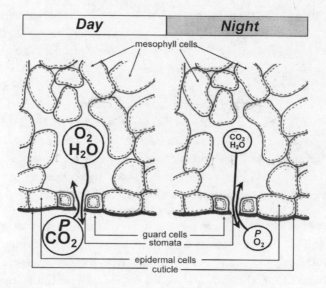

Figure 6.1: Diagrammatic cross-sections of a typical leaf showing the paths of gas exchange of CO_2 and O_2 during the day and night, the loss of H_2O, and the uptake of gaseous pollutants (P).

The aperture of the stomatal pore is not fixed in size, but is defined by the condition of the pair of guard cells that surround it. Change of shape of the guard cells results in changes in pore size. In most species changes in stomatal aperture follow a typical diurnal pattern: open during the day, permitting the entry of CO_2 for photosynthesis and the release of O_2 and water vapour, and less open (or even closed) at night. The greater inward diffusion of CO_2 for photosynthesis during the day (and outward diffusion of O_2 and water vapour) and lesser rates of diffusion at night are shown in Figure 6.1. The movement of water vapour is outward, both day and night, while the diffusion of pollutant gases is always inward. Entry through the stomata therefore presents a second obstacle to the uptake of gaseous pollutants, although small amounts of some pollutants may penetrate the leaf via the cuticle and epidermal cells. Furthermore, the functioning of the guard cells themselves, and hence the size of the stomatal pores and their regulation of the rates of diffusion of all gases, can be directly affected by several pollutants.

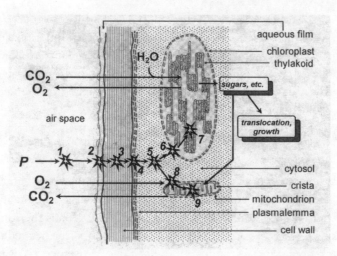

Figure 6.2: Diagrammatic section through part of a leaf mesophyll cell showing the photosynthetic and respiratory gas exchange of CO_2 and O_2 and the pathway of pollutant entry (P) into the cell organelles. The sites of potential reaction of a pollutant are: (1), the internal air space; (2), the aqueous film on the mesophyll cell surface; (3), the cell wall; (4), the cell membrane (plasmalemma); (5), the cytosol; (6), the chloroplast membrane; (7), the thylakoid; (8), the mitochondrial membrane; and (9), the cristae.

Figure 6.2 is a diagrammatic view of part of a mesophyll cell, with its cell wall, cell membrane (plasmalemma), cytosol, and two important organelles: a chloroplast and a mitochondrion. The chloroplast is the site of photosynthesis. Most of the sugars produced leave the cell and are translocated to other parts of the plant to support growth and development. In darkness, no photosynthesis can occur, but residual sugar is used in the processes of respiration carried out within the mitochondria.

The pathway followed by a pollutant gas may be similar to the daylight movement of CO_2 into the cell. However, as shown in Figure 6.2, this journey may be curtailed if the pollutant that enters the leaf air space undergoes reactions with other constituents of the air space, in the aqueous film on the surfaces of the mesophyll cells, in the cell wall, in the plasmalemma, in the cytosol, in the chloroplast's membrane or its internal thylakoid the actual site of photosynthesis), or in the mitochondrion's membrane or its internal cristae the actual sites of respiration). In some cases the reactions may result in detoxification; in others they may give rise to other toxic products or to metabolizable compounds that are of benefit to the plant.

It is convenient to visualize these steps along the pathway by analogy to Ohm's Law (which relates electrical voltage, current, and resistance) with pollutant concentration difference replacing electrical potential, flow (or flux) of pollutant replacing electrical current, and the various obstacles on the pathway as resistances. Such a model of uptake is presented in Figure 6.3, which shows the boundary layer resistance, r_{bl}, the stomatal resistance, r_s, the resistance of the cuticle, r_c, and the remaining resistances (i.e., for the stages depicted in Figure 6.2) combined for simplicity as the internal or mesophyll resistance, r_i. The overall concentration gradient that drives diffusion is from that in ambient air, C_a, to the final concentration at sites of reaction, C_o, assumed to be zero, with intermediate concentrations at the leaf surface, C_s, and in the internal air space, C_i. Thus the surface concentration, C_s, is reduced from C_a by r_{bl}, and C_i is further reduced by the parallel resistances r_s and r_c. Boundary layer resistance, r_{bl}, is high in still air, r_c is relatively constant, and r_s is much lower than r_c if the stomata are fully open.

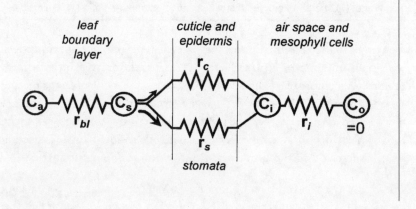

Figure 6.3: Resistance model of pollutant uptake into a leaf. C_a, C_s, C_i and C_o are pollutant concentrations in the ambient air, at the leaf surface, in the leaf interior air space, and at the final site of reaction (assumed to be 0), respectively; r_{bl}, r_c and r_s are the boundary layer, cuticular, and stomatal resistances, respectively; r_i is a composite internal resistance of the individual resistances related to the potential sites of reaction shown in Figure 6.2.

Since r_s is readily measurable, and it is frequently possible to estimate r_{bl}, the resistance model provides partial help in assessing the dose resulting from a given exposure, at least the dose to the internal air spaces. Thus, if r_{bl} is small, i.e., in breezy conditions, the product of C_a and the reciprocal of r_s provides a measure of the rate of pollutant entry or flux rate. If C_a is measured in units of $g.cm^{-3}$, and r_s in units of $s.cm^{-1}$, flux rate (given by $F = C_a.r_s^{-1}$) will be in units of $g.cm^{-2}.s^{-1}$, i.e., mass of pollutant moving per unit area of leaf surface per second. If r_{bl} is large, as in still air, flux rate is given by $F = C_a(r_{bl}^{-1} + r_s^{-1})$.

Although this approach using flux as a surrogate for dose has been validated in a few studies, its wide-scale use is limited by its need for information on boundary layer resistance, stomatal resistance, or both.

In summary, the likelihood of adverse effects on the cell is the resultant of three factors:

- The rate at which the pollutant is able to penetrate the leaf, the cell and its organelles

- The sufficiency of various defence mechanisms

- The rate at which the various defence mechanisms can respond

The balance between these rates determines the nature of the plant response — acute, chronic or hidden, as defined above. There is no sharp distinction between the levels of exposure that elicit these types of response, but the acute response, involving the rapid death of cells (usually after a few hours of exposure), results from situations in which a plant's defence mechanisms are rapidly overwhelmed by high flux rates and the amount of the pollutant taken up. Chronic and hidden injury responses occur when the defence mechanisms are still at least partly functional. Normal cell functioning at the biochemical and metabolic levels is impaired and altered, and only in the chronic case are the effects sufficient to cause local cell death.

The following sections describe the effects on plants of the major individual gaseous pollutants and some of the known effects of exposure to various combinations of pollutants, since during its lifetime, and indeed at any instant, a plant may be exposed to more than a single pollutant. In each case, acute, chronic, and hidden responses are contrasted wherever possible, and the probable mechanisms involved are discussed in relation to the uptake pathway depicted in Figure 6.2.

SULPHUR DIOXIDE (SO_2)

Sulphur dioxide has the longest history of adverse effects on vegetation of any pollutant. Although the chimney was recognized long before the Industrial Revolution as a remedial measure for the dispersal of the gases, particularly SO_2, and particulates from the smelting of ores and the burning of fuels, its benefits were largely related to human health and discomfort. With industrialization, the chimney's answer to the adage that "the solution to pollution is dilution" became inadequate — too many chimneys! Plants were not exempt from the harmful effects of the outpourings of SO_2 and smoke that typified industrial cities, as attested to by the diarist John Evelyn in his 1661 submission to King Charles II and Parliament entitled "Fumifugium: The Inconvenience of the Aer and Smoake of London Dissipated." In this he writes:

> It is this horrid Smoake ... which kills our Bees and
> Flowers abroad, suffering nothing in our Gardens to
> bud, display themselves, or ripen.

In more recent times, smelting operations in many parts of the world led to the complete denudation of the surrounding areas, for example, at Trail, British Columbia; Sudbury and Wawa, Ontario; and Copper Basin, Tennessee. Although SO_2 was not the only airborne discharge from these operations, which also included toxic metals, its quantity and the immediacy of its adverse effects ensured that little of the original vegetation could survive, even with taller and taller chimneys to disperse the diluted pollutant over wider areas.

Visual Symptoms

The visual symptoms of acute SO_2 injury observed on the leaves of most species typically involve three stages: the initial collapse of areas of leaf lamina with a water-logged appearance, followed by a brownish discoloration of the affected areas, and finally their bleaching. The final symptoms usually appear within a day of exposure, and extend through the leaf from one surface to the other. In broad-leaved species, the necrotic areas are irregular in size and shape and may anastomose to extend over veins as well as lamina, and occasionally reach the leaf margins. Figure 6.4 shows the typical bleached acute injury symptoms on a birch leaf exposed to SO_2, with a healthy leaf for comparison.

Figure 6.4: Birch leaves: healthy (left) and showing typical acute injury symptoms caused by exposure to SO_2 (right).

In plants with long narrow leaves, such as the grasses, the symptoms usually appear first at the leaf tip as a chlorosis or yellowing, and extend down towards the leaf base, often leading to the appearance of necrotic areas in stripes between the veins. In conifers, the needles similarly tend to show tip chlorosis as the first symptom, followed by a browning of the necrosing cells that may extend towards the needle base, often with a distinctly darker brown boundary between the living and dead tissues.

Acute injury to a wide range of species has been observed in many parts of the world, where the topography and meteorological conditions around local sources of SO_2 cause periodic ground-level exposures to concentrations above about 250 ppb (0.25 ppm) for several hours. However, severely adverse effects leading to rapid plant death are a rarity, and usually occur as a result of industrial or transportational accidents that lead to the release or production of extremely high concentrations of SO_2 at ground level ($>> 1$ ppm).

The initial chronic visual symptom of SO_2 injury is widespread chlorosis. In broad-leaved species this is occasionally accompanied by dispersed bleached necrotic lesions, similar to but smaller than those at the base of the injured birch leaf shown in Figure 6.4. In conifers, the chlorosis starts at the needle tip and may extend towards the leafbase in longitudinal stripes before dieback occurs. In general, therefore, the consequences of chronic exposures to SO_2 frequently resemble those of natural senescence but occur at an accelerated rate. Chronic injury to many species is more commonplace and results from prolonged exposures to lower concentrations (between about 50 and 250 ppb).

Effects on Growth

It is generally accepted that reductions in plant growth will be demonstrable if more than 5 % of the leaf area is visibly necrotic, whether as a result of acute or chronic injury. However, the effects of SO_2 lie on a continuum, ranging from death of the whole plant following massive exposures, through growth reductions following moderate to low exposures, to growth stimulations at the lowest exposure levels, especially of plants growing with an insufficient supply of nutrient sulphur from the soil. The adverse effects have been reported from innumerable studies across a wide range of crop and native species. In many cases, adverse effects on growth have been reported in the absence of any visual injury symptoms.

Response Mechanisms

The mechanisms responsible for these types of injury are not completely understood, but the important toxic agents responsible are intracellular bisulphite, HSO_3^-, and sulphite, SO_3^{2-}, formed by the pollutant's reactions with water in the aqueous film covering the mesophyll cells (site 2 in Figure 6.2):

$$SO_2 + H_2O = HSO_3^- + H^+ = SO_3^{2-} + 2H^+.$$

The observed bleaching of injured leaves is therefore not surprising given the well-known chemical action of SO_3^{2-} as a bleaching agent. The preliminary deleterious effects, however, are largely due to the fact that the formation of excessive amounts of acidic HSO_3^- and the SO_3^{2-} seriously perturbs the acid-base relationships within the cell and the functioning of the cell's membranes; the plasmalemma, the chloroplast membrane, and the mitochondrial membrane (sites 4, 6, and 8 in Figure 6.2). In addition, acidification within the chloroplast may significantly reduce the activity of ribulose-1,5-bis-phosphate carboxylase/oxygenase (rubisco) the enzyme responsible for the actual capture (fixation) of CO_2 during photosynthesis.

The stomatal guard cells themselves may be adversely affected by SO_2 at high relative humidities by becoming more turgid, causing the stomata to open wider. Since this reduces the stomatal resistance, r_s, entry of the pollutant is facilitated, which may lead to injury to the guard cells themselves and to the surrounding cells. Although the effects may be reversed if the injury is not severe and the exposure is reduced, prolonged exposures will have serious consequences, especially for tree species, because they lose the ability to control the loss of water.

However, SO_3^{2-} is also a normal intermediate in the sulphur nutrition of plants, in the process of reducing sulphate, SO_4^{2-}, taken up via the roots and translocated to the mesophyll cells of the leaf, to hydrogen sulphide, H_2S, and sulphydryl groups, -SH. These reductions take place within the chloroplast. The latter are incorporated into the S-containing amino acids, cysteine and methionine, essential constituents of proteins. The release of H_2S during photosynthesis in the light may be thought of as a relief mechanism by which plants may rid themselves of excess S resulting from SO_2 exposure.

The potential for SO_2 to provide nutritional benefit will be manifested only if the exposures are below those which induce injury and where plants are growing with suboptimal supplies of sulphur from the soil. Where a significant background level of SO_2 exists in ambient air, e.g., > 40 ppb, as occurs in many industrialized parts of the world, much of this may be utilized in plant growth. Estimates made at the University of Nottingham suggest that, in central England, the balance sheet for sulphur supplied to a wheat crop from fertilizer and from atmospheric SO_2 showed that the amount of sulphur in the harvested grain was essentially the same as the amount deposited as SO_2.

The role of SO_2 in acid rain and its effects are discussed in a later section.

OXIDES OF NITROGEN: NITRIC OXIDE (NO) AND NITROGEN DIOXIDE (NO_2)

Nitric oxide, NO, is produced during the combustion of all fuels, along with lesser amounts of nitrogen dioxide, NO_2. However, since NO is rapidly oxidized to NO_2 in the atmosphere, both are ubiquitous in the air of urban, suburban, and industrial regions, and also in the air around isolated power plants and heavy industries.

Visible Symptoms and Growth Effects

Their potential for causing severe acute injury to vegetation is limited to situations where massive concentrations, usually of NO_2, may occur as a result of accidental industrial releases, e.g., during nitric acid production. In such cases, the visual foliar symptoms are extensive areas of necrosis, similar to acute SO_2 injury but with the exception that the lesions tend to be brownish in colour and are rarely bleached.

Chronic visible injury unequivocally attributable to NO or NO_2 has rarely been observed in nature, but has been observed in greenhouses which employ CO_2-enrichment to enhance plant growth. This is achieved by burning natural gas, propane, or kerosene within the greenhouse. Since the objective is to increase the greenhouse concentration of CO_2 to about 1,000 ppm (a threefold increase over that in ambient air), ventilation must be carefully controlled to avoid the build-up of nitrogen oxides to harmful levels. In such situations, the principal oxide is NO, since there is little oxidation to NO_2, and although NO is a relatively insoluble gas, the amounts produced (> 1 ppm) may lead to growth inhibitions that completely counter the enhancement resulting from the added CO_2! One factor that mitigates against such effects is the relative stillness of greenhouse air, which results in a thick boundary layer and a correspondingly high boundary layer resistance to diffusion.

Response Mechanisms

NO and NO_2 react with water by different mechanisms, but both form nitrous, HNO_2, and nitric, HNO_3, acids. Hence, nitrite (NO_2^-) and nitrate (NO_3^-) ions will be produced in the aqueous film on the mesophyll cells following their uptake (site 2 in Figure 6.2). Nitrate and nitrite also occur in the normal pathway of nitrogen metabolism in plants, in which nitrate, taken in through the root system, is translocated to the leaves, and is first reduced in the cytosol by the enzyme nitrate reductase to NO_2^-. Nitrite then moves into the chloroplasts where it is further reduced by the enzyme, nitrite reductase, to give amino groups, -NH, the essential prerequisites for amino acid and protein synthesis.

The potential therefore exists for nitrogen oxide pollutants to confer nutritional benefit by short-circuiting the root-uptake pathway, as in the case of SO_2. But the need for -NH groups for growth far exceeds the need for -SH groups, and the demands of nitrogen metabolism in the chloroplast offer serious competition to the photosynthetic conversion of CO_2 to sugars. As a result, there is a fine line between nutritional benefit and impaired photosynthetic carbon assimilation and growth, which is highly species and even variety-specific. Thus greenhouse lettuce has been shown to be adversely affected by NO, even when grown with limiting amounts of nitrate supplied to the roots. Some grasses have been reported to show no effects of continuous daily exposures to 60 ppb NO_2 for 20 weeks, while others show more than 50 % reduction in dry matter accumulation. On the other hand, several crop species, including radish, beans, and wheat, another member of the grass family, show significant growth stimulations from low exposures to NO_2, as shown in Figure 6.5.

It is hard, therefore, to provide a clear answer as to whether the oxides of nitrogen per se are significant air pollutants for vegetation in the field. However, their significance becomes clearer when one considers their contributions to acid rain, and their interactive effects with other pollutants, as discussed in later sections.

Figure 6.5: The stimulatory effect on the growth of wheat of prolonged exposure to low levels of NO$_2$. Right: control grown in filtered air; left: grown in filtered air enriched to 80-100 ppb NO$_2$ for 3 hours (0600-0900) per day for 45 days.

HYDROGEN FLUORIDE (HF)

Hydrogen fluoride, HF, is a localized pollutant, most commonly resulting from emissions from aluminum smelting and superphosphate fertilizer manufacture. Since fluoride is not metabolized, uptake leads to its accumulation at the tips and around the margins of leaves, where its toxicity leads to necrosis. Since it is a cumulative toxin, the acute versus chronic definitions of response do not apply: symptoms appear when the local internal concentration exceeds a threshold, regardless of the exposure history and rates of uptake that led to the accumulation.

Figure 6.6: Gladiolus plant (variety Snow Princess) showing typical terminal leaf dieback and chlorosis caused by acute exposure to HF.

Typical visual symptoms of HF injury are shown in Figure 6.6, depicting the leaf-tip dieback of gladiolus. Here, as with most species, the tips or margins of the leaves are first affected, becoming chlorotic and then necrotic and brown in colour as the injury spreads. Characteristic features are the separation of the necrotic and healthy tissue by a narrow band of purplish-brown pigmentation, and the loss of the necrotic areas by breakage, resulting in truncated or ragged, shot-holed leaves. Adverse effects on growth are therefore largely the result of progressive loss of functional leaf tissue.

The localized accumulation of fluoride appears to be due to a limited ability of the plasmalemma to exclude its entry into the cell. It therefore remains in the aqueous film and cell walls and follows the transpirational stream of water to the tip and margin of the leaf. In these areas, the plasmalemma's ability to prevent uptake into the cell is overwhelmed, and the structure of the plasmalemma is destroyed, leading to a complete breakdown of cell integrity and function. There is no clear picture of the mechanism by which HF disrupts cell function, although it is a known inhibitor of several key enzymes. There is persuasive evidence that it interferes with the important regulatory roles played by calcium and magnesium in the cell and its membranes, by direct chemical reaction or the formation of fluorophosphate complexes.

PHOTOCHEMICAL OXIDANTS (SMOG): OZONE (O_3) AND PEROXYACYLNITRATES (PANS)

Following its first characterization in Los Angeles in the middle of the 20th century, photochemical oxidant (smog) has become a worldwide urban phenomenon. Its major constituent, ozone, O_3, however, is transported to many rural and pristine areas, where it may injure vegetation and lead to significant loss of crops and reduced forest tree growth.

Ozone formation in the lower troposphere is the result of the daylight-hour ultraviolet radiation of nitrogen dioxide and reactions with volatile hydrocarbons (VHCs). In urban locations, the sources of NO_2 and VHCs are largely anthropogenic, but there are significant contributions of VHCs from street trees and other vegetation in many cities. However, natural sources of NO_2 and $VHCs_s$ from vegetation also lead to the photochemical production of O_3 in more remote regions. As a result, there is a significant background concentration of O_3 (25-50 ppb) in most vegetated parts of the world. In regions with severe photochemical oxidant pollution, phytotoxic levels of peroxyacylnitrates, PANs, are frequently present.

Visible Symptoms

In addition to human respiratory effects and eye irritation, components of smog were recognized in the early 1940s by workers in California as having harmful effects on plants. Dealing first with O_3, consistent features of acute injury to the leaves of broad-leaved species are the appearance of small circular necrotic lesions visible only on the upper surfaces. Initially they appear as small water-logged areas which turn brown within a day or so and are subsequently bleached by the sun, by which time the necrosis may extend through the thickness of the leaf and become visible on the lower surface. The lesions are usually edged by a narrow ring of dark pigmentation, attributed to the deposition of tannins, surrounded by healthy green tissue. Typical symptoms on a tobacco leaf are shown in Figure 6.7. This symptomatology has led to the use of descriptive terms such as "stipple" and "fleck." In severely polluted regions, repeated occurrences of acute injury can be superimposed on a leaf, leading to anastomosis into larger necrotic areas. Visual inspection of the state of the lesions can sometimes be used to approximate the time elapsed since the different injurious exposures occurred. In fact, a particularly sensitive variety of tobacco, Bel-W3, has been used as a biomonitor in several studies around the world, to provide crude surveys of the levels of O_3 in ambient air. In narrow-leaved species, including the coniferous trees, the visible symptoms are bifacial flecks or stipples that may extend through the leaf. However, in all cases, the lesions are confined to the intercostal lamina and never appear over the leaf veins.

Chronic O_3 injury is usually revealed by the appearance of extensive chlorotic stippling or general chlorosis, which if the exposures are continuing may lead to the premature death of large areas of leaf. In many cases, the visual changes are indicative of an acceleration of natural senescence.

Although PANs are ubiquitous constituents of photochemical smog, their concentrations are rarely sufficient to cause plant injury. In Southern California, however, sufficiently high levels led to the association

Figure 6.7: Leaf of tobacco (*Nicotiana tabacum* variety Bel-W3) showing stipple symptoms of acute O_3 injury.

of the "silver leaf" symptom with exposure to ambient PANs, mostly peroxyacetylnitrate. The words are descriptive since the leaf's lower mesophyll cells are killed, leaving the lower epidermis as a thin membranous film with a silvery appearance. On a crop such as head lettuce, the symptoms are immediately visible on the exposed lower surfaces of the outermost leaves.

Effects on Growth

As with SO_2, necrotic loss of more than about 5 % of functioning leaf tissue will begin to result in impaired growth, but the effects of O_3 are more insidious: without any marked visible symptoms other than perhaps chlorosis and accelerated senescence, hidden injury can result in significant reductions in growth, as shown by the potato plant in Figure 6.8. Extensive field studies in the United States, Europe, and elsewhere have shown that significant crop losses and reductions in forest tree growth are attributable to ambient O_3. There are wide differences in sensitivity among species and varieties, but some varieties of alfalfa, green bean, clover, lettuce, grape, oat, onion, potato, soybeans, spinach and wheat are particularly at risk (see Table 6.1). Tree species similarly show a range of sensitivity, with alder, aspen, eastern white pine, and ponderosa pine being among the most sensitive.

Figure 6.8: Effects of O_3 on the growth of potato (Solanum tuberosum). Left, plant grown in filtered air; right, plant exposed to daily daytime peaks of 80 - 120 ppb O_3 for 48 days.

As the recognition of O_3 as a major air pollutant became more widespread, numerous attempts were made to quantify its adverse effects on vegetation, especially crops. Early studies using chambers and greenhouses to compare plant growth in ambient air with that in air filtered through charcoal to remove O_3 (conditions such as those used for Figure 6.8) permitted crude assessments of the magnitudes of losses caused by ambient O_3 in many locations in order to focus public and political attention on the seriousness of the situation. Table 6.1 shows such estimates of the losses of several crops induced by ambient O_3 concentrations in Ontario and several US in the early 1980s. Other chamber experiments with plants exposed to a range of O_3 levels provided some simple exposure-yield relationships for many crops, and these could be used to obtain estimates of the losses (due to increased O_3) or gains (due to reduced O_3) to crops within a region in different O_3 scenarios. Estimates of this type, expressed in terms of lost value to the producer (assuming fixed crop prices), led to amounts of approximately $9 million in 1986 for the Fraser Valley of British Columbia, and from $17 to $70 million annually in the mid-1980s for Ontario. The upper figure represented about 4 % of the $1.9 billion in Ontario crop sales. Since these figures are composites covering the major crops in a region, it must be borne in mind that some individual crops will be hit much harder than others.

Crop	Location	Yield loss (%)
Green bean	Ontario	24
	New York	26
	Massachussetts	41
	California	1
Potato	Ontario	36
	Pennsylvania	14
	New Jersey	25
Tomato	Ontario	30
	New York	33
	California	12
Alfalfa	California	11-28
Peanut	Ontario	0-20
Sweet Corn	California	9-28

Table 6.1: Some early 1980s estimates of crop losses due to ambient O_3 levels in Ontario and several US states.

While the variability in the estimates is partly due to the inevitability of growth in different seasons, different environmental conditions, species and variety differences, and weak methodology, the magnitude of the losses was such that the situation could not be ignored. A much better understanding of the quantitative response of plants to O_3 was needed in order to obtain more reliable estimates of the costs of lost agricultural production, and this led to considerable field research, aimed at improving our ability to provide reasonable estimates of the losses caused by existing and projected ambient O_3 concentrations. Three factors are largely responsible for the difficulties faced in this task.

- The first relates to the nature of exposure to O_3. Since UV from sunlight is needed, there is a diurnal fluctuation in photochemical oxidant formation, with O_3 levels usually peaking in the early afternoon.See Fig 2.5, page 46. But day-to-day variations in variables such as cloud cover and air circulation patterns can lead to marked day-to-day differences in exposure. A growing season may therefore experience several daytime episodes of potentially injurious concentrations, and some of these may occur on consecutive days. But they will tend to occur at random throughout the season, so that in a given year, plants may receive the highest exposures in their early growth stages while in another, the highest exposures may occur only later in the growing season. As a result, decisions have to be made about how best to compute the effective exposure that a crop or a stand of forest trees has received over a growing season or some other period of time. Since the usual form in which ambient O_3 data are available is as hourly or half-hourly averages, there are numerous ways in which these can be condensed to provide a single exposure index for any given period. Using data obtained from extensive field experiments on a range of major crops in different locations in the United States between 1980 and 1986 (the National Crop Loss Assessment Network, NCLAN), and on wheat in different countries in Western Europe during the 1990s (the European Open-Top Chamber Programme, EOTCP), several hundred different indices have been computed and tested to see how well they performed statistically as measures of the exposures causing observed growth reductions or crop losses.

- The second factor that complicates the selection of the "best" exposure index concerns the nature of the relationship between exposure and plant response: is it linear or non-linear, and if the latter, what form of non-linear relationship is most appropriate?

- The third factor relates to the effects of a host of environmental variables on uptake and plant susceptibility. These include physical factors such as wind (already discussed in relation to the leaf boundary layer resistance to uptake), light intensity, and temperature; chemical factors such as nutritional status and interactions with agricultural chemicals and other pollutants; and biological factors such as interactions with disease organisms, insects and other pests, and, in the case of crops, competitive interactions with weeds.

Dealing first with the issue of selecting the "best" exposure index, one objective has been to find a defensible form of exposure index which is of use in developing robust estimates of the crop losses attributable to O_3. But a closely related application is the potential use of such an index as the basis of air quality standards or objectives to protect vegetation from injury and loss. Throughout the world, air quality standards for gaseous air pollutants are currently expressed in terms of simple mean concentrations (averaged over various periods: 1 hour, 3 hours, 8 hours, 1 day, 1 year) that are not to be exceeded. While such averages have appealing simplicity, in the case of O_3 they are poor indices of exposure and poor standards for plant protection, since it was early recognized that plant responses to O_3 are non-linear and exhibit thresholds below which no effects are detectable. In other words, various defence mechanisms are adequate to cope with sub-threshold exposures. However, this means that higher exposure concentrations are more important than low concentrations and, more importantly, that simple averages are inappropriate because they treat all individual concentrations equally. Attention has therefore focused on cumulative indices that increment only when a particular threshold concentration is reached.

The outcome of extensive computational work largely based on the NCLAN studies has been that, in Canada and the United States, an index termed SUM06 has been recommended as the basis for expressing ambient O_3 exposures for use as an air quality objective or standard to protect vegetation. SUM06 is defined as the sum of all daytime hourly O_3 concentrations that equal or exceed a threshold of 0.06 ppm (60 ppb).

Based on the results of the EOTCP, European workers have adopted the AOT40 index, defined as the sum of all daytime hourly O_3 concentration that exceed a 40 ppb threshold. The conceptual distinction between these two indices is shown in Figure 6.9a, but there is a close relationship between the two indices, as shown in Figure 6.9b.

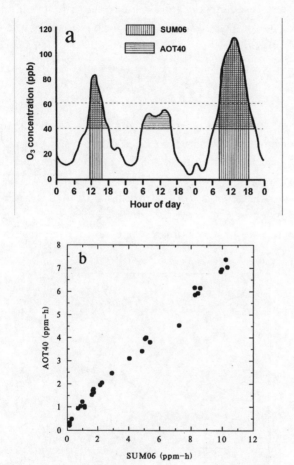

Figure 6.9: Comparison between the sum06 and AOT40 indices for o_3 exposure. a) Typical hourly O_3 profiles over three consecutive days illustrating the methods used to calculate the SUM06 and AOT40 exposure indices. (b) The close relationship between the SUM06 and AOT40 indices for O_3 calculated for three successive broccoli crops grown in an experimental field exposure facility at the University of British Columbia.

The North American and European approaches have also differed with respect to the choice of response function. In Europe, the AOT40 has been used to define linear yield effects, while North American workers have favoured a non-linear approach. The arguments in favour of a threshold-based exposure index can be applied equally well to the selection of a non-linear response function, and although many curvilinear functions have been studied, the Weibull function has been used extensively in the analysis of NCLAN data, expressed in the form:

$$y = \alpha \bullet e^{-\left(x/\sigma\right)^{\lambda}}$$

where y is yield or some other measure of growth, x is an exposure index, α is the asymptotic maximum yield at zero exposure, and σ and λ are parameters that control the shape of the curve. A Weibull response curve fitted to experimental data on bush bean yield is shown in Figure 6.10. This shows the lack of yield depression until a threshold of O_3 is approached beyond which the curve falls more steeply to a point of inflection, after which it declines more slowly, ultimately reaching zero at infinity.

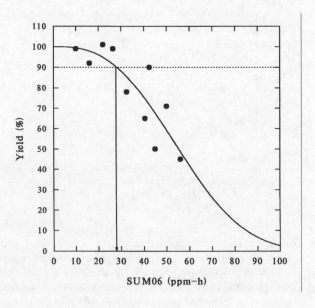

Figure 6.10: Weibull yield response curve for bush bean grown under 10 levels of O_3 exposure in a field experiment at the University of British Columbia.

The outcome of the NCLAN studies, which comprised a total of 56 response functions similar to that in Figure 6.10 for different years, locations, and major crops (accounting for 70% of all US cropland), indicated that exceeding summertime 3-month exposures with a SUM06 index of 26.4 ppm-h would lead to more than a 10% yield loss of half the major crops; to protect 75% of crops to the same extent would need a more stringent 16.5 ppm-h. For deciduous and coniferous trees, exceedances of 3-month SUM06 values of 31.3 and 42.6 ppm-h, respectively, have been suggested as likely to cause more than 10% growth reductions.

From the EOTCP studies, an AOT40 index of 3.0 ppm-h has been proposed in Europe as the critical 3-month exposure level for wheat, above which yield losses of 5%or more will occur. For trees, a 6-month AOT40 of 10 ppm-h has been proposed as the critical level for 10% growth reductions.

In both situations, it is clear that achieving the quoted values will not prevent greater losses to some crops or greater growth reductions in some tree species. At the same time, there is abundant evidence to indicate that the exposures quoted may be too conservative and that they may be exceeded without adverse effects on even the most sensitive species, because of the roles played by various environmental factors in affecting uptake and susceptibility.

While the preceding discussion has focused on the application of exposure indices to the establishment of air quality objectives or standards, the values quoted are derived from the range of improved crop response models produced by the NCLAN and EOTCP studies over several years. These have paved the way for more robust assessments of the losses from ambient O_3, expressed either as yields or in monetary terms, than those presented above. For example, an analysis of all the US regions producing corn, soybean, wheat, cotton and peanuts yielded a total benefit (cost) of $1.3 billion (1978 dollars) with a mean annual reduction in O_3 concentration to 40 ppb from 53 ppb (the mean level for the regions in 1978). A similar analysis for corn, soybean, cotton, wheat, sorghum and barley produced a total benefit of $1.7 billion for a 25% reduction in 1980 O_3 levels. Since the essential underpinning response relationships for forest trees are not nearly as well developed as for agricultural crops, unambiguous estimates of the economic impact of O_3 on forests are premature, although figures for losses from all forms of air pollution (especially acid rain and O_3) ranging from \$1.5 billion (1981 Canadian dollars) in eastern Canada to \$1.75 billion (in 1978 in US dollars) for the eastern US have been published.

Response Mechanisms

Since O_3 is a highly reactive oxidizing agent there are many potential locations for it to react following its entry into the leaf air space. Based on its known in vitro reactions with sulphydryl groups in key amino acids such as cysteine, and with C=C double bonds in fatty acids, most proteins and lipids are potential targets, together with various unsaturated volatiles it meets in the interior air space. Since membranes consist of phospholipid-protein matrices, the plasmalemma and chloroplast and mitochondrial membranes (4, 6, and 8 in Figure 6.2) are vulnerable. And since they regulate so many of the cell's functions, any membrane dysfunction may lead to serious adverse effects.

Because of its reactivity, it seems doubtful that O_3 can penetrate far into the cell. It seems most likely that it will react in the air space, aqueous film, cell wall, and plasmalemma (1, 2, 3, and 4 in Figure 6.2) and that more deep-seated effects are caused by the further penetration of various toxic reaction products. Non-invasive techniques such as chlorophyll fluorescence and electron spin-resonance spectrometry together with studies using ultra-microscopy have clearly demonstrated that O_3 can adversely affect both Photosystems I and II, inhibit the activation of rubisco within the chloroplast and several mitochondrial functions in vivo and induce structural changes. But this does not mean that O_3 itself is the direct cause.

On the other hand, the guard cells are directly exposed to O_3, and usually respond by slow closure of the stomatal pores. Indeed, in an early study, the resistance to acute O_3 injury in one variety of onion was related to the ultrasensitivity of its stomata, whose closure reduced the entry of the pollutant. Differing sensitivities have since been found among varieties of many crop species. However, the closure response may be a mixed blessing — although entry of O_3 is restricted, so too is CO_2 uptake, which results in reduced photosynthesis. Furthermore, repeated exposures usually lead to a loss of the closure response, and a dampening of the normal diurnal opening-closing cycle so that the stomata tend to remain partly open both day and night. Because of the key role played by the stomata in overall gas exchange, such dampening results in less CO_2 uptake during the day and more water loss at night, both of which may lead to impaired growth.

There is a report suggesting that, having passed through the stomata into the air space, the O_3 concentration (C_i in Figure 6.3) falls to close to zero, which indicates either that it has reacted in the air space or that the aqueous film, cell wall, and plasmalemma present so many reaction sites that there is a steep concentration gradient drop from the concentration passing through the stomata to that at the mesophyll cell surface. In terms of the electrical model of uptake shown on Figure 6.3, this would mean that the early components of the internal resistance, r_i, are extremely low. Another suggestion is that O_3 reacts in the air space with endogenous unsaturated volatiles such as ethylene, C_2H_4, to produce even more highly reactive free radicals, but these have not been identified. However, the reaction of O_3 with unsaturated cellular constituents such as lipids by the process of ozonolysis has been shown to produce hydroxyhydroperoxides (HHPs), and it has been suggested that is the HHPs that constitute the major toxic agents within the plant cell following O_3 uptake.

The anti-oxidants ascorbic acid (and its peroxidase enzyme system) and α-tocopherol are important constituents of leaf cells that can react with O_3, HHPs, and other reaction products of O_3 such as hydrogen peroxide, H_2O_2, and the free radicals superoxide (O_2^{β}) and hydroxyl (HO^{β}). Ascorbic acid, in particular, occurs in the aqueous film and cell wall as well as throughout the cell. Indeed, in some species, it constitutes as much as 10% of the soluble leaf carbohydrate. It therefore provides at least two lines of defence against O_3 (2 and 3 in Figure 6.2), protecting the plasmalemma, and may also provide possible defences against further penetration of the cell. Failure of the cell wall defence mechanisms to protect the plasmalemma is manifested by the appearance of water-logged flecks as the first visible signs of acute leaf injury following membrane breakdown and the leakage of cell fluids into the air space.

OTHER GASES

There are numerous other phytotoxic gases that occasionally cause injury to vegetation. Many of these are industrial chemicals such as chlorine (Cl_2), hydrogen chloride (HCl), ammonia (NH_3), hydrogen sulphide (H_2S), and carbon disulphide (CS_2), which may cause injury to vegetation around industrial plants as a result of fugitive emissions or through accidental releases. In such situations, however, attention properly focuses on human health effects, which are of greater concern.

Ammonia is also released through many agricultural activities, which in several regions of the world may lead to significant background levels of NH_3 in ambient air. However, no direct adverse effects on plants have been reported, although NH_3 may interact with other pollutants to modify their effects, and plays a role in acidic precipitation because of its neutralizing capabilities.

Although carbon monoxide (CO) is notoriously poisonous to humans and most other animals, it has no significant adverse effects on higher plants at comparable concentrations, because of their ability to oxidize it to CO_2 in the mitochondria.

Mention has already been made of the release of H_2S by plants as a means of reducing the harmful effects of SO_2. Although plant injury has been reported from exposures to H_2S concentrations greater than 100 ppb, lower levels are stimulatory. Since the odour threshold in humans is below 1.5 ppb, remedial action to remove the malodour usually ensures that phytotoxic levels are rarely reached.

Ethylene, C_2H_4, is the only gaseous hydrocarbon of any significance as a phytotoxic air pollutant. Ironically, it is a naturally produced plant hormone, and is responsible for the ripening process of many fruits. However, prolonged exposures to concentrations as low as a few parts per billion can cause growth deformities, chlorosis, and flower drop; such concentrations may occur from time to time around industrial sources of C_2H_4 as a result of fugitive emissions and accidental releases.

ACID RAIN

As a result of reactions in the atmosphere, gaseous SO_2 gives rise to sulphuric acid, H_2SO_4, and NO_2 to nitric acid, HNO_3. Both are strong acids which, when dissolved in raindrops cause significant acidification of rainwater. Similar acidification may also occur in fog water droplets. However, although studies with simulated acid rain (water containing various concentrations of H_2SO_4 and HNO_3) sprayed onto leaves have reported the occurrence of visible injury in the form of small necrotic lesions, the acidities used were usually considerably greater than those observed in acid rain in the field. Indeed, the only reports of such symptoms having been seen in the field appear to come from observations of the effects of extremely acidic fogs in California, which result from a unique combination of meteorology and ambient air containing O_3 as well as H_2SO_4 and HNO_3.

However, acid rain has many adverse effects on plants at the ecological level because of its effects on soil. The balance in the soil of chemical elements that can be absorbed by plant roots is largely regulated by its acidity. With increased acidification, the leaching of important nutrient cations such as potassium, magnesium and calcium is accelerated which may lead to deficiency disorders and impaired plant growth. In many soils, acidification may also lead to the solubilization of aluminum from rock and soil particles as aluminum hydroxide, $Al(OH)_3$, which is toxic to the roots of many species.

As a result, acid rain has rightly been identified as a contributory cause of forest declines in the eastern United States and northern and central Europe. However, these are not simple cause-and-effect situations, since there is ample evidence to implicate O_3 as another factor in the forest decline syndrome.

COMBINATIONS OF GASEOUS POLLUTANTS

Air pollutants rarely occur in isolation. In the industrial world, significant levels of SO_2, NO, NO_2, O_3, and other gases may be present in the ambient air, although only one may be predominant. Combinations of significant pollutant levels may be sequential or concurrent, i.e., as mixtures. However, except in the case of local episodes of high levels of pollutants such as SO_2, exposures to mixtures are infrequent. The most common exposure pattern is sequential, with two or more pollutants reaching peak levels at different times of day or on successive days, with or without periods of overlap.

In the case of concurrent exposures, much information on the effects on plants has been obtained under experimental conditions with relatively high concentrations of binary and ternary mixtures such as SO_2-NO_2, SO_2-O_3, SO_2-HF, HF-O_3 and SO_2-NO_2-O_3. However, with the exception of some SO_2-NO_2 studies, most of the information is of little relevance to the real world, because of both the unrealistic high levels and the artificial exposure regimes employed, although it includes examples of antagonistic (less than additive), additive, and synergistic (more than additive) effects. The SO_2-NO_2 studies of interest were conducted using levels of both gases known to occur in the United Kingdom (20-40 ppb) and showed that (1) NO_2 reversed the SO_2-induced stomatal opening that occurs at high humidities; (2) SO_2 inhibited the detoxification mechanism provided by the NO_2-induced induction of the enzyme nitrite reductase; and (3) these effects translated into synergistic growth reductions in several grass species.

Figure 6.11: Response of wheat to daily sequential exposures to NO_2 and O_3 for 45 days. Left: control in filtered air; centre: exposed to 80-100 ppb O_3 for 6 hours from 0900; right: exposed to 80-100 ppb NO_2 for 3 hours from 0600, followed by 80-100 ppb O_3 for 6 hours.

There have been very few studies of the effects of sequential exposures to different pollutants. However, a couple of studies of the effects of NO_2-O_3 sequences are particularly relevant since NO_2 is the photochemical precursor of surface-level O_3. Hence, diurnal exposures to NO_2 will normally precede exposures to O_3. An investigation of the effects of daily 3-hour exposures to 80-100 ppb NO_2 followed by 6-hour exposures to 80-100 ppb O_3 revealed different responses among three crops: bush bean, radish and wheat. With the first, the NO_2 pretreatment reduced the inhibition of growth caused by O_3, while in the last two, it increased the inhibition caused by O_3 alone. In the case of wheat, the NO_2 exposures by themselves were stimulatory (as shown in Figure 6.5), but they caused increased susceptibility to O_3, as shown in Figure 6.11. One explanation is suggested by a subsequent study with radish which showed that the NO_2 pretreatment caused decreased stomatal resistance during the day, i.e., wider stomata, leading to increased O_3 flux rates and uptake.

These and other studies of air pollutant combinations illustrate the hazards of trying to predict the outcome of exposures to such combinations based upon knowledge of the responses to the individual pollutants. They also explain why, to date, no satisfactory general plant response models have been developed to accommodate the range of pollutant combinations that may occur in ambient air.

INTERACTIONS OF GASEOUS POLLUTANTS WITH ENVIRONMENTAL FACTORS AND GLOBAL CLIMATE CHANGE

Many environmental factors affect growth per se, and many of these affect plant response to air pollutants. For example, plants grown in shade tend to be more susceptible than those of the same species growing in full sun. Many interactions have been reported between pollutants and mineral nutrient status, but the evidence is fragmented with more (or less) of nutrients such as nitrogen, phosphorus or potassium having been reported as affecting susceptibility both positively or negatively. However, one consistent observation has been that drought stress usually reduces pollutant impact. Unfortunately, drought adversely affects growth and accelerates senescence; it is a hollow victory for a plant to avoid injury from, say, O_3, only to succumb to the lack of water!

Current concerns about climate change are dealt with in a subsequent chapter. However, two features of the changing global climate that have the potential to modify plant responses to air pollutants are increases in CO_2 levels and mean temperatures. Mention has already been made in a previous section of the use of CO_2 enrichment in greenhouses to promote vigorous plant growth. A doubling of present-day atmospheric levels of CO_2 to about 700 ppm has been used in several experimental investigations of its effects on the impact of O_3. A common but not universal finding has been that the resulting increased photosynthesis provides some degree of protection against injury and growth inhibition. However, when the elevated CO_2 is accompanied by modest increases in temperature in the range of temperature rises forecast for the next century by most climate models, the protection may disappear because of the differential effects of increased temperature on different growth and development processes. For example, the three-year European Union "ESPACE-wheat" study involving 25 experiments in nine locations included a study with CO_2 doubling at ambient and ambient $+$ 2.4°C temperatures, with and without added O_3. Although CO_2 tended to counteract the negative impact of O_3 on wheat yield, the effect was minimized by the warmer temperatures. Furthermore, a multiple linear regression of wheat yields from all 25 experiments revealed temperature as a significant variable with a negative coefficient. However, there has been insufficient experimentation to date to provide definitive information about CO_2-temperature-air pollutant interactions.

A similar situation exists with respect to interactions of air pollutants with increased surface levels of ultraviolet-B (UV-B) radiation. The sparse data are mostly contradictory and preclude the making of any definitive statements about how increasing UV-B levels may affect plant response to pollutants.

Other important environmental factors with which air pollutants may interact at the plant level are disease-causing organisms (plant pathogens) and insects, mites, and other pests. Numerous studies have shown that pollutant-induced necrotic injury may facilitate infection by pathogens. There is also evidence of increased severity of disease in the absence of visible injury. For example, O_3 has been found to increase the incidence of mildew on broccoli.

Numerous interactions with insects are known. These range from the increased bark beetle infestations of ponderosa pine weakened by O_3 in Southern California to O_3-attributed increases in infestations by aphids, beetles, weevils, and other pests on several crop species. SO_2 predisposes white pine to mite infestations but reduces the severity of attacks by the white pine weevil. HF, too, has been found to be either stimulatory or inhibitory to different pests of crops and forest trees. A pollutant may affect an insect pest directly, or through effects on the host plant on which it feeds, or through subtle effects such as changes in feeding preference. There are numerous reports in the literature of each type of response.

ECOLOGICAL IMPACTS

Although pathogen and pest interactions are ecological in nature, the focus of the preceding sections has been on pollutant effects on plants as individuals or populations of the same species/variety, e.g., crops. Most natural ecosystems are characterized by a diversity of species; not surprisingly, therefore, sensitive species which are unable to withstand the stress imposed by air pollutants will tend to die out, leaving room for more tolerant species to proliferate. This modifies the natural succession of species, both by allowing the upsurge of previously minor species and, if the dominant species is sensitive, causing drastic changes in speciation.

Terrestrial ecosystems, whether large or small (e.g., forests, grasslands, meadows, fallen logs), have both structure and function. Their structure relates to species diversity and abundance; their function relates to how the species interact with each other and their physical and chemical environments. The major role in the functioning or dynamics of all terrestrial ecosystems played by microorganisms is rarely recognized, although they are largely responsible for many essential features such as the recycling of nutrients, the breakdown of organic wastes, and the maintenance of a balance of gases in the air. Since the effects of acid rain are mediated through the soil, as discussed above, disturbance of the functioning of the communities of soil microorganisms by increased acidity plays an important role in the effects on higher plants.

Historically, the most dramatic ecological effects have been those around major industrial sources of SO_2 and HF. Here, the number of surviving species is observed to decline steadily as one moves closer to the source. In some cases the hardiest survivors are species which were minor components of the original vegetation or may be "foreign" invader species that have become well established. For example, the lowly lichens, *Lecanora conizaoides* and *L. dispersa*, "like" SO_2, and can be found in many industrial cities and regions of Europe as the dominant lichens on buildings, walls, and trees, but are rare in areas with no SO_2 pollution.

The complex ecological ramifications of air pollution are well illustrated by the effects of O_3 on the San Bernardino Forest in Southern California. Two fire-resistant tree species, ponderosa and Jeffrey pines, normally dominate the fire-climax system, but continuous exposure to O_3 has caused growth reductions in both, accompanied by the premature shedding of needles. Species that are more O_3-resistant but less fire-resistant have tended to proliferate in the understory, which, together with the thicker carpet of decaying needles, creates the conditions for catastrophic fires that jeopardize the remaining overstory trees. The thicker carpet of shed needles also changes the litter decomposition patterns, with the fungal microflora of the needles weakening the natural microbial and arthropod decomposer community and slowing the rate of decomposition. As a result, the release of nutrients into the soil is reduced, which adds to the woes of the overstory species and shifts the nutrient balance in favour of other species.

Studies of forest decline in Europe and the eastern United States have revealed similarly complex interactions among tree species of differing sensitivity to O_3 or acid rain or both, and the soil microflora.

EPILOGUE

Many topics have had to be omitted or their discussion curtailed in this brief survey of the effects of air pollutants on vegetation. But one take-home message for the reader must be that, in spite of what we now know (and understand) about these effects, there is still much to be learned, from the ecological level down to the cell and its functioning.

Similarities between plants and man in their responses to air pollutants were alluded to in the Preamble. These are essentially all at the enzyme level and are particulary true of the mechanisms for detoxifying free radicals.

The statement was also made that plants are more sensitive than humans to some pollutants, CO and H_2S being notable exceptions. A partial explanation lies in the fact that, in spite of uptake into leaves being a passive process, for a given ambient concentration of SO_2, NO_2 or O_3, more pollutant reaches the mesophyll cells of leaves than the alveolar cells of the lungs, even during exercise, as suggested by the following calculations, which admittedly contain several approximations and assumptions.

Assume a pollutant concentration of 100 ppb (100 nL L^{-1}) in both cases. For plants with 10 m^2 of leaf area (e.g., a small tree or shrub, 2 m^2 area of rice paddy, or 3 m^2 area of wheat field) and leaves whose total mesophyll cell surface is 20 times the leaf's surface area, wind speeds greater than 4.8 km h^{-1} (1.3 m s^{-1}) will reduce the boundary layer resistance to close to zero and, from experimental evidence, it can be calculated that the uptake rate through the stomata is approximately 60 mL h^{-1}. (This would be reduced in still air.) Further assuming that the thickness of the mesophyll cell walls is 0.5 m, the wall volume that receives the pollutant is 125 mL, and the dosage to this volume (next to the plasmalemma) is 480 mL L^{-1} h^{-1}.

Turning to the lung, assuming a breathing rate of 120 min^{-1} under exercise and a lung volume of 2 L, the ventilation rate is 14,400 Lh^{-1} and the intake of pollutant is 1.4 mL h^{-1}. Further assuming that an alveolar surface area of 100 m^2 and that the thickness of the cell layers between the alveolar surface and the blood is 0.5 m, giving a tissue volume of 50 mL, the dosage it receives will be 29 mL L^{-1} h^{-1}, more than an order of magnitude less than that received within the foliage. Taking the comparison a stage further, a human body weight of 75 kg would equate to more than 50 m^2 of rice, but to absorb the amount received by the exercising human would only require about 0.12 m^2 of rice and 0.18 m^2 of wheat.

While the foregoing example illustrates why plants may be more sensitive than people, it also illustrates the important role that plants play as absorbers of pollutants, even though they may sacrifice themselves in the process! We mostly take this assistance offered by the plant world for granted and, while we may concede that plants are the essential primary producers in the earth's life-support system, we often fail to recognize the role that vegetation plays in protecting human health. The primacy of human health over other concerns is well illustrated by the application of the US Clean Air Act which requires the definition of primary (human health) and secondary (human welfare) standards of air quality for the major pollutants. With regard to O_3, in spite of the evidence for the greater sensitivity of many plants which would suggest that the secondary standard be more stringent than the primary, both standards are equated and defined based on health considerations. Perhaps a way needs to be found to relate effects on plants directly to health effects. Then perhaps some of the funds available for medical research related to pollution might become available to permit plant scientists to answer some of the outstanding questions!

ACKNOWLEDGEMENTS

No specific references have been made to published research, but the author wishes to acknowledge the work of many graduate students and colleagues throughout the world that has been referred to. He is also indebted to the late Professor Alan Wellburn of Lancaster University for all too infrequent but highly invigorating discussions, including the time spent in developing plant-human comparisons such as the one above, another version of which can be found in his book, cited below.

FURTHER READING

AGRAWAL, S.B. & AGRAWAL, M. (eds.) 2000. Environmental Pollution and Plant Responses. Lewis Publishers, Boca Raton, FL.

FLAGLER, R.B. (ed.) 1998. Recognition of Air Pollution Injury to Vegetation: A Pictorial Atlas, 2nd edition. Air & Waste Management Association, Pittsburgh, PA.

HECK, W.W., TAYLOR, O.C. & TINGEY, D.T. (eds.) 1988. Assessment of Crop Loss from Air Pollutants. Elsevier Applied Science, London.

JACOBSON J.S. & HILL, A.C. (eds.) 1970. Recognition of Air Pollution Injury to Vegetation: A Pictorial Atlas. Air Pollution Control Association, Pittsburgh, PA.

LEFOHN, A.S. (ed.) 1992. Surface Level Ozone Exposures and Their Effects on Vegetation. Lewis Publishers, Boca Raton, FL.

TRESHOW, M. (ed.) 1984. Air Pollution and Plant Life. John Wiley & Sons, Chichester, UK. (A second edition is in preparation.)

WELLBURN, A. 1994. Air Pollution and Climate Change: The Biological Impact. Longman Scientific & Technical, London.

In addition, the reader may wish to refer to the various Air Quality Criteria Documents for the major pollutants prepared by the US Environmental Protection Agency, and to various scientific journals, such as Atmospheric Environment, Environmental & Experimental Botany, Environmental Pollution, Global Change Biology, The Journal of the Air & Waste Management Association, The Journal of Environmental Quality, New Phytologist, Plant Cell & Environment, and Water, Air & Soil Pollution.

Chapter 7
Community Odour Issues

Bohdan W. Hrebenyk and Bridget A. Mills

Over 50% of complaints received by air pollution control agencies are related to ambient odours in the community, and the number of complaints is growing annually. Furthermore, environmental awareness about the health perception of odours, annoyance reaction to odours, and increased number of health complaints linked to odours is also increasing [2,3,6,49]. As a result, odour mitigation is already a major focus of these agencies, and odour issues are expected to rise in importance as increased residential land use encroaches upon industrial and agricultural properties.

With respect to health, most odours are believed to constitute a public nuisance rather than a health hazard [6]. Consequently, odour-related issues have traditionally been managed at the provincial and municipal levels as a nuisance issue. In general, regulatory legislation related to air pollution does not directly acknowledge odours as potentially causing an adverse health impact. Furthermore, such legislation provides little regulatory guidance regarding the handling of odour-based health complaints and any possible policy and/or technology-based measures that can be implemented to mitigate the complaints.

A number of physiological manifestations of offensive odours have been reported in published literature [7,8,9,10,11], including nausea, vomiting, headache, loss of appetite, impaired nutrition, curtailed water intake, disturbed sleep, upset stomach, and hampering of proper breathing. At elevated concentrations, an annoying odour may become a nasal irritant, although not all odours cause irritation at high concentration. Some recent advances in odour research point to a possible combination of both non-toxicological (psychological and psychogenic) and toxicological (physiological) mechanisms for odour-related health effects (i.e., health symptoms may involve a complex interplay between biological and behavioural/psychosocial influences). Consequently, there is a need for a multi-disciplinary approach to further research. Much of that research is currently being funded by the agri-food industry, because of community odours from the confinement of large numbers of livestock (e.g., cattle and pigs) in feedlots.

HUMAN RESPONSE TO ODOURS

Although humans are regarded as microsmates (poor smellers) compared with other mammalian species, it does not necessarily follow that our sense of smell is poor; the issue rather is that people are often not conscious of many olfactory stimuli [1]. Smell plays a significant part in many psychic processes and behaviour patterns. It is essential to taste; it affects sex life, motivation and memory (including learning, health, and feelings of security and well-being primarily via conditioning mechanisms); and it has an alarm function in some life-threatening situations (e.g., in detecting gas fumes).

Our knowledge and understanding (physically and biologically) of how the sense of smell operates is poor. No satisfactory general theory exists to explain the sensation of smell (i.e., how the nose and the brain detect and distinguish an odour) [1, 6], and little is known as yet about its mechanics. It is not known exactly what properties of chemical substances cause sensations, even whether it is the chemical characteristics of the substance or, to mention just one possibility, the shape of the molecule[1].

The lack of knowledge with respect to smell stems from the fact that the olfactory constituents are relatively inaccessible for study; scents and olfactory sensations do not have a readily measurable property such as wavelength; olfactory sensations are triggered by chemical substances of very different kinds; odours are generally mixtures which in addition can react with the environment in all kinds of ways before we perceive them; and, finally, people display wide differences in their sensitivity to smells and their appreciation of smells.

The Physiology of Smell

In evolutionary terms, the sense of smell is an old one with relatively few direct connections with the youngest part of the brain, the left neocortex. It does, however, have many well-developed connections with the older brain structures that regulate emotions and motivation, including the so-called limbic system, the brain stem ("neural chassis"), and the pituitary gland (primary hormonal system gland). One result of this connection is that we do not in the first instance rationalize and verbalize what we smell, but have an immediate reaction to the smell and a tendency to act in accordance with it. In other words, people do not generally convert an olfactory perception into a considered intellectual judgement, followed by consciously controlled behaviour; smelling something generally leads to emotionally coloured, and sometimes even intuitive, actions.

In simple terms, the physiological response to odour stimuli involves the olfactory organ, the rhinencephalon, and the trigeminal nerve. The actual organ of smell (olfactory organ) is located at the top of the nose, a little below eye level. Access to the olfactory organ is via the nostrils and the throat. The olfactory organ consists of a mucus layer, the nasal epithelium and a supporting layer (the lamina propria). The mucus layer is responsible for dissolving odour molecules, and the degree to which odours are perceived is dependent on the properties (i.e., composition, thickness, and viscosity) of this layer. Variation in the thickness and viscosity of the mucus layer can be caused by a number of factors including simple colds and hormone levels. This variation explains to some degree variations in odour perception among individuals. The epithelium of the olfactory organ consists of three kinds of cells: sensory cells, support cells, and basal cells. The sensory cells are naked neurons (i.e., they are in direct contact with the outside world, although they are embedded in mucus). The sensory cells are joined here into nodes, which combine to form the olfactory nerve (first cranial nerve).

The rhinencephalon structure of the brain is where the first processing of signals takes place. Subsequently, the signals are analyzed and linked together with other information in the olfactory cortex. This process affects primarily the general activity of the right brain.

The trigeminal nerve (fifth cranial nerve) is responsible for "feeling" in the face. In the nasal and oral cavities, the nerve registers pain (dental), heat (and burning), and irritation (and tickling) through nerve receptors which are sensitive to temperature, pressure, and touch. Stimulation of the trigeminal nerve initiates protective responses. The trigeminal nerve generally reacts to high concentrations of chemical irritants, which include certain odorants, especially harmful odorants. Stimulation in this case registers as irritation or pain, and triggers protective physiologic reflexes, alerts the exposed individual to danger, and initiates escape behaviour [25].

Thus, the olfactory organ mainly reacts to low concentrations of odorants. When the trigeminal system is activated (as the concentration of harmful substances increases), signals from the olfactory system are muted. When the odour is not aggressive, the trigeminal system is generally not activated [1]. Therefore, in interpreting smelling capacity, it is important to consider the interaction between the olfactory and trigeminal systems. Many substances, such as alcohol and turpentine, are perceived by both systems [1].

From the perspective of potential impacts on human health, it is worth noting that the direct exposure of sensory cells to the outside world creates a pathway for certain pathogenic or poisonous substances, as well as viruses, into the brain. Substances that are absorbed by the olfactory hairs and that — usually as a result of continuing stimulation — are not adequately removed remain in the olfactory epithelium. As a result of the rapid process of division of the base cells, these substances can make their way quite quickly to the brain, where they may result in harmful effects, including nerve tissue damage and nervous system effects [1].

Olfaction

Olfaction may be defined as the perception or characterization of smell resulting from the stimulation of the olfactory organ. The process of olfaction considers four primary odour characteristics; detectability, quality, intensity, and acceptability.

Detectability — The detectability of an odour is related to its concentration. The concentration at which an odour is first perceived (but not identified) is referred to as the *odour threshold* or *detection threshold*. This value varies among individuals in a population sometimes by as much as two-to-three orders of magnitude [2], and reported threshold values are usually mean concentrations based on the lowest odour concentration that can be detected by 50% of the population. For example, if a volumetric amount of odorous gas requires 9 units of odour-free air to be diluted until the odour is just barely detectable by 50% of the population (as determined by an odour panel), the original odorous gas is said to have an odour threshold of 10, which is numerically equivalent to 10 odour units (10 o.u.).

In general, the threshold detection values of dangerous substances are relatively low, and substances are detected before they reach a harmful level. There are exceptions, however, such as odourless carbon monoxide [1].

Quality or Character — The concentration at which an odour is recognized as having a characteristic odour quality is termed the *recognition threshold*. Typically, this concentration is 1.5 to 10 times higher than the detection threshold [2]. The odour quality is a purely subjective descriptor of an odour's aesthetic impression (i.e., what it smells like — fishy, hay, nutty, creosote, turpentine, rancid, sewer, ammonia, etc.). However, odour descriptions from the general public tend to be unreliable. Experimentation with exposures to odorants has demonstrated that an individual's vocabulary for describing smells is generally very limited. Furthermore, a significant portion of surveyed individuals may be unable to describe the smell in any terms at all [3]. This phenomenon may be related to the paucity of connections between olfactory sensations and the left neocortex, the system which houses the language centres [1].

Intensity — The intensity of a given odour is defined as the perceived strength of the odour sensation. Intensity increases as a function of concentration according to the following power function [4]:

$$S = KI^n$$

where   S = perceived intensity of sensation
         I = physical intensity of stimulus (odorant concentration)
         n = slope of the psychophysical function
         K = y-intercept

The slope and intercept of the function vary with the type of odorant. Odours with high slope values dissipate more quickly with dilution, while odours with low slope values are more difficult to eliminate as they are perceivable at lower concentrations. This means that for two odorants, a particularly pungent odour at very low concentration may be perceived to be more intense than a less pungent substance at a higher concentration. In addition, the ability of humans to distinguish different odour intensities is highly subjective. Studies indicate that changes in concentration on the order of 25-33% are needed for an individual to recognize a different odour intensity [2].

Acceptability — The odour acceptability, which is also referred to as the *Hedonic tone*, is an indication of the pleasantness or unpleasantness of the odour. Hedonic tone is often a matter of association [3] and is influenced by subjective experience, frequency of occurrence, odour character, odour intensity, and duration [4].

Smell Sensitivity and Smell Tolerance

All kinds of diseases or congenital defects may underlie differences in the ability of individuals to detect an odour, but even among normal, healthy people the sense of smell varies enormously. Two extremes are general anosmia, an inability to smell, and hyperosmia, an over sensitivity to olfactory stimuli. Approximately 96% of the population have a normal sense of smell, while 2% are hypersensitive and 2% are insensitive (hyperosmic and anosmic, respectively) [2,4]. Moreover, depending on the circumstances, there is a great deal of variation within the same individual. Factors affecting smell sensitivity are associated with human characteristics, environmental conditions, chemical (odorant) properties, and exposure events, as discussed below.

Human Characteristics

Age — Small children are generally either tolerant of smells or relatively indifferent to them. An appreciation of smells heightens during puberty and is associated with the production of sex hormones. As people age, their responses to smells grow more subjective and richer in associations. Optimum sensitivity occurs between 30 and 40 years of age. Between the ages of 50 and 60, loss of smell occurs gradually. Three-quarters of the population over the age of 80 are anosmic, as are half the people between 65 and 80 [1].

Sex — The olfactory capacity of women is superior to that of men on all fronts; threshold values for many substances are considerably lower, and the whole hedonic palate of smells is wider and deeper [1]. Furthermore, sensitivity increases for some women before or during ovulation [5].

Culture — No essential differences in olfactory capacity have been observed in people from different cultures [1]. However, the range of smells on offer varies considerably from country to country. As a result, certain cultures differ in smell recognition.

Smokers — The olfactory capacity of smokers is usually worse than that of non-smokers [1]. Shortly after smoking, a smoker will smell less because of adaptation to the smoke and the effects of nicotine. However, there is also the question of loss of smell due to direct tissue damage caused by smoking. The severity of damage and resulting diminished sense of smell is a function of how long and how much a person has smoked.

Physical and Emotional Health — In general, the capacity for smell is greatly affected by overall physical and physiological condition. A number of health conditions affect sensitivity to odours: the common cold can practically eliminate the sense of smell for a short time; migraine sufferers have reported that their sensitivity to odours increases before or during migraine attacks; neurological diseases (e.g., Parkinson's) and glandular diseases (e.g., Addison's) can greatly increase sensitivity to odour [5]. For example, patients with Addison's disease may be up to 100,000 times more sensitive to odours than average healthy individuals in the general population [48].

Environmental Conditions

Temperature and Relative Humidity — Increasing temperature and relative humidity result in an increased concentration of an odorant. In addition, increasing levels of humidity have been found to alter the sensory perception of certain odours [5].

Background Odours — Background odours can interact with and/or mask another odour.

Work Environment — Exposure to certain substances can have directly harmful effects on a person's sense of smell [1]. This includes volatile substances such as sulphuric acid, acetone, ammonia, benzene, carbon monoxide, and formaldehyde, as well as metals such as lead, silver, chromium, mercury, and cadmium. The extent of damage (and potential for recovery/reversibility) is a function of exposure concentration and duration.

Context — Most people are more tolerant of odours at work than at home, and are particularly bothered by odours when they are trying to eat, sleep, relax, or entertain their friends. Even pleasant odours can be bothersome if they occur in the wrong place or at the wrong time [5]. For example, the smell of baking bread is perceived as welcome in the home, but frequent exposure to the same odour from a large commercial bakery may be perceived as annoying.

Chemical (Odorant) Properties

Concentration — As a rule of thumb, many substances which cause a stench not only stink less as the concentration decreases, but gradually even begin to be pleasant. For example, tetrahydrothiophene, which is added to natural gas, smells like coffee at low concentration; ozone irritates breathing passages, but in low concentration smells fresh and pleasant [1].

Effect of Mixtures — Almost all smells are composed of mixtures of chemical compounds. The olfactory organ can distinguish several hundred thousand odours, provided they are presented separately. In mixtures, the olfactory organ does not perform very well, and we generally perceive mixtures as a single odour [1]. When attempting to identify components of mixtures, unpleasant components are usually recognized more easily than pleasant ones. Mixing odorous substances can alter the properties of the individual constituents, and the final intensity of the mixture is rarely the sum of the constituent parts. For example, the removal of one of the odorous components of a mixture can lead to a more foul- smelling mixture [1].

Exposure Events

Adaptation — Adaptation or olfactory fatigue occurs after prolonged exposure to an odour. It is associated with temporary desensitization to that odour and is a result of the weakening of the reaction of the sensory cells due to exhaustion [1].

Habituation — Habituation occurs after prolonged exposure to a smell, particularly if the smell is neither alarming nor unpleasant. This loss of sensitivity, or perhaps increase in tolerance, is believed to result at the brain level due to "boredom" [1].

Sensitization — Individuals may become sensitized to a particular odour as a result of repeated exposures. This is distinct from adaptation [2].

Conditioning and Memory — Smells can serve as memory aids, and a smell can evoke a certain mood with the attendant memories [1]. After experiencing an odour strong enough to cause nausea or other unpleasant effects, a person may continue to have similar reactions to that odour even when it is very faint [5].

HEALTH EFFECTS OF ODOURS

Research linking odours to adverse human health impacts is relatively sparse. Consequently, our understanding of the relationship between reported health effects from exposure to odorous substances is poor. Such distressing symptoms as nausea, headache, loss of sleep, loss of appetite, impaired breathing, and even allergic reactions may result from exposure to foul odours, especially when they occur during the night [48]. Even if the chemical components individually or collectively responsible for the foul odours have not been specifically identified as toxic substances by the usual criteria, such reactions clearly represent a matter for public-health concern and attention under the World Health Organization's definition of health (i.e., "a state of complete physical, mental and social well-being and not merely the absence of disease or infirmity").

There exist two distinctly different schools of thought with respect to odour-related health effects in situations where the concentrations of odorants are below threshold limit values (TLVs) established for occupational exposures, namely:

- Non-toxicological odour-related health effects (psychological or psychogenic mechanisms)

- Toxicological health effects (physiological mechanisms)

The former assumes that odours per se do not cause adverse health effects, and that most odours constitute a public-health nuisance rather than a health hazard. As such, and barring any direct evidence of acute toxicity, the theory assumes that most symptoms reported by individuals exposed to community odours are acute in onset, self-limited in duration, and subjective. This implies that current standards for occupational exposure to chemical substances are both applicable to, and provide a sufficient margin of safety for, members of the general public.

The alternative to the non-toxicological effects theory argues that the scientific studies which are used to support the non-toxicological theory are inadequate to support conclusions about cause and effect, and that few of the studies include adequate clinical and laboratory evaluations for assessing the basis of symptoms. It has been suggested that relevant toxicological data in those studies were downplayed and that some of the findings cited as being supportive of a psychological origin of odour-related symptoms were actually suggestive of dose-response effects consistent with a toxicological origin [26]. Moreover, recent advances in odour research point to a possible combination of both non-toxicological (psychological and psychogenic) and toxicological (physiological) mechanisms (i.e., a complex interplay between biological and behavioural/psychosocial influences) resulting from low-level concentrations of some chemical substances [47].

The significance of this debate about the non-toxicological versus toxicological effects of odours on human health rests with the fact that most regulatory statutes on community odours are based on the assumption that odours constitute a public nuisance rather than a public- health hazard. As such, the issue of odour and health effects is addressed by regulatory agencies on a case-by-case basis. In order for an odour to be considered a cause of health impacts, the perception of the odour must be accompanied by a clear adverse physiological response (i.e., a symptom). The perception of smell alone is not considered to represent a health impact.

The issue of non-toxicological versus toxicological effects of odours on human health is discussed below.

Non-Toxicological Odour-Related Health Effects

The influence of odours on the health and comfort of human beings is difficult to prove [6]. Odours per se are usually not the cause of organic disease. However, an odour or odorant may incite an allergic response. Thus, the presence of an odour may precipitate attacks of asthma or may aggravate other allergic conditions. In many cases, it is difficult to determine whether an allergic patient was affected by an odour or by the odorant substance itself.

Schroeder [6] identifies two basic types of adverse human reactions to odours in ambient air: (1) *disease states*, including causation or aggravation, and (2) annoyance reactions, including action taken to abate perceived annoyance [7].

Some highly toxic substances, such as hydrogen sulphide, are associated with offensive odours, but the dangerous properties of these substances do not derive from the odour itself. In this case, odour is valuable in serving as a warning of the presence of an injurious gas. Generally, odour bears no relationship to toxicity, and some highly poisonous gases are odourless or may even have a pleasant odour (e.g., hydrogen cyanide). The ratio of the olfactory threshold to maximum acceptable concentration needs to be considered in this instance.

Schroeder [6] indicates that variations in response to odour are caused by demographic variables (sex, age, marital status, income and occupation, and differences in individual or collective attitudes towards a pollution source). He states that in a community setting, annoyance at odour exposure is reported more frequently by persons with a propensity towards neurosis, sensitivity to aircraft noise, and displeasure with other aspects of the community.

The theory of non-toxicological effects of odorants assumes that when community exposures are confined to sub-irritant levels of one or more odorant compounds, and in the absence of any evidence of other mechanisms for acute toxicity, explanation of acute odour-triggered symptoms must invoke non-toxicological, odour-related mechanisms. These mechanisms have been postulated to include innate odour aversions, innate pheromonal phenomena, odour-related exacerbation of underlying conditions, odour-related aversive conditioning, odour-related stress-induced illness, mass psychogenic illness, and recall bias. Shusterman [25] provides a discussion of the possible mechanisms as follows.

Innate Odour Aversions

Notwithstanding individual factors, everyday experience indicates that there are many odours that are perceived by individuals as either pleasant or unpleasant. New born babies have been found to react with predictable facial expression to nominally pleasant and unpleasant odours, which has been interpreted as evidence for the existence of innate odour aversions [31] and similar patterns have been observed across different cultures [32]. The term *reflex nausea* has been used to refer to involuntary visceral responses to odours [33].

Innate Pheromonal Phenomena

Odorant chemicals that trigger hormonal or reflex behavioural responses in an organism are termed *pheromones*. For example, researchers have documented an effect of odorous androgenic steroids secreted in sweat in regulating the female estrus cycle. Shusterman [25] states that the relationship, if any, of such phenomena to potential adverse health effects from environmental odour pollution is, at present, purely conjectural.

Odour-Related Exacerbation of Underlying Conditions

The basis of this mechanism is that a pre-existing medical condition may result in hypersusceptibility to odours. Such pre-existing conditions include bronchial asthma and "morning sickness." It has also been speculated that pre-existing psychological conditions (e.g., hypochondriasis or somatization disorder) may render some individuals more symptomatic in response to odorant stimuli.

Odour-Related Aversive Conditioning

Shusterman [25] reports that many investigators [34, 35] have documented what appear to be conditioning phenomena after acute over exposures to irritant (or other acutely toxic) chemicals. After the initial traumatic exposure, these individuals report that they experience a variety of symptoms in response to low-level odorant exposures, including the panic or hyperventilation symptom cluster (i.e., anxiety, sweating, tachycardia, "air hunger," paresthesias, light headedness, and nausea). Despite the apparent utility of this learning theory in explaining some odour-related symptoms, Shusterman acknowledges that exposures of a magnitude sufficient to produce aversive conditioning are rare in environmental (as distinct from occupational) settings. Nonetheless, Shusterman suggests that it is possible that more subtle types of associational learning may influence individuals' responses to environmental odours.

Odour-Related, Stress-Induced Illness

Shusterman et al [36] noted that symptom prevalence near three hazardous waste sites was related to both the degree of environmental worry and the frequency of odour perception. The authors suggested that environmental odours may precipitate (cue) acute stress among individuals who perceive the odour source as a toxicological risk. A range of physical effects are attributed to psychological stress including elevations in blood pressure, gastric motility, and scalp muscle tension; coronary artery disease, peptic ulcers, and chronic hypertension. Shusterman concludes that, although an intuitively plausible mechanism, the causal role of environmental odour pollution in the development of chronic stress-related illnesses is conjectural.

Mass Psychogenic Illness

Illness clusters that involve epidemic fainting, nausea, hyperventilation, or panic symptoms have been termed *mass psychogenic illness*. Mass psychogenic phenomena are suspected when symptoms spread rapidly through an enclosed population (e.g., workplace or school) and no credible causal agent can be identified. In such situations, ambient odours frequently play an important role in the propagation of alarm, often against a backdrop of psychosocial stressors [37, 38, 39]. Shusterman [25] notes, however, that rapidly spreading symptoms are not generally characteristic of community health complaints documented to date near environmental odour sources.

Recall Bias

Recall bias occurs when an adverse health outcome, the publicity surrounding an environmental issue, or another factor (such as odour perception) affects the accuracy of recall for a particular symptom. For example, Knasko [43] concluded that the belief that odours are harmful may trigger physical symptoms or exacerbate existing symptoms. Further, this belief may cause recall bias such that individuals report having experienced odours and symptoms where one or the other may not even have existed. Epidemiological studies of odour-related health effects in which there is a uniform elevation of reported symptoms, particularly those that involve multiple organ systems, may be indicative of recall bias rather than an indication of actual adverse health effects.

Toxicological Health Effects

Ziem [26] presents an argument which refutes the non-toxicological theory on the basis that the scientific process for the development of threshold limit values (TLVs) is flawed and that there is insufficient research on long-term, low-level chemical exposure effects on humans. The few compounds that have been studied for chronic, low-level effects have very rarely been evaluated for neurologic (central, peripheral, autonomic), neurobehavioural, immune, endocrine, reproductive, and pulmonary effects.

Ziem argues that the studies reviewed by Shusterman [25] to support the non-toxicological theory are inadequate to support conclusions about cause and effect, and few of the studies included adequate clinical and laboratory evaluations for assessing the basis of symptoms. According to Ziem [26], the available research literature indicates that sub-TLV health effects are not uncommon [27, 28], and that scientists rarely know the minimum exposure levels necessary for a specific toxic effect. Minimum toxic dose estimates for the general population grossly overestimate the doses that can affect sensitive individuals [29]. Ziem [26] states that it is an axiom of medicine that when investigating the origins of illness, physiological causes must be ruled out before ascribing psychological causes — this has simply not been done for illnesses associated with low-level chemical exposure.

Ziem [26] suggests that many non-specific conditions frequently accompany many legitimate chronic medical disorders, and that such conditions can be mediated by neurohormones, toxins and endocrine and immune abnormalities [30], as well as by stress or psychiatric disorders.

The non-toxicological conditioning theory is not well supported by studies on multiple chemical sensitivity at Johns Hopkins University.

Ziem [26] concludes that given the current state of knowledge and the absence of essential research, odour-related complaints cannot ethically be dismissed as non-toxicological curiosities. Multiple chemical sensitivity and similar conditions associated with sub-TLV levels of environmental chemicals deserve to be investigated rigorously, notwithstanding that past progress appears to have been impeded by political considerations, and that future investigations may present problems for industry and its insurers [26].

Some examples of studies which support the toxicological argument for health effects from odours are as follows:

- Respiratory symptoms and reflex, transitory apnea (cessation of breathing) [13] can result from inhalation of VOCs (volatile organic compounds) at a concentration that produces pungency (i.e., sensory irritation, including stinging, burning, piquancy, prickling, freshness, and tingling).

- There seems to be a reflex mechanism that is responsible for the increase in airway resistance and bronchoconstriction that results from irritant stimuli in the nasal cavity [14]. Muscular contraction of bronchial tubes upon irritation restricts airflow and minimizes intake.

- Hoarseness of voice can also occur and can be measured using spectral frequencies of the voice [15]. However, there are individual differences in the concentrations of VOC that produce these symptoms, as well as individual differences in the degree to which persons find these symptoms bothersome.

- Odorous irritants can set up a low-grade neurogenic inflammation with leukocyte (white blood cell) recruitment that predisposes to hyperactivity and allergy [16].

- Anaphylaxis can be triggered by chemical odours [18].

• Persons who complain about environmental odours seem to experience an increase in nasal resistance, respiration rate, and heart rate after exposure to odours [17]. It has been suggested that persons who report problems with odours may also be more aware of the irritant effects of volatile compounds as they interact with the trigeminal nerve endings in the nasal cavity.

• Olfactory pathway kindling and long-term potentiation (LTP) may account for physical symptoms from chemical exposures [19, 20, 21, 22, 23]. Kindling is a phenomenon that occurs when repetitions of sub threshold stimuli summate, triggering seizure activity in brain cells that had previously functioned normally. Long-term potentiation refers to the persisting enhancement of synaptic responses resulting from high frequency stimulation of excited pathways. It has been suggested that kindling and LTP register information about past high-dose and/or cumulative low dose chemical exposures, increasing the likelihood of limbic responsivity to subsequent low-dose exposures. Limbic dysregulation could then produce a range of behavioural, autonomic, and endocrine dysfunctions that are under limbic control or influence.

• The incidence of eye and nasal symptoms, cough, and headache among children living in the two Finnish communities exposed to malodorous sulphur compounds associated with pulp mills was higher than among those living in the non-polluted community [44]. These results correlated well with a similar and statistically significant adult study [46].

• Residents in a community exposed to total reduced sulphur (TRS) compounds from a large sulphate pulp and paper mill equipped with advanced odour-elimination techniques and very low emission levels reported significantly more cough and headache than subjects in a reference community [45]. Acute respiratory infections were also more common, and the prevalence of hay fever was greater in the polluted area.

Combined Mechanisms

According to Shusterman (personal communication), recent research by Zald and Pardo[47] showing that pleasant and unpleasant odours activate different areas of the brain has been of particular importance to the understanding of odour-related effects. As summarised by Schiffman [12], Zald and Pardo [47] reported alterations of activity in the amygdala (a brain centre that is involved in emotional processing) during aversive olfactory stimulation. The amygdala is a conglomerate of related nuclei, each nucleus having specific anatomical connections and functions. Zald and Pardo [47] measured regional cortical blood flow (rCBF) using positron emission tomography (PET) in 12 healthy women who were exposed to highly aversive odours (sulphides), moderately aversive odours (garlic breath, natural gas, and motor oil), and pleasant smells (fruits, flowers and spices). They concluded that amygdalar activity depends on the hedonic properties of odorants, and that unpleasant odour increases CBF in the left amygdala. This research has significant implication for purely psychosocial (non-toxicological) theories of odour-related effects because the results suggest that odour and health effects may be linked by a variety of mechanisms, which may be both non-toxicological and toxicological.

It has been suggested that the strong hedonic aspect of odour can affect mood due to the anatomical overlap of the olfactory and limbic (emotional) systems in the brain. A study of odours emanating from large-scale hog operations on the mood of nearby residents found that exposed persons had significantly more tension, more depression, more anger, less vigour, more fatigue and more confusion than control subjects [24]. The authors concluded that both innate physiological responses and learned responses may contribute to the impairment of mood. Unpleasant odours that produce impaired mood and stress may influence health via biological mechanisms that include immune changes [34] or hippocampal damage [35].

A wide range of both physical (acute and chronic) and psychosocial effects were reported in the vicinity of an oil refinery in Oakville, Ontario [40, 41, 42]. Acute physical effects included exacerbation of asthma, sinus congestion, cough, upper and lower respiratory tract infections, eye irritation, headaches, earaches, nausea, vomiting, insomnia, and dizziness. Chronic physical effects included reduced immunity, aggravation of heart disease, hypertension in relation to chronic anxiety, lethargy, weakness, and adverse effects on pregnancy outcomes. Psychosocial effects included general lack of enjoyment of the outdoors, anger, anxiety, depression, irritability, stress on family relationships, and a sense of lack of control. These effects were frequently linked to perceived odours and visible evidence of emissions from the refinery in the form of flares and smoke. With respect to specific odorous pollutants, the authors reported negative effects on pulmonary function for school children at 10-20 ppb of sulphur dioxide, and increases in hospital admissions for respiratory problems related to acute exposure to 24-hour average or maximum levels of sulphur dioxide of about 30 ppb. These studies suggest that modest health effects may be observable below current regulatory ambient air quality objectives and guidelines.

Similarly, a wide range of both physical and psychosocial effects were noted by Legator et al. [50] from chronic, low-level exposure to hydrogen sulphide. Symptoms suggestive of effects on the central nervous system (CNS) were 2-3 times higher in regions having average H_2S concentrations in the low parts per billion range compared with unaffected regions, while respiratory symptoms were 4-6 times higher in the exposed communities.

ODOUR REGULATION

Reflecting the non-toxicological view of odour effects, community odour issues in North America and Europe are often regulated on the basis of a subjective determination of the degree of nuisance caused by a source of odour emissions, as opposed to setting a contaminant concentration level which must not be exceeded. In most jurisdictions, odour is not even specifically defined as an air pollutant. Regulations often simply require that a source must not cause any undue or unacceptable odour impacts, without specifying exactly what constitutes an "undue" or "unacceptable" impact. Any potential toxicological aspects of the chemical constituents of odorous emissions may be addressed separately through traditional health risk assessment techniques. However, these techniques do not address the sorts of toxicological issues raised by Ziem [26], or the evidence of combined mechanisms suggested by the work of Zald and Pardo [47]. At present, there is no practical way to deal with such health-related issues from a regulatory perspective.

Odour investigations by regulatory agencies generally take place on a case-by-case basis, and only after odour complaints have been lodged by the public. Government inspectors are then sent out to investigate and, based on their assessment, the source of the odourous emissions may be forced to either retrofit odour controls and/or pay a fine. In extreme cases, the control requirements set by the pollution control agency may cause a facility to either relocate or permanently shut down its operations.

As a general rule, public complaints about nuisance odours do not usually arise when odours are at the odour threshold (i.e., 1 odour unit). In fact, odour recognition thresholds (i.e., the concentration at which half the population can identify the odour and successfully describe it) are generally 3-5 times higher than the odour threshold. As odour intensity increases to 10 times the odour threshold value, odour is detected universally, and there is an annoyance reaction that consistently results in odour complaints.

Due to the inconsistent policies of various pollution control agencies, the level of "acceptable" odour impact that is permitted varies across jurisdictions. In Canada, the province of Ontario has used an unofficial guideline of 1 odour unit (10 minute average) in regulating sources which cause annoyance in surrounding communities. Although there is no official regulatory policy requiring the use of this exposure limit, the limit has appeared as a requirement in some control orders and Certificates of Approval (Air) issued by the Ontario Ministry of Environment for specific facilities in recent years. A number of agencies in the United States still define odour nuisance in terms of an ambient standard based on the number of dilutions required to render an odour undetectable (<1 odour unit). Some US regulatory agencies have no specified limits on how frequently a facility can cause an odour in the community, while others set numerical limits in terms of percent frequency of occurrence between 1 and 10 odour units. Most of these agencies require that sources meet a maximum ambient odour impact level not exceeding 7 odour units in residential or commercial areas.

Similarly, during the 1990s, the Netherlands tried to implement a national odour policy based on a number of rule-of-thumb values to determine whether an industrial facility required additional controls to reduce its odour impacts. Odour emissions from new sources were not allowed to cause an odour impact greater than 1 odour unit more than 0.5% of time on an annual basis. Existing sources which produced ambient odours of less than 1 odour unit 98% of the time were considered to be acceptable in the sense that no serious annoyance was expected in the large majority of cases. Odour concentrations of 1-5 odour units less than 2% of the time were considered "normal" values for most odours and sources, although large-area sources and high stacks tended towards the "relaxed" end of the range (i.e., 5 odour units) while low-level, intermittent sources and unpleasant odours (e.g., from rendering plants) were regulated at the "stringent" end of the range (i.e., 1 odour unit). Serious community annoyance was expected for sources causing an impact of more than 10 odour units at least 2% of the time, and these sources were required to implement odour control measures to reduce ambient impacts. The attempt to implement the Dutch policy on odour control was abandoned in 1995 as unfeasible for practical considerations. The national policy on odours reverted to the ALARA principle (As Low As Reasonably Achievable), and specific odour concentration levels for the frequency of complaint-level odours are no longer used. In essence, the Dutch policy has reverted to dealing with odour issues on a case-by-case basis.

The experience of the Dutch government and regulatory agencies in North America reflects the fact that odour is a sensation rather than a substance, and the odour concentration, as expressed in odour units, is not necessarily an accurate measure of odour intensity. Community complaints about odours do not always correlate with odour intensities, and other factors such as the socio economic level of a neighbourhood, the presence or absence of an active civic association, the degree of news media attention being given to the problem, and a sense of futility on the part of the citizens (i.e., they give up and quit complaining) all contribute to the frequency of complaints registered by regulatory agencies. In a sensitized community where citizens have been exposed to an odour over a long period of time, a considerable emotional burden may contribute to the frequency of complaints from specific individuals, such that a small number of complainants may account for a large proportion of the complaints registered. As such, odour complaint statistics alone do not provide an absolute measure of the extent or severity of odour problems in a community, although they can be used to derive insight into the nature of the problem. With the increasing awareness about the potential health effects of odours and the increased number of health complaints linked to odours, even a handful of odour complaints from a community may be sufficient to draw the attention of government inspectors to a source of odour emission, and trigger a review of the process and operation of that facility.

REFERENCES

[1]   Vroon, P., Smell, the Secret Seducer, Farrar, Straus and Giroux, New York (1997).

[2]   Greater Vancouver Regional District, GVRD Air Quality Management Plan Working Paper Odour Management, GVRD Communications and Education Department (June 16, 1993).

[3]   Beck, L., New Jersey's Approach to Odour Problems, Recent Developments and Current Practices in Odour Regulations, Control, and Technology — Papers from an International Specialty Conference. Air and Waste Management Association, Detroit, Michigan, October 23-26, 1989.

[4]   Cha, S.S., Odour Thresholds for Chemicals with Established Occupational Health Standards, Recent Developments and Current Practices in Odour Regulations, Control, and Technology — Papers from an International Specialty Conference. Air and Waste Management Association, Detroit, Michigan, October 23-26, 1989.

[5]   The Environmental Health Committee of the South Riverdale Community Health Centre, Environmental Information: Effects of Odour Pollution and Sensitivity to Odours contained in What's that Smell? — Odour Pollution in Central and Eastern Toronto, 126 Pape Avenue, Toronto, Ontario.

[6]   Schroeder, W.H., Air Pollution Aspects of Odorous Substances. A Literature Survey, Publications and Training Division, Technology Development Branch, Air Pollution Control Directorate. EPS 3-AP-75-1 (1975).

[7]   Turk, A., Odour Source Inventories, Pollution Engineering, Aug., pp. 22-24 (1972), cited in [6].

[8] US Department of HEW, Preliminary Air Pollution Survey of Odourous Compounds — A Literature Review, US Department of HEW, Public Health Service, NAPCA, # PH 22-68-25) (1969), cited in [6].

[9] Altner, H., Neurological Responses to Odorants, Paper presented at the Conference on the Dose-Response Relationships Affecting Human Reactions to Odorous Compounds, Cambridge, Mass., (1971), cited in [6].

[10] McCord, C.P. & Witheridge, W.N., Odours: Physiology and Control, McGraw Hill Book Co., New York (1949), cited in [6].

[11] Petri, H., Assessing the Health Hazards of Gaseous Air Pollution Staub 25: 50 (1965), cited in [6].

[12] Schiffman, S.S., Livestock Odours: Implications for Human Health and Well-Being, Journal of Animal Science (5): 1343-55 (May 1998).

[13] Ware, J.H. et al., Respiratory and Irritant Health Effects of Ambient Volatile Organic Compounds. The Kanawha County Health Study, Am. J. Epidemiol. 137:1287-1301 (1993), cited in [12].

[14] Nolte, D., & Berger, D., On Vagal Bronchoconstriction in Asthmatic Patients by Nasal Irritation, Eur. J. Respir. Dis. Suppl. 128:110-15 (1983), cited in [12].

[15] Wolfe, V., et al., Acoustic Correlates of Pathologic Voice Types, J. Speech Hear. Res. 34:509-16 (1991) cited in [12].

[16] Eccles, R., Rhinitis as a Mechanism of Respiratory Defense., Eur. Arch. Oto-Rhino-Laryngol. Suppl. 1:S2-S7 (1995), cited in [12].

[17] Doty, R.L., et al., Olfactory Sensitivity, Nasal Resistance, and Autonomic Function in Patients with Multiple Chemical Sensitivities, Arch. Otolaryngol. Head Neck Surg. 114:1422-27 (1988), cited in [12].

[18]   Saunders, R.L., et al., Odour-Associated Idiopathic Anaphylaxis. A Case Report, Allergol. Immunopathol. (Madr) 23:35-37 (1995), cited in [12].

[19]   Bell, I.R., White Paper: Neurophychiatric Aspects of Sensitivity to Low-Level Chemicals: A Neutral Sensitisation Model, Toxicol. Ind. Health 10:277-312 (1994), cited in [12].

[20]   Bell, I.R,. et al., Increased Limbic System Symptomatology and Sensitizability of Young Adults with Chemical and Noise Sensitivities, Environ. Res. 70:84-97 (1995), cited in [12].

[21]   Bell, I.R., et al., Neuropsychiatric and Somatic Characteristics of Young Adults with and without Self-Reported Chemical Odour Intolerance and Chemical Sensitivity, Arch. Environ. Health 51:9-21 (1996), cited in [12].

[22]   Bell, I.R., et al., Self-Reported Illness from Chemical Odours in Young Adults without Clinical Syndromes or Occupational Exposures, Arch. Environ. Health 48:6-13 (1993), cited in [12] and [42].

[23]   Bell, I.R., et al., Possible Time-Dependent Sensitization to Xenobiotics: Self-Reported Illness from Chemical Odours, Foods, and Opiate Drugs in an Older Adult Population, Arch. Environ. Health 48:315-27 (1993), cited in [12].

[24]   Schiffman, S.S., et al., The Effect of Environmental Odours Emanating from Commercial Swine Operations on the Mood of Nearby Residents, Brain Res. Bull. 37:369-75 (1995), cited in [12].

[25]   Shusterman, D., Critical Review: The Health Significance of Environmental Odour Pollution, Arch. Environ. Health 47:76-87 (1992).

[26]   Ziem, G.E., Illness from Chemical "Odours": Is the Health Significance Understood? Arch. Environ. Health 47:88-91 (1992).

[27]   Roach, S.A., & Rappaport S.M., But They Are Not Thresholds: A Critical Analysis of the Documentation of Threshold Limit Values, Am. Ind. Med. 17:727-53 (1990), cited in [26].

[28]   Ziem, G.E., & Castleman B.I., Threshold Limit Values: Historical Perspectives and Current Practice, J. Occup. Med. 31:910-18 (1989) cited in [26].

[29]   Calabrese, E.J., Pollutants and High Risk Groups: The Biological Basis of Increased Susceptibility to Occupational and Environmental Pollutants, Wiley-Interscience, New York (1978), cited in [26].

[30]   Extein, I:, & . Gold M.S, Medical Mimics of Psychiatric Disorders, American Psychiatric Association, Washington DC: (1986), cited in [26].

[31]   Steiner, J.E., Innate, Discriminative Human Facial Expressions to Taste and Smell Stimulation, Ann NY Acad Sci 237:229-33 (1974), cited in [25].

[32]   Schleidt, M., et al., Pleasure and Disgust: Memories and Associations of Pleasant and Unpleasant Odours in Germany and Japan, Chem. Senses 13:279-93 (1988), cited in [25].

[33]   Cain, W.S., & Garcia-Medina M.R., Possible Adverse Biological Effects of Odour Pollution. Proceedings of the 73rd Annual Meeting of Air Pollution Control Association, Montreal, No. 80-23.2, (June 22-27, 1980), cited in [25].

[34]   Schottenfeld, R.S., & Cullen M.R., Recognition of Occupational Induced Posttraumatic Stress Disorders, J. Occup. Med. 28:365-69 (1986), cited in [25].

[35]   Shusterman, D., et al., Behavioural Sensitization to Irritants/Odorants after Acute Overexposures, J. Occup. Med. 30:565-67 (1988), cited in [25].

[36]   Shusterman, D., et al., Symptom Prevalence and Odour-Worry Interaction near Hazardous Waste Sites, Environ. Health Perspect. 94:25-30 (1991), cited in [25].

[37]   National Institute for Occupational Safety and Health, Epidemic Psychogenic Illness in an Industrial Setting — Pennsylvania, MMWR 32:287-94 (1983), cited in [25].

[38]   Boxer, P.A., et al., An Epidemic of Psychogenic Illness in an Electronics Plant, J. Occup. Med. 26:381-85 (1984), cited in [25].

[39]   Hall, E.M., & . Johnson J.V, A Case Study of Stress and Mass Psychogenic Illness in Industrial Workers, J. Occup. Med. 31:243-50 (1989), cited in [25].

[40]   Institute of Environment and Health, Community Health Effects in the Vicinity of the Petro Canada Refinery in Oakville, Ontario, Regional Municipality of Halton Health Department, January 1992.

[41]   Sider, D., A Cross-Sectional Survey of Community Health Effects in the Vicinity of the Petro Canada Oakville Refinery, Regional Municipality of Halton Health Department, 1993.

[42]   Institute of Environment and Health, Further Study of Community Health Effects in the Vicinity of the Petro Canada Refinery in Oakville, Ontario, Regional Municipality of Halton Health Department, November 1994.

[43]   Knasko, S., Performance, Mood, and Health During Exposure to Intermittent Odours, Arch. Env. Health 48(5):305-8 (1993), cited in [42].

[44]   Marttila, O., et al., The South Karelia Air Pollution Study: The Effects of Malodorous Sulfur Compounds from Pulp and Paper Mills on Respiratory and Other Symptoms in Children, Environ. Research 66:152-59 (1994).

[45]   Partti-Pellinen, K., et al., The South Karelia Air Pollution Study: Effects of Low-Level Exposure to Malodorous Sulfur Compounds on Symptoms, Arch. Environ. Health 51(4):315-20 (1996).

[46]   Jaakkola, J.J.K., et al., The South Karelia Air Pollution Study: The Effects of Malodorous Sulfur Compounds from Pulp and Paper Mills on Respiratory and Other Symptoms, Am. Rev. Respir. Dis. 142:1344-50 (1990), cited in [44].

[47]   Zald D.H., and Pardo J.V., Emotion, Olfaction and the Human Amygdala: Amygdala Activation During Olfactory Stimulation. Proc. Natl. Acad. Sci. USA 94:4119-24 (1997), cited in [26].

[48]   First, M.W., Public Health Aspects: Management of Environmental Odours, Appendix A of Odours from Stationary and Mobile Sources, National Academy of Sciences, Washington DC (1979).

[49]   Sparks, P.J., et al., An Outbreak of Illness Among Aerospace Workers, West J. Med. 153:28-33 (1990,) cited in [12].

[50]   Legator, M.S., et al., Health Effects from chronic low-level Exposure to Hydrogen Sulphide, Arch. Environ. Health. 56:123-31 (2001).

Chapter 8

Public Decision Making: Standard Setting, Economic Valuation, Risk Assessment, and Public Debate

David V. Bates, Robert B. Caton, and Michael Brauer

This chapter begins with a very brief summary of some current air quality standards and guidelines (or objectives) to preface a more detailed discussion of the standard-setting process and its place in public decision-making. The summary places the Canadian objectives in the context of other North American and international standards and guidelines.

CURRENT STANDARDS, GUIDELINES AND AIR QUALITY INDICES

Air quality guidelines and standards have been adopted to protect public health from the negative effects of environmental pollutants. As one example, the World Health Organization (WHO) has developed guidelines that encompass the routinely measured pollutants, as well as others. The WHO documentation of their current air quality guidelines provides an excellent overview of standards, guidelines, and their basis, and is available on-line at <http://www.who.int/peh/air/Airqualitygd.htm>. While these guidelines apply to air pollutants indoors or outdoors, standards that are adopted by specific countries are limited to outdoor air. The application of specific indoor air quality standards is rare, and there are numerous examples of indoor air concentrations exceeding levels of outdoor air quality standards. Appendix II of this volume lists current outdoor air pollution standards for the US and Canada, and the guidelines of the WHO. Research is increasingly suggesting that there is little evidence to indicate no-effect thresholds related to the health effects of outdoor air pollution. For example, the most recent version of the WHO Guidelines for Air Quality does not set guideline values for particulate matter (PM) but instead includes a quantitative relationship between PM concentrations and various health impacts (risks). This is based upon the absence of scientific evidence to support a no-effects threshold concentration for airborne particulate matter. These relationships allow any individual country to manage air pollution by assessing the health effects associated with different levels. On this basis, most standards are not thought to be purely health-based, but are rather an application of scientific information in the political context of any given jurisdiction. See Appendix II for details.

Appendix II summarizes some standards and guidelines from selected jurisdictions and agencies. The information is not intended to be exhaustive, but rather to illustrate the similarities (or dissimilarities) across jurisdictions and agencies.

Air quality indices have been developed as a simple way to inform the general public about pollution conditions. There is currently no standardized global air pollutant index, although many countries develop an index based upon the US Environmental Protection Agency (EPA) Pollutant Standards Index (PSI) or the recent revision called the Air Quality Index (AQI). Information on the US AQI may be found at an EPA Web site: <http://www.epa.gov/airprogm/oar/oaqps/airnow/ aqibroch/index.html>. The PSI and AQI are based on the measurement of five pollutants: carbon monoxide, sulphur dioxide, nitrogen dioxide, ozone, and PM_{10}. The values for each pollutant are converted to a scale from 0 to 500, with only the highest value being reported. A value of 100 represents the air quality standard while a value of 300 represents the level of harmful air quality. Values below 50 are described as good air quality. At different index levels, precautionary statements are included to advise the public on actions to reduce their risk of health effects associated with air pollution. It is important to note that these indices do not take into account the effects of the combination of pollutants. Further, they are designed as tools to help communicate urban air pollution measurements to the public and are not meant to be the basis of management strategies. They do not themselves indicate whether health effects will be experienced by any given individual.

A Canadian air quality index has never gained national acceptance, but indices similar to the US AQI are used by several jurisdictions in Canada, such as the Greater Vancouver Regional District and the Province of Ontario (where the index levels are based, essentially, on the Canadian National Ambient Air Quality Objectives and the Canada-Wide Standards for PM and Ozone). Smog advisories to citizens based on index levels are now provided in eastern Canada and the Lower Mainland of British Columbia. An initiative is currently under way to develop a national air quality index that would be applied consistently across Canada.

STANDARD SETTING

The process of setting a standard differs in different jurisdictions. The procedure used by the US EPA is exemplary and involves the following steps:

1. Preparation of a criteria document [1], which summarizes the existing scientific database and is reasonably complete. A large number of individuals help to prepare, review and approve this document, and discussions of it are in the public domain.

2. Approval of the criteria document by the Clean Air Science Advisory Committee (known as CASAC), an arm of the Science Advisory Board of EPA.

3. Preparation of a staff paper by EPA [2] that attempts to synthesize the database and interpret major results. It may extend the database by calculations of populations at risk etc., and it makes a recommendation of possible limits (upper and lower) for a standard. The economic impact of a possible standard is then reviewed within the government.

4. Proposal of a standard by the Administrator of EPA, followed by media reaction, intense lobbying, and a final proposal after 60 days of input.

This process is remarkably open, with public and lobbying interests intervening at various stages. Minutes of meetings discussing the criteria document, and of the meetings of CASAC, are available for public review.

In Canada the standards development process historically has been essentially closed to external scrutiny compared with its US counterpart, and has produced general guidelines (designated as objectives) rather than national, enforceable standards. The process has been changed in recent years to permit more stakeholder, public, and expert input as the Canada-Wide Standards (CWS) development process has been implemented under the auspices of the Canadian Environmental Protection Act (CEPA). A development committee is established for each pollutant or related group of pollutants, under the direction of a chairperson.

Standards development under this process is supported by a science assessment document developed by staff of Environment Canada and Health Canada (with some external review) that is similar in intent to the US EPA's criteria documents. The development of CWS documents and the final standards themselves are not governed by a mandated process. Standards are subject to federal-provincial agreements about implementation and applicability and are not enforceable as legal sanctions, unless the subject pollutant has been declared "toxic" under the provisions of CEPA. The latter gives the federal government some additional authority to carry out information-gathering and assessment activities.

During 1999 and 2000, the Canada-Wide Standards process produced consensus national ambient air quality standards for particulate matter ($PM_{2.5}$) and ozone. These standards supplement the Canadian National Ambient Air Quality Objectives, but are still subject to implementation at the level of individual provinces. Progress on the development of other standards and implementation of the PM and ozone standards can be followed on the Canadian Council of Ministers of the Environment (CCME) Web site at <http://www.ccme.ca/3e_priorities/3ea_harmo nization/3ea2_cws/3ea2.html>. CCME maintains a newsgroup for the CWS process that provides up-to-date information regularly (CWS List-serv).

Canada-Wide Standards have been developed for both particulate matter ($PM_{2.5}$) and ozone, and PM_{10} has been declared CEPA-toxic (Canada Gazette, Part 2, May 11, 2001); ozone (and its precursors, NOx [nitrogen oxides] and VOCs [volatile organic compounds]) is still subject to a proposed designation (Canada Gazette, Part 1, June 9, 2001), and $PM_{2.5}$ has not been separately designated. In 2000, the precursors of secondary PM_{10} (identified as SO_2, NOx, VOCs, and ammonia) were proposed to be declared CEPA-toxic in order to provide authority to control direct and indirect (secondary) components of PM (Canada Gazette, Part 1, July 15, 2000). The complex linkages among all of these designations (NOx is a precursor of both ozone and PM_{10}, and some VOCs are precursors of ozone but not PM_{10}, for example) suggests that the implementation of these initiatives will be fraught with difficulties, especially in the context of Canadian federal-provincial implementation.

Also in 2000, ozone management was addressed in an annex to the Canada-US Air Quality Agreement, harmonizing the two countries' approaches to a common problem. It had long been recognized that southern Ontario, and Michigan and Ohio to the west, and New York state to the south (and extending further into the Midwest, Southeast and Northeast), constituted a regional airshed in which transboundary movement of ozone and its precursors was important. The amendments to the 1991 Air Quality Agreement between the US and Canada discussed this problem in Annex III, and in Annex II the Agreement was modified to add important co-operative aspects to deal with the issue. Annex II contained some new and significant provisions, such as the following:

- To develop joint analyses including research and applications that contribute to tracking of human health and environmental responses to controls

- To develop common emission inventories and join in analyses of cost-effective emission reductions

- To evaluate the adequacy of monitoring networks

- To undertake certain specific obligations on either side of the border

In agreeing on these issues, the two governments went much further than before in ensuring comparable ozone strategies on either side of their long border.

The World Health Organization (WHO) convenes meetings of experts from different countries. In the recent update of the Guidelines for Air Quality [3], there were 15 experts from 11 countries, 3 observers, a representative from the European Community, and staff members of WHO. They conduct a brief review of current relevant data, but concentrate on arriving at a consensus about a numerical standard. The final report is incorporated into the WHO Guidelines for Air Quality, and each section provides some scientific references. There is no coordinated public input into the process.

Other jurisdictions, such as Australia, use a modified WHO process, with some public input as the discussions of scientific data are held.

Recent reviews published in Sweden constitute "criteria" documents on which a decision about a standard on ozone may be based [4, 5, 6, 7].

There are several important points to note about standards (infringement of which carry some sort of penalty) and guidelines (which are some sort of "wake-up call" to be used for planning purposes).

- The present epidemiological data on particulate pollution do not indicate that there is a threshold below which no adverse health effects occur [8, 9]. A particulate standard should therefore acknowledge that some adverse effect may well occur in regions within the attainment of the standard. The new WHO Guidelines for Air Quality recognized this [3] (see Appendix II). The Canadian CWS PM standard implementation to date has also recognized this fact.

- The ozone standard has been much influenced by controlled exposure studies of normal individuals, summarized in Chapter 4. The decisions about an appropriate standard may well be influenced in the future by the demonstration that even a 1-hour level of 70 ppb does not prevent adverse effects in field workers [10]. The consistent and coherent data on respiratory hospital admissions are also of great importance. The Swedish papers on ozone referred to above, recommended an 8-hour exposure to not more than 40 ppb of ozone. The Canadian CWS for ozone specifies a maximum 8-hour exposure of 65 ppb within an air quality management jurisdiction (fourth highest measurement annually, averaged over three consecutive years).

- The older Canadian National Ambient Air Quality Objectives (guidelines) use the words: "maximum acceptable," "maximum desirable," and "maximum tolerable" to describe three levels of targets for air quality management. These qualitative words are confusing and would be better avoided altogether. The Australians use the word "detrimental" in place of the Canadian "maximum tolerable." This is a good deal more specific. The US EPA does not use such qualifying words at all, but refers to primary (human health-based) and secondary (all other impacts) standards.

• In some situations, proper protection requires a very short-term standard. Thus, with very large point source emitters of SO_2 (which exist still), it is sensible to base a standard on a maximum 10-minute ground level concentration, as recognized in the WHO standard. Asthmatics are very sensitive to SO_2, and have been shown to be immediately affected (within minutes) by concentrations not much above 0.25 ppm. They would not be adequately protected by an SO_2 standard that set only an annual average. The WHO Guidelines for Air Quality [3] noted: "Based upon controlled studies with asthmatics exposed to SO_2 for short periods, it is recommended that a value of 500 μg/m^3 (0.175 ppm) should not be exceeded over averaging periods of 10 minutes." The US EPA has not yet recommended a 10-minute standard, but it did note the occurrence in the US of a significant number of ground-level exceedances of 0.5 ppm for 10 minutes, and even a few over 0.75 ppm close to major point sources.

• There is often some confusion over which parts of the process involve "science" and which do not. There are two essential areas in which a judgement has to be made but which are not amenable to a scientific process. These are:

a) Decisions about using data from animal experiments in the calculation of human risk, and

b) Decisions about when a causal inference is to be made from data indicating an association between pollutant levels and some health outcome. (This is discussed in Chapter 5.)

In some cases, as with dioxins (the family of polychloro-para-dibenzodioxins), for example, animal data are very important in signalling the danger of a substance to biological systems. In other cases, of which lead is an example, animal data contributed little to the understanding of human risk, which depended on the interpretation of epidemiological studies, particularly of children.

One of the authors has noted elsewhere [11], that a final judgement on a suitable standard involves an attempt to integrate data from epidemiological studies, controlled exposure studies, and experimental animal exposures. It is generally recognized that such tasks involve a very high level of intelligent function; in a sense, they are comparable to juggling with objects of different shapes and weights, which is far more difficult than with similar items. Some years ago, someone engaged in this process observed:

> Animal toxicology studies ask the wrong questions but give perfect answers; Epidemiological studies ask the right questions but give imperfect answers; Clinical studies give perfect answers to questions of unknown relevance.

This neatly sums up the inherent difficulty in attempting to synthesize such disparate information. It is important to acknowledge that in an open society, those responsible for this task must come from a variety of backgrounds — a fact recognized by the membership of the CASAC Committee which, in the US EPA, has to approve the emphasis and analysis involved in a scientific criteria document on a given pollutant before the Administrator considers the question of a numerical standard.

There is no doubt that the processes that precede the promulgation of a standard, as followed by the US EPA, are very important in the evaluation of all the available information and of the relative strength of different sections of it; this is particularly important in the case of epidemiological data, the discussion of which usually involves far more time and dialogue than is the case with animal experiments or controlled exposures. The entire process assists society to arrive at some consensus on the level of protection that should be afforded, and the possible benefits that might follow enforcement of stricter standards. This process should be fully in the public domain. This is a requirement that has proven more difficult to organize in countries with a parliamentary system of government than in the US [12]. In the US, in addition, the courts play an important role in the national standards-setting process. The recent example of the remanding and subsequent confirmation of the new PM and ozone standards by a US District Court and the Supreme Court, respectively, may have helped to clarify some of the legal issues attached to EPA's regulatory authority. At this level of legal debate, it is unlikely that public issues were illuminated.

However complicated or inexact the process of standard setting may be, nevertheless it is important to note that it is most unlikely that the public health would be adequately protected unless such standards, objectives, and perhaps even guidelines are in place.

ECONOMIC VALUATION OF THE EFFECTS OF AIR POLLUTION

Economic analysis of the effects of air pollution has been carried out in the form of cost-benefit analysis for more than 30 years [13, 14]. Cost-benefit analysis is but one of a suite of approaches to evaluating environmental impacts. It is the most commonly used method, but it is not the most comprehensive. The cost side of the ledger, expressed as the direct and indirect expenditure costs of controlling emissions to certain levels or achieving ambient air quality standards, is fairly straightforward — although not without uncertainties. Benefit estimates have normally been based on welfare economics and pollution damage costs expressed as willingness-to-pay or willingness-to-accept compensation to avoid the damage, in monetary terms, by those who are deemed to be affected. Direct, real (i.e., out-of-pocket) expenditures, such as actual health care costs to treat respiratory disease, or lost days of work, are included in such analyses and are reasonably accessible and un-controversial. Valuing less tangible avoided damages, such as the value of lengthened lives or of a child's school attendance, however, has been fraught with disagreement. Such analysis must evaluate both market and non-market (externality) factors. We do not attempt to treat this subject in the detail that would be necessary to address the more controversial aspects fully; instead, we present the results of some of the major, widely accepted studies to illustrate the dimensions of this evolving field.

The following figure illustrates the steps in the complex process of placing an economic value on the effects of changes in air quality.

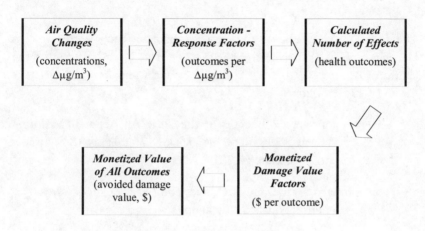

Figure 8.1: Schematic of air quality economic valuation process.

The most convincing use of cost-benefit results, as suggested by the use of Δ in the graphic (symbolizing a change in concentration), is in comparing the effects of policy proposals or regulatory requirements to a reference baseline scenario in the absence of the measures. The analysis is based on the changes in emissions and air quality that are estimated to result from the policy measures and the marginal value of associated air quality improvements. The credibility of cost-benefit value is stronger in relative terms, that is, in describing changes in air quality, than in representing the absolute value of air pollution effects at a point in time.

When the first edition of this book was written in 1971, Lave and Seskin's analysis of existing levels of pollution in the US, in economic terms, had just appeared [15]. At that time, there was considerable uncertainty as to whether the translation of exposure-effect regression coefficients into dollars was an acceptable exercise. In 1989, a committee convened by the US Congress reviewed the economic valuation of the adverse effects of air pollution, and concluded that the margins of error of such estimates were so large that there was little to be gained by such analyses. Yet, in the 1990 Clean Air Act Amendments (in section 812), Congress disregarded this advice and required the EPA to conduct periodic assessments of the benefits and costs of the Act. There are now a considerable number of these estimates, which may be summarized as follows.

The first EPA response to the congressional instruction appeared in October 1997 as a retrospective analysis of the costs and benefits of the Clean Air Act from 1970 to 1990 [16]. The conclusions from the executive summary are as follows:

- The total monetized benefits of the Clean Air Act realized during the period from 1970 to 1990 range from $5.6 trillion to $49.4 trillion, with a central estimate of $22.2 trillion.

- By comparison, the value of direct compliance expenditures over the same period equals $0.5 trillion.

- Subtracting costs from benefits results in net, direct, monetized benefits ranging from $5.1 trillion to $489.9 trillion, with a central estimate of $21.7 trillion, for the 1970 to 1990 period.

- The lower bound of this range may go down and the upper bound may go up if analytical uncertainties associated with the compliance costs, macroeconomic effects, emissions projections, and air quality modelling could be quantified and incorporated in the uncertainty analysis. While the range already reflects many important uncertainties in the physical effects and economic evaluation steps, the range might also broaden further if additional uncertainties in these two steps could be quantified.

- The central estimate of $22.2 trillion in benefits may be a significant underestimate due to the exclusion of large numbers of benefits from the monetized benefit estimate (e.g., all air toxics effects, ecosystem effects, and numerous human health effects).

This study also included a table of "central estimates of economic welfare value per unit of avoided effects," in 1990 dollars, shown in Table 8.2.

More recently [16], a prospective cost-benefit analysis of the Clean Air Act for 1990-2010 has confirmed the conclusions respecting the earlier period, but indicate a diminishing, but still significant, net benefit relative to the required investment in control and administrative costs.

Another important report has been on the benefits of reductions in acid rain [17]. The authors concluded:

> The results of this assessment show that the potential health benefits of reductions in exposure to sulfate aerosols in the eastern United States as a result of the SO_2 emissions reductions required by Title IV are substantial. Based on what we believe is a reasonable interpretation of the available epidemiological and economic evidence on potential health effects of sulfate aerosols and their monetary value, we estimate that the annual health benefits of Title IV required reductions in SO_2 in 2010 in the eastern United States are more likely than not to fall between $12 billion and $78 billion, with an estimated mean value of $40 billion. There is reason to expect some possible upward bias at the higher end of this range, and the results of the sensitivity analyses suggest that there is a good chance that the benefits in 2010 fall between $12 billion and the estimated mean of $40 billion. Annual health benefits for eastern Canada resulting from the U.S. reductions in SO_2 emissions would add as much as one billion dollars to the U.S. benefit totals in both 1997 and 2010.

An independent analysis that comes to similar conclusions may be found in reference [18].

Another cost-benefit analysis compared the economic disbenefits of different modes of generating electricity with the costs of the different technologies in New York State [19].

A detailed and conservative analysis of adverse health costs in Los Angeles [20] concluded that to pay for the current health disbenefits, one would have to impose a tax of 3 cents per mile on every automobile, and 53 cents per mile on every heavy diesel truck.

Other estimates have included an early one for Los Angeles [21] and for San Francisco [22]; the authors of these studies have reviewed some of their methodology and the problems encountered [23].

Estimates on a smaller scale included one conducted for Vancouver and the Lower Fraser Valley of British Columbia [24], with a population of about 2 million people. This concluded that agricultural crop damage amounted to $4.4 million yearly, and that adverse effects of PM_{10} and ozone on human health brought the range of total damage value to between $490 million and $1,035 million per year in 1995. In these estimates, a PM_{10} response threshold of 10 micrograms/m^3 was assumed.

A calculation completed for the Ontario Medical Association [25] estimated costs for each region of Ontario, and produced a model that local people could use to calculate their own costs based on their local pollution levels. For Ontario as a whole, the direct (actual) health costs attributable annually to air pollution were about $600 million.

In all of these studies, the major uncertainties were described in some detail. The following problems require individual discussion:

- The problem of whether to assume some "threshold" number arises acutely when considering the PM_{10} and $PM_{2.5}$ data. As the most recent papers on $PM_{2.5}$ results have shown, there is no evidence for a statistical threshold. In some studies, however, some lower threshold for an effect has been assumed. The assumption has a considerable effect on the economic valuation. For example, if one assumed a no-effect threshold of 20 micrograms/m^3 for PM_{10} in the Vancouver study cited above, the effects on morbidity and mortality — and associated avoided damage values — were reduced by more than half.

- For a long time, the problem of how to cost premature mortality was a stumbling block in economic estimates. It was agreed that the age of the individual had to be taken into account; and analyses of such things as the amounts awarded by workers' compensation boards in the case of accidental death of an employee, and of awards in the case of aircraft accidents, in combination with revealed preferences in expenditures to reduce personal risk (for example, investing in anti-lock braking systems in cars), has led to a general consensus that a median figure of about $4 million is appropriate, provided it is adjusted for age. A similar value has been used in Canadian valuation work (i.e., about $4 million CDN).

Some current analyses express avoided mortality benefit in terms of the value of a statistical life year (i.e., a marginal change in life expectancy).

• There is, however, no certain way of deciding which estimates of mortality should be used. The EPA retrospective cost-benefit study quoted at the beginning of this section decided to use only the extensive and more or less unanimous data bank of results from time-series studies of daily mortality and particulate pollution. However, the longitudinal American Cancer Society (ACS) study described in Chapter 4 would give a mortality estimate several-fold larger than that derived from time-series studies. And the longitudinal data from the US Six-Cities Study (Harvard School of Public Health) would give an estimate several times larger than that. Which of these should be chosen? Does it make any sense to use all of them and arrive at some mean figure? In the event, the EPA study elected to use the longitudinal data from the ACS study. Statistical weighting of a range of values (often using randomly selected values from a range using Monte Carlo sampling techniques) has been used frequently to represent the possible distribution of overall value that might be implied.

• There have been attempts to evaluate morbidity costs, but different studies show considerable differences in these. Most of the studies make no attempt to estimate medication costs, but depend only on hospital emergency or admission data, or on the broad evidence of days of restricted activity when these have been shown to be pollution-related. Few estimates take any account of possible but undemonstrated long-term effects of air pollutants. This is partly because these effects are so difficult to measure. If all the data on air pollution in Britain that were published between 1956 and 1972 are reviewed, one would conclude that cigarette smoking was the cause of chronic lung disease, and that air pollution acted only by increasing mortality in specific episodes. The role of air pollution in aggravating or even causing chronic lung disease was not assessed (though it must have been present), even though it was shown in 1965 that FEV1 (forced expired volume in one second) levels were lower in comparable men living in more polluted cities [26]. This would indicate that survival (life expectancy) had probably been affected.

• Loss of visibility is clearly an economic disbenefit. Initial attempts to quantify this depended on calculations of loss of tourist income, or of inconvenience to flying. It then came to be realized that in the case of such locations as the Grand Canyon, which began to be affected by aerosols resulting from emissions from a distant power plant, more was at stake than was reflected in some possible local loss of tourist income. Many people sampled for their opinion who lived many miles away and had no immediate intention of visiting it expressed the view that if visibility became impaired in the Grand Canyon, a "national treasure" had been defiled. So what would the affected population be in such a case? Two hundred fifty million? More narrowly, populations may resent the brown haze of visible air pollution or the loss of sight of distant mountains — and some efforts have been made to quantify this. If the population affected is large, then the economic disbenefit of loss of visibility may be very large indeed, even if a low dollar value is put on each individual's willingness to pay to avoid the impact.

These considerations lead to the question of public perceptions about air pollution. This was the subject of a detailed study conducted in a steel industry town, Hamilton, in Canada [27]. A survey of 402 households elicited the responses summarized in Table 8.1.

Factor	Percentage of respondents expressing concern (%)	Percentage of these reporting moderate or extreme (%)
Industrial black smoke	82	90
Air pollution (all types)	71	85
Black soot	70	91
Traffic exhaust	57	81
Water	45	87
Soil	22	76

Table 8.1: Results of a public opinion survey conducted in Hamilton, Ontario [27], regarding public perceptions about air pollution.

Similar surveys in other regions, particularly those impacted by heavy traffic, have generally elicited similar responses. This should be seen in the context of continually improving air quality in all jurisdictions in North America in which air quality management has been taken seriously.

Another way of assessing economic costs is to concentrate on a detailed analysis of the costs entailed by one disease. This has been done recently by Krahn and his colleagues [28] in the case of asthma in Canada. The example is important because it illustrates the complexity of what is being attempted.

The authors included the following as direct costs: in-patient care, emergency services, physician and nursing services, ambulance use, drugs and devices, outpatient diagnostic tests, research, and education. Indirect costs were: loss due to absence from work, inability to do housekeeping, need to care for children absent from school because of asthma, time spent travelling and waiting for medical care, and premature death from asthma. All the costs were in 1990 Canadian dollars. The direct costs were estimated at $306 million, $124 million of which were drug costs. These were estimated by direct reference to the pharmaceutical manufacturers. The largest component of indirect costs was illness-related disability. Total costs were estimated between $504 and $648 million annually in Canada.

This cost represents 0.4% of the total economic burden of illness in Canada, and 7.1% of the burden of respiratory disease as a whole. As a percentage of total costs, hospital care was similar to other respiratory diseases and all diseases; but drug costs were much higher for asthma, and premature death costs were lower. Research accounted for about 0.25% of costs. The costs of asthma in the US have been estimated at $2,997 million ($11.54 per capita), compared with Canadian costs of $7.47 per capita. Drug costs were comparable, but in-patient, emergency, and physician costs were all higher per capita in the US. The costs for Canada were generally similar to those computed for New South Wales in Australia.

Few economic estimates can contain such detail as this. However, the costing of an acute asthma episode at $32 US noted in Table 8.2 looks like an underestimate, since the Canadian authors [28] estimated a hospital emergency visit as costing at least $120, and even this is likely to be an underestimate in view of careful costing which has been undertaken in Vancouver, which suggests a figure four or five times higher [29].

The first major European analysis of health costs associated with air pollution in Europe has recently been published [30]. In this, the fraction of PM_{10} attributable to exposure to vehicle emissions was calculated; calculations of adverse health effects in France, Austria, and Switzerland were then made; the regressions relating these to PM_{10} were used; and various economic valuations were applied. The conclusion was reached that the overall health costs amounted to about 1.7% of the gross domestic product of those countries.

As the 1989 Committee of Congress noted, [40] the economic valuation of the adverse health effects of air pollution is an inexact science — but it seems that it is possible to fix some upper and lower margins, such that of the lower margin one can say "it is unlikely to be less than this," and of the upper margin "it is unlikely to be more than that." A useful question to ask is whether the estimated benefits of a policy in monetary terms are of sufficient magnitude to offset the estimated costs. This balance point (the so-called critical value) should be used to advise decisions, not prescribe them.

The process is nevertheless important, because politicians have come to demand an analysis of probable cost-benefit relationships before agreeing to any restrictive legislation.

Endpoint	Valuation ($, mid-estimate)
Mortality (shortened life)*	4,800,000 per case
Heart attacks	587,000 per case
Strokes	587,000 per case
Hospital admissions	
Respiratory	7,500 per case
Ischemic heart disease	10,000 per case
Congestive heart disease	8,000 per case
Respiratory illness & symptoms	
Upper respiratory illness	18 per case
Lower respiratory illness	10 per case
Acute bronchitis	45 per case
Acute respiratory symptoms	17 per case
Work loss days	83 per day
Restricted activity days	38 per day
Asthma attacks	32 per case
IQ changes	
Lost IQ points	5,550 per IQ point
Incidence of IQ < 70	52,700 per case
Hypertension	680 per year per case
Decreased worker productivity	Direct economic value
Visibility	Direct economic value
Household soiling	Direct economic value
Agriculture (net surplus)	Change in economic surplus

Table 8-2: Central estimates of economic welfare value per unit of avoided effects, in 1990 US dollars [16]. * Adjusted for age.

In spite of all the reservations about methodology that have been expressed, the general conclusion seems to be valid that, so far, the economic benefits of reductions in air pollution of all kinds — broadly interpreted — have far exceeded the costs incurred over a 30-year period in the United States.

FACTORS LEADING TO UNDER - OR OVERESTIMATES OF RISK VALUE

Overestimates

Since the association between particulate matter and daily mortality plays such a large part in these estimates, the question of estimating the disbenefits consequent upon premature mortality has dominated the discussion. In this connection, the issue of possible "harvesting" (advancing death of seriously ill people by a few hours or days) has been settled by a number of studies which have demonstrated that it is not a major factor. A British study of health costs did not compute actual costs because of the uncertainty in relation to "harvesting" [31].

Another issue is whether any threshold should be assumed; as noted above, this exerts a major effect in regions where levels of particulate pollution are generally low. Although no statistical threshold can be demonstrated (and specific attempts have been made to demonstrate one), it can be argued that, from a biological point of view it must exist, and therefore to ignore it must lead to an overestimate. Estimates of the costs associated with premature mortality, and the necessary correction for age, are bound to vary; this question can be settled only by new analyses or data.

Overestimates may also result from analyses that view pollutant effects individually, costing effects attributed to NO_2, CO, or SO_2 as if these were separate from effects due to particulate matter. This can be avoided if only the effects from $PM_{2.5}$ are considered in the analysis, with the possible addition of ozone.

Underestimates

A number of factors point to present estimates as being necessarily lower than the actual value of air quality improvement benefits:

- No account is taken of effects on the prevalence of diseases such as asthma or heart disease. If such an effect exists, it would appear as a discrepancy between the time-series calculated association with mortality and the long-term effects on survival found in longitudinal studies; it may be significant that the estimates based on longitudinal studies are at least double and possibly triple those calculated from time-series data.

- Estimates based on time-series analyses only do not take account of the lag (between pollution exposure and outcome) in the effect, nor of death certification in which one disease may be listed as the primary cause but another listed as a secondary effect. Distributed lag models cause the estimate of response to be about doubled.

- It is not evident that secondary costs have been properly considered. If school absences for respiratory illness are caused by ambient ozone levels, how should such an absence be valued? Also, any long-term effects of such induced illnesses are ignored nor is any account taken of such factors as reduced lung development.

- Medication costs are generally ignored, although as noted in Chapter 4, they have been shown to rise in relation to air pollution levels. It is difficult to cost perceptions of annoyance, though there is no doubt that these exist [32].

There seems little doubt that efforts to estimate the economic costs of air pollution will continue. The methodology will always be controversial, yet considerable progress has been made to eliminate major factors in such estimates.

Provided that the uncertainties — in both directions — are freely acknowledged, such estimates are likely to play a useful role in policy formulation.

DECISION MAKING AND PUBLIC DEBATE

Decisions on new policies or developments that will impact the environment are difficult and contentious. We (the authors) have participated in a number of such issues and suggest that the following are common factors in such processes:

- An analysis of environmental impact, dealing with local meteorology, topography, exposed population and socioeconomic factors, and calculated impact should be basic to any hearing process. Various individuals, including the proponent and some members of the public will have joined the political issues before such information is available.

- There is a recognized (and understandable) tendency for proponents (whether private or public) to expect that environmental impact assessments reflect a bias favourable toward the project. In some cases, the proponent may seek to modify such assessments when they are in draft to make them appear more favourable. One model that has been used successfully in a number of jurisdictions is for the regulatory or hearing body to contract for an independent assessment (proponents still pay the expense of the assessment).

- For these reasons, all environmental impact assessments must be critically reviewed by others, and the cross-questioning and discussion of leading issues should be in a semi-formal setting and be in the public domain. This process cannot be avoided or sidestepped. The modelling of probable future emissions and their ground-level concentrations, for example, is not an exact science, however quantitative the analysis may appear, and such exercises require careful examination.

- The hearing board or other body constituted to prepare a final assessment of the project, should report in public and within a reasonable time of a public hearing.

The questions raised are often difficult. We have recently encountered problems with heavy diesel trucks involved in a major construction project having to pass within 40 yards of an elementary school and its playground — is this an acceptable exposure? What conclusion should be reached about PM_{10} emissions from antiquated "beehive burners" operated by a wood fabrication company that is a major local employer and argues that these are necessary if the industry is to be maintained? Does a detectable odour of styrene from a fibreglass fabrication plant constitute a sufficiently serious nuisance that remedial steps should be ordered? Does the emission of formaldehyde from a wood-processing plant constitute a health hazard? If so, what emission standard should be applied, and how should it be enforced?

It is our experience that many jurisdictions do not yet recognize that responsible decision making in a free society requires careful and structured procedures to resolve these kinds of issues. Many members of the public believe that proponents may have had undue influence on local councils or on local emission licensing procedures, and such views are often expressed at public meetings before anyone has a real idea of what is proposed and what the likely environmental impact will be. It needs to be constantly emphasized that proper scientific evaluation by truly independent parties should precede the political process of decision making. This is not to suggest that the scientific assessment should prescribe the course of a decision, rather that it be used appropriately to qualify and inform the decision.

How do members of the public approach decision making in the presence of uncertainty? Dr. Ray Neutra and his colleagues in the California Department of Health Services studied the public response to the question of what should be done in the face of a possible impact of electromagnetic fields on human health [38]. They comment that stakeholders operate "under different policy frameworks that lead to differences in preferred action." Starting with the most "hard-line" and progressing toward the softest, these are:

1. Requiring virtual certainty of a problem before acting on it.

2. Adhering to a "utilitarian" framework that aims at "the most good for the most people at the least cost." This is favoured by economists and regulators.

3. A "social justice" framework that "aims at protecting the most vulnerable regardless of cost."

4. A "non-interventionist" framework that prefers voluntary non-governmental approaches to environmental risk regardless of the degree of confidence that there is a problem.

The authors note that the differences in approach to precaution should ideally be resolved in a transparent and fair political process.

RISK PERCEPTION AND RISK COMMUNICATION IN DECISION MAKING

Descriptions of environmental risks and their imputed values supported by all of the foregoing types of analysis and arguments are generally poorly communicated to the public. Public perception of the seriousness (or acceptability) of a risk, say, exposure to a peak or long-term concentration of an air pollutant, is strongly influenced by many factors. Some of these are captured in the title of a recent paper by one of the pioneers in the development of risk communication, Paul Slovic: *Trust, Emotion, Sex, Politics, and Science: Surveying the Risk-Assessment Battlefield* [39]. Public (or private) decision making will be influenced by all of these factors (and more). Slovic argues:

> Risk assessment is inherently subjective and represents a blending of science and judgement with important psychological, social, cultural and political factors... The limitations of risk science, the importance and difficulty of maintaining trust, and the complex, socio-political nature of risk point to the need for a new approach — one that focuses upon more public participation into both risk assessment and risk decision making in order to make the decision process more democratic, improve the relevance and quality of technical analysis, and increase the legitimacy and public acceptance of the resulting decisions.

Morgan [33] points out that decisions based on risk analysis and assessment often focus on the numerical balance of costs and benefits without considering the important additional democratic value of equity. He argues for a "hybrid" approach in which efficiency and equity are both appropriately weighted in influencing decision making respecting environmental risks. This is a difficult challenge for modern, economically driven societies. The moral and ethical dimensions of risk-based (or risk-influenced) decisions are emphasized in a paper by Moore [34], who questions the propriety of using cost-benefit analysis in setting health-based environmental standards.

The issues discussed here are the subject of an entire issue of the journal *Environmental Science and Technology* (vol. 34, no. 8, April 15, 2000). Farrow et al. [35] point out in their introduction to a dozen papers on the subject of economic valuation of the environment one of the dilemmas of modern economies:

> When all is said and done about valuation, what's the purpose? Policy-makers, advocates, and managers need, in a complex world, to differentiate between better and worse alternatives. It is much easier to distinguish better from worse in one dimension or in as few of them as possible. Valuation methods claim to measure different impacts in monetary terms that can be consistently and logically added and subtracted. The impacts come first, for there is no valuation without a physical state of the world, but economists sit atop a demand for reaching a single bottom line.

We believe that public decision making regarding air quality can benefit from an open, objective critical assessment of the scientific and economic factors associated with proposed policy changes or development projects—as long as accountable public participation processes are followed. The outcomes are too important to be left to technocrats.

Two recent examples of the application of cost-benefit analysis to public decisions in Canada have been assessed by the National Round Table on the Environment and the Economy (NRTEE) and the Royal Society of Canada (RSC). The first dealt with a joint government-industry approach to evaluating proposals to reduce the sulphur content of gasoline and diesel fuels [36]. NRTEE's analysis of the decision-making process is instructive. It points out some of the successes and pitfalls of the expert panel approach that was used to prepare input for a government working group that made the final recommendations for policy and regulations. The case study analysis is provided on the NRTEE Web site: <http://www.nrtee-trnee.ca/eng/programs/>. To quote from their summary:

The disagreements over the extrapolation of findings of the Health Panel and the debate about the methodologies and tools employed to generate the findings represent the fundamental challenge to the Sulphur Panel Process. This challenge may be defined by the existence of two opposing viewpoints: a) the feeling that the expert panel findings represented the best available scientific advice and were a sound basis for regulation, and b) the feeling that the results were too speculative to base a decision on.

Two of the authors both participated in this process (as members of the health and atmospheric science panels, respectively) and saw the conflicting viewpoints at first hand. We concur that the disagreements were a healthy part of the process. We would have preferred that the proceedings were more open to external (i.e., non-expert) scrutiny and believe that this would have produced a more complete public understanding of the complex issues involved.

The second Canadian example is the recent assessment by an Expert Panel of the Royal Society of Canada of the socio economic evaluation tools used in the development of the Canada-Wide Standards for PM and Ozone [37]. Although critical of many of the details of the content and application of the analysis tools, the RSC Panel endorsed the role of cost-benefit analysis in environmental policy and regulatory decision making. The panel pointed out a serious shortcoming of the technocratic process that has evolved for standards development in Canada, namely, that the process was confined to cost-benefit analysis only without assessing multiple attributes ("accounts") that address less tangible effects (including macro-economic effects). The panel also pointed out that the process would have generated much stronger stakeholder and public support if it had been conducted more openly and transparently.

These examples point out a weakness in current approaches to public evaluation of environmental effects of economic development. As noted above, development causes real impacts on our biophysical environment. Just because we cannot (or choose not to) measure or quantify them, they are nonetheless real. Impacts may be insignificant because they are reversible (rare) or because ecosystems can adapt to them, or they may be truly irreversible, leading to unsustainable pressure on ecosystems. Science can help elucidate the best available information on the nature of the impacts and their risks, but open, systematic public consideration of the inevitable complexities, in which all reasonable perspectives on the issue(s) at hand are encouraged to be expressed, is essential. Such deliberations need not consume inordinate amounts of time and expense.

REFERENCES

[1]   Air Quality Criteria for Ozone and Related Photochemical Oxidants. 3 volumes. Office of Research and Development, US Environmental Protection Agency, Research Triangle Park, NC 27711, USA. EPA/600/P-93/004cF. July 1996.

[2]   Review of the National Ambient Air Quality Standards for Particulate Matter: Policy Assessment of Scientific and Technical Information. OAQPS| Staff Paper, Office of Air Quality Planning and Standards, US Environmental Protection Agency. April 1996.

[3]   WORLD HEALTH ORGANIZATION, Guidelines for Air Quality, WHO, Geneva, 2000, 190 pp.

[4]   COTGREAVE, I.A., Absorption and Metabolic Fate of Ozone — the Molecular Basis of Ozone-Induced Toxicity, Scand J Work Environ Health 22, Suppl 3, 15-26, 1996

[5]   SUNDELL, J., & ZUBER, A., Ozone and Other Photochemical Oxidants in Ambient and Indoor Air — Properties, Sources and Concentrations, Scand J Work Environ Health 22 Suppl 3, 5-14, 1996

[6]   BYLIN, G., Controlled Human Studies of Ozone Exposure, Scand J Work Environ Health 22 Suppl 3, 52-71, 1996.

[7]   NYBERG, F., & PERSHAGEN, G., Epidemiologic Studies on Ozone, Scand J Work Environ Health 22 Suppl 3, 72-98, 1996.

[8]   SCHWARTZ, J., & ZANOBETTI, A., Using Meta-Smoothing to Estimate Dose-Response Trends Across Multiple Studies, with Application to Air Pollution and Daily Death, Epidemiology 11:666-72, 2000.

[9]   DANIELS, M.J., DOMENICI, F., SAMET, J.M., & ZEGER, S.L., Estimating Particulate Matter-Mortality Dose-Response Curves and Threshold Levels: An analysis of daily time-series for the 20 largest US cities, Am J Epidemiol 152:397-406, 2000.

[10]   BRAUER, M., BLAIR, J., & VEDAL , S., Effect of Ambient Ozone Exposure on Lung Function in Farm Workers, Am J Respir Crit Care Med 154:981-87, 1996.

[11]   BATES, D.V., Standard-Setting as an Integrative Exercise: Alchemy, juggling, or science? In: Inhalation Toxicology, edited by U. Mohr. Springer-Verlag, New York & Heidelberg. 1988. See pages 1-9.

[12]   BATES, D.V., Environmental Health Risks and Public Policy: Decision-making in free societies, University of Washington Press, Seattle. Dec 1994. pp 117.

[13]   HALVORSEN, R., & RUBY, M.G., Benefit-Cost Analysis of Air Pollution Control, Lexington Books, D.C. Heath & Co. 1981. Pp 264.

[14]   KOPP, R.J., KRUPNICK, A.J., & Toman, M., Cost-Benefit Analysis and Regulatory Reform: An Assessment of the science and the art, Resources for the Future, Discussion Paper 97-19, January 1997.

[15]   LAVE, L.B., & SESKIN, E.P., Air Pollution and Human Health, Science 169:723-33, 1970.

[16]   US ENVIRONMENTAL PROTECTION AGENCY, The Benefits and Costs of the Clean Air Act 1970 to 1990, Prepared for the US Congress by the US Environmental Protection Agency, October 1997 (the "retrospective study"). Followed by The Benefits and Costs of the Clean Air Act 1990 to 2010, US EPA Report to Congress, November 1999 (the "prospective" study).

[17]   CHESTNUT, L.G., Human Health Benefits Assessment of the Acid Rain Provisions of the 1990 Clean Air Act Amendments, EPA Contract No. 68-D3-0005. November 1995. (Hagler-Baily Consulting, Inc., P.O. Drawer O, Boulder, Colorado 80306-1906)

[18] BURTRAW, D., Krupnick, A., Mansur, E., Austin, D., & Farrell, D., The Costs and Benefits of Reducing Acid Rain, Resources for the Future, Discussion Paper 97-31-REV, July 1997.

[19] ROWE, R.D., LANG, C.M., CHESTNUT, L.G., LATIMER, D.A., RAE, D.A., BERNOW, S.M., & WHITE, D.E., The New York Electricity Externality Study, Volume I: Introduction & Methods. pp 835. Volume II: Appendices. pp 720. Oceana Publications Inc. December 1995.

[20] SMALL, K.A., & KAZIMI, C., On the costs of Air Pollution from Motor Vehicles, J Transport Economics & Policy 29:7-32, 1995.

[21] HALL, J.V., Economic Assessment of the Health Benefits from Improvements in Air Quality in the South Coast Air Basin, Final Report to South Coast Air Quality Management District Contract No. 5685. June 1989. California State University Fullerton Foundation.

[22] HALL, J., BRAJER, V., & KLEINMAN, M., The Economic Value of Quantifiable Ozone and PM_{10} Related Health Effects in the San Francisco Bay Area. Final Report to the Bay Area Air Quality Management District. October 1995.

[23] HALL, J.V., WINER, A.M., KLEINMAN, M.T., LURMANN, F.W., BRAJER, V., & COLOME, S.D., Valuing the Health Benefits of Clean Air, Science 255:812-17, 1992.

[24] BOVAR-CONCORD ENVIRONMENTAL Economic Analysis of Air Quality Improvement in the Lower Fraser Valley, Report Prepared for the BC Ministry of Environment, Lands & Parks, Environmental Policy Branch; BCE 42149687. Bovar-Concord Environmental, November 1995.

[25] DSS MANAGEMENT CONSULTANTS, Illness Costs of Air Pollution: Phase II: Estimating Health and Economic Damages, Prepared for Ontario Medical Association by DSS Management Consultants Inc. (1886 Bowler Drive, Pickering, ON L1V 3E4 [905] 839 8814). July 2000.

[26]   BATES, D.V., ibid.

[27]   ELLIOTT, S.J., COLE, D.C., KRUEGER, P., VOORBERG, N., & WAKEFIELD, S., The Power of Perception: Health risk attributed to air pollution in an urban industrial neighbourhood, Risk Analysis 19:621-34, 1999.

[28]   KRAHN, M.D., BERKA, C., LANGLOIS, P., & DETSKY, A.S., Direct and Indirect Costs of Asthma in Canada, 1990, Can Med Assoc J 154:821-31, 1996.

[29]   BEHBEHANI, N.A., GRUNFELD, A., & FITZGERALD, J.M., Health Care Costs Associated with Asthma: A prospective economic analysis, Can Respir J 6:521-25, 1999.

[30]   KUNZLI, N., KAISER, R., MEDINA, S., STUDNICKA, M., CHANEL, O., FILLIGER, P., HERRY, M., HORAK, F. Jr., PUYBONNIEUX-TEXIER. V., QUENEL, P., SCHNEIDER, J., SEETHALER, R., VERGNAUD, J.-C., & SOMMER, H., Public-Health Impact of Outdoor and Traffic-Related Air Pollution: A European assessment, Lancet 356:795-801, 2000.

[31]   ECONOMIC APPRAISAL OF THE HEALTH EFFECTS OF AIR POLLUTION, Department of Health:, London: The Stationery Office.1999. Pp 130.

[32]   OGLESBY, L., KUNZLI, N., MONN, C., SCHINDLER, C., ACKERMAN-LIEBRICH, U., LEUENBERGER, P., & THE SAPALDIA TEAM, Validity of Annoyance Scores for Estimation of Long Term Air Pollution Exposure in Epidemiologic Studies, Am J Epidemiol 152: 75-83, 2000.

[33]   MORGAN, G., Risk Management Should Be about Efficiency and Equity, Environmental Science & Technology 34(1):32A-34A, 2000.

[34]   MOORE, C., The Impracticality and Immorality of Cost-Benefit Analysis in Setting Health-Based Standards, Tulane Environmental Law Journal 2(2), Summer 1998.

[35] FARROW, R.S., Goldburg, C.B., & Small, M.J., Economic Valuation of the Environment: A special issue, Environmental Science & Technology 34(8):1381-1461, 2000.

[36] NATIONAL ROUND TABLE ON THE ENVIRONMENT AND THE ECONOMY, Reducing Sulphur in Gasoline and Diesel Fuel — Case Study, Web document: http://www.nrtee-trnee/eng/programs/health/SULPHUR_e.htm.

[37] THE ROYAL SOCIETY OF CANADA, Report of an Expert Panel to Review the Socio-Economic Models and Related Components Supporting the Development of Canada-Wide Standards for Particulate Matter and Ozone. S.E. Hrudey, Chair. June 2001.

[38] NEUTRA, R.R., VON WINTERFIELD, D., FLORIG, K., & BERNSTEIN, B. The Precautionary Principle and Policy Options in the Face of Possible Risk from Power Frequency Electric and Magnetic Fields (EMF). Personal Communication.

[39] SLOVIC, P., Trust, Emotion, Sex, Politics, and Science: Surveying the Risk Assessment Battlefield, Risk Analysis 19(4):689-701, 1999.

[40] BLODGETT, J. Health Benefits of Air Pollution Control: a discussion Congressional Research Service Report for Congress, Feb 27, 1989. Library of Congress.

Chapter 9
Air Quality Management

Morris Mennell and Kamal K. Bhattacharyya

INTRODUCTION

The preceding chapters provide information on sources and characteristics of air pollutants, their transport and transformation in the atmosphere, and their impacts on public health and the environment. Sufficient evidence exists to indicate that people throughout the world are experiencing the adverse public health, environmental, and economic impacts of increasing air pollution. These negative impacts threaten the quality of life at every level, from the health of the individual citizen to the long-term survival of humans and natural ecosystems around the world.

Traditionally, cities have been economic centres, and they are still the driving forces of economic and social development. As centres of concentrated human activity, urban areas are generally the major sources of air pollution. While economic development and urbanization can bring improvement to people's income and lifestyles, if carried out in an unsustainable way, they can also result in a deterioration of the quality of the air in the region. There is increasing concern about the rapid pace of urbanization in many parts of the world, and about the extent of air pollution associated with it.

Over the years, our understanding about the influence of air pollutants on our health, environment, and economy on a local, regional, and global scale has improved immensely. In most regions, poor air quality results from pollutants emitted from sources within the region. The ambient level of air pollutants in a region also depends on topography and meteorological conditions, which influence dispersion of pollutants, and physical/chemical atmospheric processes, which form secondary pollutants. Moreover, air pollutants emitted in an urban area do not remain confined within its boundaries but can travel hundreds or even thousands of kilometres from their origin, causing detrimental impacts in many downwind cities and ecosystems. In a very complex fashion, all these factors determine the pathway and fate of air pollutants from source to destination. Transboundary movement of air pollution has become an international problem in many parts of the world. Long-range transport of certain persistent air pollutants has become a global problem. In addition, there is the over arching issue of global climate change caused by the discharge of greenhouse gases such as carbon dioxide when fossil fuels are burned.

There are many strategies and techniques to reduce emissions and improve air quality. These include prohibiting the sale of toxic substances such as lead in gasoline; regulations to require removal of contaminants in the industrial stack or motor vehicle tailpipe; economic incentives to encourage the use of cleaner raw materials, fuels and production processes; economic disincentives to make higher-polluting production or activities more expensive; and land use and transportation policies and services to minimize urban sprawl and single-occupant vehicle use. Air quality management is the process of determining the community goals for ambient air quality, assessing whether the current air quality complies with those goals and, if not, developing and implementing an air quality management plan which sets out a comprehensive and cost-effective set of initiatives to reach the clean air target.

This chapter provides an overview of regional and global air quality issues, approaches to management of these issues, the information necessary for identification of regional air quality problems, and how an air quality management plan (AQMP) is developed and implemented to address such issues. The importance of public consultation during AQMP development and implementation is also discussed.

AIR QUALITY ISSUES

At present, seven air quality issues, four regional and three global, are of recognized concern:

The regional air quality issues are:

- Urban smog

- Visibility impairment

- Acidic deposition

- Hazardous air pollutants or air toxics

The global issues are:

- Greenhouse gases

- Stratospheric ozone depletion

- Persistent organic pollutants

Regional Air Quality Issues

Urban Smog — The word *smog* originated in the United Kingdom in the early 1900s and referred to the unique atmospheric condition resulting from a combination of smoke and fog. In winter the city of London often experienced dense, stagnant fog. Coal was the main fuel for industry and for home heating in and around the city, and coal-burning emissions caused severe episodes of air pollution during foggy days, when dispersion of air emissions was very limited. The term *photochemical smog* came into use in the 1960s to describe the air pollution condition in the areas surrounding Los Angeles. The main constituent of photochemical smog is ozone which is formed in the lower atmosphere by complex reactions among certain air pollutants on warm sunny days.

Only recently has the term *smog* been used to describe what people see as polluted, brownish, hazy air hanging over urban areas and their surroundings. In its Phase 2 Federal Smog Management Plan, issued in November 1997, the Government of Canada identified ground-level ozone and particulate matter as the main constituents of smog [1].

A description of ozone and fine particulate matter and other air pollutants which contribute to their formation, as well as their emission sources, is found in Chapters 2 and 3. One of the major precursors of secondary fine particles is gaseous ammonia, which reacts with primary pollutants such as sulphur and nitrogen oxides in the atmosphere to form sulphate and nitrate particles, respectively. Ammonia gas is emitted mostly from agricultural and animal husbandry activities. Other sources of ammonia are fuel and waste combustion, chemical industry, and refrigeration facilities.

Visibility Impairment — One of the obvious signs of poor air quality in most urban areas is the haziness of the atmosphere. The conditions which promote haze formation are complex, and depend on weather conditions and relatively high levels of air pollutants such as particulate matter, aerosols, ozone and other pollutants. A detailed discussion of visibility impairment is provided elsewhere (See page 370).

Acidic Deposition — Acidic deposition, or acid rain as it is commonly known, occurs when primary air pollutants like oxides of sulphur and nitrogen are converted in the atmosphere into sulphuric and nitric acid droplets, and sulphate and nitrate particles. These acidic substances are deposited back to earth's surface as dry particles or with rain, fog, or snow. The descriptions of these primary pollutants and their sources of emissions are given in Chapter 2. The formation of acidic particles and the effects of acidic deposition on vegetation and materials are discussed in Chapters 3, 6, and 11, respectively.

Hazardous Air Pollutants — Hazardous air pollutants (HAPs), also referred to as air toxics, are chemical substances and trace metals present in the atmosphere as gas, liquid droplets, and solid particles. HAPs are released into the atmosphere as volatile organic compounds (VOCs) and particles from a variety of sources, as described in Chapter 2.

Global Atmospheric Issues

Some air pollutants and gases are responsible for global issues such as climate change, depletion of the stratospheric ozone layer, and persistent organic pollutants. As these issues are dealt with in other chapters, only brief descriptions of the contributors to these issues and their status are described below.

Greenhouse Gases [2] — Until recently, a relatively constant amount of greenhouse gases (GHGs) in the earth's atmosphere has maintained our planet's average temperature in a range suitable for human and natural life as we know it. These gases maintain a balance between the energy reaching the earth and that escaping into space. Human activities, particularly since the 19th century Industrial Revolution, have been upsetting the earth's energy balance by releasing an increasing amount of GHGs and other substances, as well as through deforestation and land use. The increased levels of these gases in the atmosphere are warming the average surface temperature of the earth by trapping more heat, as more energy is retained in the earth's atmosphere than is lost to space.

The major greenhouse gases include carbon dioxide (CO_2), methane (CH_4) and nitrous oxide (N_2O). These gases are emitted from both natural and anthropogenic (human-made) sources. Water vapour is another GHG, but human activities do not have a direct effect on its emission rate. Major natural sources of GHGs include volcanic eruptions, forest fires, living organisms, decomposition of vegetation and animal material, and soil. Carbon dioxide is the second most abundant greenhouse gas. The primary anthropogenic source of CO_2 emissions is the burning of fossil fuels and the decomposition of wastes containing carbon. Other industrial processes such as cement and lime manufacturing also release carbon dioxide. Deforestation contributes indirectly to the build-up of CO_2 by removing the sinks for the gas through the release of the carbon stored in the trees.

Methane is discharged to the atmosphere during the mining and transportation of coal; oil and gas exploration and distribution; solid and liquid waste treatment and disposal; and agricultural practices, including rice paddies and the raising of cattle and livestock. Nitrous oxide is generated mainly during combustion of fossil fuels and wastes, and by certain industrial activities and agricultural practices.

There are also several powerful GHGs generated entirely by human activities. These are referred to as ozone-depleting substances (ODS), a group of chemical compounds which are associated with stratospheric ozone depletion, another global issue described below.

Each GHG has a different lifetime and ability to trap heat in the atmosphere. For example, while methane can remain in the atmosphere for 11 years, the lifetime of some ODS ranges from 10,000 to 50,000 years. The heat-trapping ability or global warming potential (GWP) of GHGs varies widely. On a per mass basis, CH_4 traps 21 times and N_2O absorbs 310 times more heat than CO_2. The GWP of some ODS compounds is thousands of times greater than that of carbon dioxide. [3]

Uncertainties still remain about the scientific details of the problem, the extent of its impacts, and the manner in which the effects will be felt. In spite of uncertainties, the countries of the world agreed to initiate actions following the "precautionary principle," to address the problem through the 1992 United Nations Framework Convention on Climate Change at the Earth Summit in Rio de Janeiro.

Subsequently, in December 1997, a Protocol to the United Nations Framework Convention on Climate Change was agreed to by over 160 nations in Kyoto, Japan [4]. One of the most important provisions of the Kyoto Protocol set binding limits on emissions of GHGs for 38 developed countries (Annex B Parties) which are responsible for the major portion of the current emission levels. These countries are to reduce emissions by an average of 5.2% below 1990 levels in the years 2008-12. The Protocol also provides significant incentives for developing countries to control their emissions as their economies grow.

In January 2001, in Shanghai, the member governments of the Intergovernmental Panel on Climate Change (IPCC) issued the Third Assessment Report of Working Group I [5]. Some of the major findings in the report include:

- "An increasing body of observations gives a collective picture of a warming world and other changes in the climate system."

- "Emissions of greenhouse gases and aerosols due to human activities continue to alter the atmosphere in ways that are expected to affect the climate."

- "There is new and stronger evidence that most of the warming observed over the last 50 years is attributable to human activities."

- "Human influences continue to change atmospheric composition throughout the 21st century."

- "Anthropogenic climate change will persist for many centuries."

Ozone-Depleting Substances [2, 6] — A layer of ozone in the stratosphere, or upper atmosphere, protects the earth by shielding it from harmful intense ultraviolet (UV) radiation. Since the 1930's the chemical industries have been producing a group of synthetic chemicals containing carbon and halogens (chlorine, bromine, and fluorine). In the 1970's it was discovered that intense ultraviolet radiation from the sun in the stratosphere could break loose chlorine and bromine atoms from these chemicals. The loose chlorine and bromine atoms could then attack and destroy the ozone layer. Further evidence since then, in particular the discovery of the depleted ozone layer, or so-called "ozone hole," over Antarctica has confirmed the destructive potential of these chemicals.

Because of their ability to deplete the stratospheric ozone layer, these chemicals are commonly called ozone-depleting substances, or ODS. These chemicals include chlorofluorocarbons (CFCs), hydrofluorocarbons (HFCs), perfluorocarbons (PFCs), hydrochlorofluorocarbons (HCFCs), brominated fluorocarbons (halons), sulphur hexafluoride (SF_6), carbon tetrachloride (CCl_4), methyl bromide (CH_3Br), and methyl chloroform ($C_2H_4Cl_3$). These are extremely stable compounds, and some of them could remain in the atmosphere for several hundreds of years and move up to the stratosphere. This means that one of these substances discharged into the atmosphere now may still float in the stratosphere and destroy the ozone layer hundreds of years in the future. The ODS have been used widely for a variety of purposes — as a cooling agent in refrigerators and air conditioners in houses and cars, as a foaming agent for manufacturing insulation and paddings, as propellants in aerosol spray cans, as solvents and cleaning fluids, as a sterilant in hospitals, and as a fire-extinguishing agent.

The depletion of ozone layer also leads to some cooling of the stratosphere, as a result of its reduced ability to absorb solar energy. However, it is now recognized that some ODS, in particular HFCs, HCFCs, PFCs, and SF_6, are powerful greenhouse gases in their own right [3]. Since the stratospheric ozone layer protects the earth, the impacts of its thinning or disappearance will be felt globally one way or another. Because of this global concern, the use of major ODS is being phased out worldwide under the international agreement known as 1987 Montreal Protocol and subsequent amendments to it signed in London (1990), Copenhagen (1992), and Nairobi (1994).

Persistent Organic Pollutants — As described in Chapter 2, persistent organic pollutants (POPs) belong to a group of volatile organic compounds. The primary reason for POPs being classified as a global issue is that they threaten human health, wildlife, and the environment in every region of the world. POPs are very stable compounds, highly toxic and bioaccumulative, i.e., they concentrate in living organisms through absorption in fatty tissue. These chemical compounds are discharged from human activities, and upon release they persist in the atmosphere for decades before breaking down. In addition, POPs are transported globally from their origins to destinations through a process known as the "grasshopper effect." POPs used in one region of the world evaporate during warm season and are transported and deposited in a relatively colder region. As the latter region becomes warmer, the deposited POPs are evaporated again and deposited back to earth in a cooler region further afield. This process of evaporation-transportation-deposition is repeated a number of times until POPs are finally deposited in the coldest polar regions.

Out of a large number of POPs, 12 priority chemicals have been recognized for international action under the United Nations Environment Programme (UNEP). These include: 8 pesticides (aldrin, chlordane, dichlorodiphenyltrichloroethane (DDT), dieldrin, ebdrin, heptachlor, mirex, and toxaphene), 2 industrial chemicals (hexachlorobenzene, also a pesticide, and polychlorinated biphenyls), and 2 products of incomplete combustion of fossil fuels and wastes (dioxins and furans). Because of the global concern, a legally binding international treaty under UNEP was finalized by 122 countries in December 2000 [7]. Initially, the treaty requires "minimization and elimination" of 12 chemicals; some are to be banned immediately, while the use of others will be phased out over a period of time.

AIR QUALITY MANAGEMENT

Government regulatory initiatives to control excessive air pollution began in industrialized nations in the late 19th and early 20th centuries. For the most part, the focus of these early air pollution control programs was to reduce excessive emissions from major industrial sources located near mid-sized communities and large cities. Regulations focused on end-of-pipe solutions, and were limited by the technical effectiveness and perceived affordability of available control technology. This single-source focus gave way to a more comprehensive air quality management approach in the latter half of the 20th century, when urban areas grew to mega cities, industrial production evolved from the processing of basic commodities to complex operations handling numerous toxic chemicals, and emissions from motor vehicles and commercial and residential building heating and air conditioning increased exponentially. As air pollution in cites increased, so too did the level of scientific understanding and societal awareness of the serious impacts of air pollution on public health and the environment, and the economic costs and benefits of reducing emissions to address these unacceptable impacts. More recently, long-range and global issues such as acid rain and global climate change have heightened the need for timely and effective air quality management programs to deal with local, regional, national, international, and global air quality problems.

A comprehensive air quality management approach is more rational, fair and cost-effective than the earlier ad hoc regulatory initiatives. It is based on a scientific assessment of the problem and the effects, with inclusive public and stakeholder review of costs and benefits of potential solutions leading to adoption of sustainable air quality policy and standards which can be implemented in a reasonable time frame.

A regional air quality management plan (AQMP) describes the present state of the ambient air quality in a region, how it has been changing in recent years, what the trends look like if no action is taken, and what can be done to achieve clean air and ensure that it remains so. It sets a course of action to attain the air quality goals and objectives for a region, and it prescribes both short - and long-term policies and pollution control strategies. The policies and emission control measures which reduce air pollution within a region will, in turn, result in a concomitant decrease in discharges into the atmosphere of pollutants and gases contributing to global issues. Hence, local actions to reduce air pollution contribute to the achievement of overall social and environmental benefits.

In recognition of the above, one of the 27 basic principles adopted at the United Nations Conference on Environment and Development held in Rio de Janeiro in June 1992 was Agenda 21 [8]. Agenda 21 is a framework for a cooperative global action plan for environmental management and sustainable development. Towards this end, Chapter 28 of Agenda 21, "Local Authorities' Initiatives in Support of Agenda 21" (i.e., "Local Agenda 21") particularly encourages local initiatives on environmental matters. It provides guidance and a framework for local planning. The "Basis for Action" under Chapter 28.1 of Agenda 21 states:

"Because so many of the problems and solutions being addressed by Agenda 21 have their roots in local activities, the participation and cooperation of local authorities will be a determining factor in fulfilling its objectives. Local authorities construct, operate, and maintain economic, social, and environmental infrastructure, oversee planning processes, establish local environmental policies and regulations, and assist in implementing national and sub-national environmental policies. As the level of governance closest to the people, they play a vital role in educating, mobilizing, and responding to the public to promote sustainable development."

The following sections provide an overview of the general approach to the design, development, and implementation of a regional Air Quality Management Plan, and brief descriptions of the key elements of the process for a typical AQMP. Particular local authorities may need to adopt a different procedure in order to address their unique issues and to conform to regional requirements.

Involvement of the general public and stakeholders in the development and implementation of an AQMP is an important part of the whole process. Their input should be sought at various stages of the process, as deemed appropriate by the air management planning authority. An outline of the public participation and consultation process is provided in a separate section in this chapter.

Air Quality Management Approach

Historically, air pollution regulatory agencies have taken a single issue approach to improve regional air quality. Efforts have been made to address issues, such as smoke, particulate matter, carbon monoxide, ground-level ozone, sulphur dioxide and acidic deposition separately by developing and implementing control measures to reduce emissions of a particular pollutant or pollutants causing the issue, as illustrated by the following examples.

In the United States, with the passage of the first federal Clean Air Act, 1970 and subsequent 1990 Clean Air Act Amendments by the Environmental Protection Agency (EPA), the single-issue approach has been utilized to improve air quality in non-attainment areas. A non-attainment area is defined as a region where the levels of an air pollutant persistently exceed federal ambient air quality standards. The state within which the designated non-attainment area is located is required to develop a State Implementation Plan (SIP) explaining how the state will implement control measures to reduce emissions of the particular pollutant, or its precursors, to bring the area back into attainment [9]. The EPA has been designating various non-attainment areas for ozone, carbon monoxide, sulphur dioxide, and, lately, fine particulate matter, and requiring the responsible states to develop and implement SIPs.

In the early 1980s sulphur dioxide (SO_2) was regarded as the major contributor to acidic precipitation. In 1985 Environment Canada, in cooperation with eastern provinces, initiated its efforts to reduce SO_2 emissions through the Eastern Canada Acid Rain Program [10]. A similar approach was taken in Canada in the mid-1980s with respect to reduction of ambient ozone (O_3) levels in three designated areas in Canada, as well as to protect "clean" areas from further deterioration. As nitrogen oxides (NO_X) and volatile organic compounds (VOCs) are the precursors of O_3, the Canadian Council of Ministers of the Environment (CCME) outlined a series of emission reduction measures for these two pollutants in the NO_X/VOC Management Plan — Phase 1, 1990 [11]. The Greater Vancouver Regional District, a regional authority in British Columbia, developed its 1994 Air Quality Management Plan with a primary focus on addressing the issue of ground-level ozone in the airshed [12].

In 1991, the Canada-US Air Quality Agreement was signed to address transboundary effects of SO_2 and NO_X emissions and reduce acidic precipitation in both countries [13]. Similar single-issue approaches have been taken in Europe to address local and regional air quality problems associated with acidic precipitation and ground-level ozone. Subsequently, international efforts were made, primarily through the United Nations Economic Commission for Europe (UNECE), to address various air quality issues. Several European countries, Canada, and the US participated in the UNECE Long-Range Transboundary Air Pollution Convention in 1979, and developed acid rain protocols on SO_2 emission (1985 and 1994), and ground-level ozone protocols on NO_X (1988) and on VOC (1991) [14].

Harmonized Air Quality Management

In the past decade, a new understanding has emerged about the complex physical and chemical processes in the atmosphere which give rise to regional and global air quality issues, and the interrelation among many of these issues. The major atmospheric processes include formation of secondary pollutants in the atmosphere from primary (directly emitted) air contaminants, dispersion and movement of air pollution within an airshed, and transboundary and long-range transport of air pollutants.

As shown in Table 9.1, the interrelationships or linkages among air quality issues mainly stem from the fact that several common air pollutants contribute, either directly or indirectly as a precursor, to more than one

Air quality issue	Air contaminant or greenhouse gas									
	CO	VOC	NO_x	SO_x	PM	NH_3	CO_2	CH_4	N_2O	ODS
Smog Ground-level ozone	*	+	+ or -							
Inhalable particulates		+	+	+	+	+				
Visibility degradation		+	+	+	+	+				
Acidic deposition			+	+	+	*				
Hazardous air pollutants		+				+				
Global climate change **				-	-	-	+	+	+	+ or -
Stratospheric ozone depletion										+

CO — carbon monoxide, VOC — volatile organic compounds, NOX — nitrogen oxides, SOX — sulphur oxides, PM — particulate matter, NH_3 — ammonia, CO_2 — carbon dioxide, CH_4 — methane, N_2O — nitrous oxide, ODS — ozone-depleting substances; + = significant contribution, - = negative contribution (i.e., lessens the severity of the impact), * = minor contribution, ** = frequently referred to as global warming

Table 9.1: Air pollutants and gases contributing to air quality issues.

It is evident from Table 9.1 that while most pollutants are significant contributors to one or more air quality issue, some reduce the levels of the key pollutant and lessen the impact of certain issues. The extent of the contribution of these pollutants on different issues varies widely too, as some have a major role in one issue but play a minor part in another issue. Some specific examples are as follows:

- Five common air pollutants (CO, VOC, NO_X, SO_X and PM) give rise to most local air quality issues.

- NO_X and VOCs are major precursors of ground-level ozone, and CO has a minor role. NO_X in concentrations higher than that needed for normal atmospheric reactions for ozone formation becomes an ozone scavenger, actually reducing the resulting concentration of ozone in the air.

- NO_X and SO_X are major contributors to acidic deposition, while CO_2 also produces some acidity in precipitation.

- SO_X, NO_X and VOCs contribute to fine particles and aerosol formation.

- SO_X is a precursor to fine PM and aerosol formation, impairing visibility and causing cooling effects which may counteract some of the potential impacts of global climate change.

- While ODS cause lowering of atmospheric temperature through stratospheric ozone depletion, some ODS are powerful green house gases which contribute to global warming.

Another interesting fact is that air contaminants and greenhouse gases which give rise to various air quality issues are emitted from several common source categories, as shown in Table 9.2. The magnitude of different pollutants emitted from various source categories varies considerably, and so the relative contributions of a particular source type to different air quality issues also differ. However, the potential exists to reduce impacts of several air quality issues through implementation of control measures to reduce emissions of multiple pollutants from one source category. It is also evident from Table 9.2 that the pollutants and gases which contribute to most air quality issues are emitted mainly from combustion-related sources.

Air quality issue	Source category for emissions of air contaminants and greenhouse gases						
	Industry and utilities	Transportation	Agricultural	Waste disposal	Residential/ institutional	Fugitive*/nat ural	Long-range Transport
Smog Ground- level ozone	✔	✔	✔	✔	✔	✔	✔
Inhalable particulates	✔	✔	✔	✔	✔	✔	✔
Visibility degradation	✔	✔	✔	✔	✔	✔	✔
Acidic deposition	✔	✔		✔	✔		✔
Hazardous air pollutants	✔	✔	✔	✔	✔		✔
Global climate change	✔	✔	✔	✔	✔	✔	✔
Stratospheric ozone depletion	✔	✔			✔		✔

* including road dust re-entrained by motor vehicles

Table 9.2: Emission sources of air pollutants and gases contributing to air quality issues

In view of the common origins and interrelationships of air contaminants and greenhouse gases giving rise to several air quality issues, there is a growing realization of the need for an integrated or harmonized air quality management approach to address a number of issues together. It is logical to pursue a harmonized multi-effect/multi-pollutant comprehensive strategy for effective management of local, regional and global air pollution problems. A coordinated evaluation of several air quality issues together can lead to the development of integrated management policies. Such an approach will ensure that a solution chosen for one air quality issue will not create negative consequences for another air quality issue.

A multi-issue approach to air quality management offers an opportunity to apply pollution control measures to a particular source to reduce emissions of several pollutants at the same time. Application of control measures for more than one pollutant from a particular source sector will be cost-effective in the long run , as it reduces the possibility of unplanned incremental requirements for future installation of control techniques on the same source. The major advantage of pursuing a multi-issue approach to air quality management is that proactive, anticipatory strategies can be adopted to prevent future deterioration of air quality. Through an integrated air quality management approach regulatory authorities will be able to reduce greenhouse gas emissions while addressing regional air quality issues.

The development of a comprehensive harmonized management strategy is likely to take more time initially. Various emission reduction measures for different pollutants must be assessed and the impacts of such measures on more than one air quality issue have to be evaluated before the optimum air quality benefits can be determined. However, there will be overall benefits from such a strategy in the long run. A multi-issue approach to air quality management would result in overall reduced environmental and social costs associated with air pollution. There will be time and resource savings by the regulatory agency and overall cost savings by industry and other emission sectors in the implementation of the harmonized emission reduction measures.

In recognition of the potential benefits of integrated air quality assessment and management, several current national and international initiatives have adopted this approach. International agreements are being negotiated to deal with transboundary issues. National regulations and guidance documents are also being issued to require local authorities to prepare regional air quality management plans. Some examples are provided below.

In Canada, "Towards National Acid Rain Strategy" for post-2000 was issued in October 1997. It included measures to control both precursors of acid rain, SO_2 and NOX, and recognized their contribution to secondary particle formation and global climate change [15].

The "Phase 2 Federal Smog Management Plan" was issued by the Canadian government in November 1997. Smog is defined in this management plan to include both ground-level ozone and particulate matter [16].

In 1996, the province of Ontario issued a discussion paper, "Towards a Smog Plan for Ontario," for public consultation to address the local issues of ground-level ozone and fine particulates [17]. However, it identified the linkages of other regional and global air quality issues with smog, and the potential overall benefits of implementing the measures proposed in the plan.

An international Protocol to Abate Acidification, Eutrophication and Ground-level Ozone was signed in December 1999 by several European countries, Canada, and the US to address multiple air quality issues arising from transboundary pollution [18]. Also, the 1991 Canada-US Air Quality Agreement was amended through an Ozone Annex in December 2000 to improve air quality by reducing cross-boundary air pollution flows from one country to another [19].

Since the issuance in 1997 of revised ambient air quality standards for ozone and particulate matter, the US EPA has been developing an implementation plan and guidance documents for state and local governments to develop state implementation plans for designated areas where the new standards are not being attained [20].

The European Council (EC), under Council Directive 96/62/EC on Air Quality Assessment and Management, requires member states to assess air quality throughout their countries. In the regions where the limit values for air pollutants, as defined in "Daughter Directives," are exceeded, the member states are required to develop programs for compliance with limit values within a specified period [21]. In 1998, the EC issued a guidance document to assist member states in assessment of regional air quality.

In the United Kingdom, as a part of air quality strategy, air quality objectives for several air pollutants were issued in January 2000, and the local authorities were required to designate Air Quality Management Areas (AQMA) [22]. For the purpose of designating an AQMA, the local authorities are provided with a Framework for Review and Assessment of Air Quality by the Department of the Environment, Transport and the Regions (DETR). Under the Environment Act of 1995, the DETR and the National Assembly for Wales have issued a number of Local Air Quality Management guidance documents to assist local authorities in developing action plans and strategies [23].

In Australia, the government has recently issued *Clear the Air*, outlining the Air Pollution in Major Cities Programme focusing on six air pollutants to which the majority of the population is exposed [24]. At a state level, in

1998 the New South Wales government issued its Action for Air, a 25-year air quality management plan which outlines an integrated approach to address several air quality issues affecting a number of areas [25].

In 1996, the United Nations Environment Programme and the World Health Organization published *Air Quality Management and Assessment Capabilities in 20 Major Cities* to assist countries in developing appropriate air quality management strategies to reduce air pollution levels in urban areas [26].

REGIONAL AIR QUALITY MANAGEMENT PLANNING PROCESS

While the principles of air quality management planning can and are being used in the development of clean air programs at the provincial/state, national, and international levels of government, the discussion here will focus on the development of air quality management plans for local or regional jurisdictions or airsheds.

The term *airshed* or *air basin* is generally used to describe an area where geographic or meteorological conditions hinder the transport of air pollutants away from the community or region. The most obvious example of an airshed is a mountain valley where air pollutants are frequently trapped by surrounding mountain slopes and an atmospheric inversion aloft. Mexico City is one example of this type of airshed. A variation on the airshed bounded on all sides by mountains is a coastal area, such as the city of Vancouver and the Lower Fraser Valley in British Columbia, or Los Angeles, California, where mountains form the landward borders of the airshed and the complex meteorology at the seacoast also frequently acts as a barrier to the effective dispersion of urban air pollutants. Other very large cities may not have significant geographic barriers to inhibit the free flow of polluted air away from the urban area, but the large size of the city may itself hinder the effective transport of air pollutants out of the populated urban area. Toronto, Ontario, and Houston, Texas, are examples of this situation.

As mentioned in the previous sections, several national and international agencies have developed guidance documents for local and regional authorities to develop and implement regional air quality management plans. Although each local or regional authority needs to design its process to conform to specific local needs and requirements, the essential steps involved in the development and implementation of an air quality management plan typically include the following components:

- Determination of jurisdictional roles

- Establishment of AQMP policies, goals, and objectives

- Identification of air quality issues

- Selection of air pollution control strategy options

- Development of emission reduction measures

- Implementation of the AQMP

- Tracking of implementation and updating of the AQMP

Community input to the entire AQMP development and implementation process is very important. The public and other stakeholders should be consulted frequently throughout the AQMP process. This aspect is discussed in more detail in a later section.

Jurisdictional Roles and Institutional Barriers

Historically, local authorities were set up for the primary purpose of administering social and community matters within their designated political boundaries. With increasing concern over environmental matters, local governments are being empowered to deal with air, water, waste water and solid waste matters too. However, air pollution by nature does not remain confined within political jurisdictions. Accordingly, regional management of air pollution is best done on an airshed or air basin basis in a geographical area that experiences similar air quality issues caused by local and regional sources of air pollution. Hence, depending on the location, an airshed could encompass land areas governed by several local authorities.

From administrative perspectives, the responsibilities for managing or regulating the various air pollution sources within a large city or an airshed rest with different levels of government. A typical distribution of regulatory responsibilities and services related to air quality management is as follows:

- **Local and Regional Government**

  - Land use and public transportation

  - Commercial business licensing

  - Regional air quality management*

  - Regional air quality monitoring*

  - In-use motor vehicle emission inspection and maintenance programs*

- **State or Provincial Government**

  - Public health*

  - State/provincial air quality standards*

  - Regional air quality management

  - Industrial emission standards and regulation*

  - Motor vehicle licensing

  - Emission standards for new motor vehicles*

  - In-use motor vehicle emission inspection and maintenance programs

- **Federal Government**

  - Public health

  - National ambient air quality objectives and standards

  - National emission standards for major industries

  - National emission standards for new motor vehicles

  - International transboundary transport of air pollution

  - National commitments and programs for GHG emission management

- **International Agencies**

  - Emission standards for aircraft and ships in international service

---

* Shared responsibility with, or delegated from, a more senior level of government.

Within various levels of government, different agencies or departments may be responsible for functions such as air quality management, land use planning, and transportation system planning and operations, all of which have direct and indirect impacts on local air quality. These agencies or departments may operate from fundamentally different perspectives, depending on their mandate, priorities, and staff expertise.

Because of involvement of multiple organizations, a cooperative partnership approach to regional air quality management is essential. Only through a joint effort can the authorities effectively address common regional air quality issues. A partnership approach also provides opportunities for the authorities to consolidate their resources in AQMP development and implementation.

In view of the above, establishment of a multi-agency committee to oversee the development of an AQMP is considered essential. This committee can ensure that the needs and concerns of the parties involved are properly identified and resolved. It is also prudent to identify lead agencies to coordinate and manage distinct tasks. If a lead agency lacks authority to act on certain matters related to the task, institutional barriers should be removed to empower the agency to fulfill its responsibility. The multi-agency partnership approach will also be helpful in building stakeholder support during the AQMP development process, as well as at the time of its implementation.

AQMP Goals, Policies, and Objectives

Recognizing that a regional airshed is a limited natural resource shared by all, the decisions on setting goals and policies to manage air quality should reflect local environmental, economic, and social values. Because of the complexities of the air pollution problem, management of regional air quality is relatively more difficult than that of water or land contamination.

The overall goals and basic principles of environmental management are usually spelled out in local legislation, and regulatory authorities are required to abide by these goals and principles. In addition, a local authority has to comply with several national and international policy initiatives on air pollution while developing a regional AQMP, so the goals and policies of one regional AQMP may vary from those of another. However, all AQMPs appear to have several common goals and policies, such as: (1) protection of human health and environment through attainment of ambient air quality standards, (2) cleaning up of "dirty areas" and maintaining "clean areas clean", (3) reduction or prevention of air pollution through application of best available control technology (in some cases, irrespective of costs or economic achievability), (4) development of regional strategies for sustainable development, (5) taking local actions to address the global climate change issue, and (6) promotion of public awareness and community involvement in management of air quality issues.

The objectives of an AQMP should be to put in practice the goals and policies set out by regional decision makers with the support of the community. The formulation of objectives is an important step towards development of an overall emission control strategy. Typically, an AQMP should be:

- Effective — in achieving the desired air quality goals

- Efficient — in both technical and economic terms

- Fair and just — allocation of emission reduction responsibilities to all sources

- Flexible — allowing for uncertainties in the AQMP and for mid-course revisions

- Transparent — easily understandable by all

- Supportable — supported by the public and stakeholders

- Implementable — timely and efficient implementation of AQMP recommendations

Four-Phase Process of Air Quality Management

The management of regional air quality is a four-phase cyclical process, as illustrated in Figure 9.1. During the first phase of the cycle, the regional air quality problem is defined by identifying the type and extent of the existing air quality issues in the region. The ranking of the current air quality issues should take into account both the degree of compliance with established health and environmental objectives and standards, and any preferences of the majority of residents in the community to maintain higher regional health and environmental standards for air quality than those which may have been established by national and provincial governments. Upon determination of the air pollution problem, the second phase of the cycle begins with the assessment and development of means to address the identified problem. In the third phase, implementation of emission control strategies and measures prescribed in the AQMP is carried out. At the next phase, the implementation of the AQMP measures is evaluated to determine their effectiveness. Even if the AQMP implementation is successful in mitigating the initial air pollution problem, the cycle should be repeated to ensure that the air quality situation remains under control and no additional air pollution issues arise.

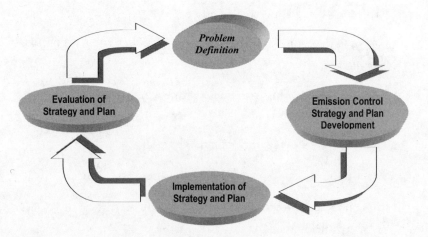

Figure 9.1: Steps in the management of regional air quality, starting with the definition of problems.

Identification of Issues and Problem Definition

The three essential prerequisites for identification of regional air quality issues and development of an AQMP are: (1) an air quality monitoring system to indicate the level of compliance of regional air quality with applicable air quality objectives and standards, (2) a current estimate and future forecast of emissions rates of all air contaminants which contribute to present and future air pollution problems, and (3) results of regional air quality modeling studies to provide guidance on current and future air pollution mechanisms and emission reduction proposals.

The key roles and capabilities of these three tools are illustrated in Figure 9.2. The prevalent air quality issues within an airshed are identified by assessment of existing air quality monitoring results and the emissions of air pollutants from all sources in the region. The potential future air quality is determined by application of an air quality model and emission forecast data. These tools are also necessary to assess the effectiveness of the AQMP strategies and measures, to determine the need for modifications to the AQMP, and to redefine air quality problems and priorities on an ongoing basis.

Air Quality Monitoring

Measurement of air pollutant concentrations at various key monitoring locations in the region provides information on the state of ambient air quality in the airshed. An assessment of the monitoring data will show if the applicable ambient air quality standards are being met. Depending on the number of monitoring locations, the air contaminants measured, and the length of the monitoring record, the results also provide information on the trends in the levels of the monitored pollutants. Air quality monitoring data assessment also identifies the deficiencies in the existing monitoring program and the areas for improvement.

Obviously, the more extensive the air quality monitoring system, the better the overall picture of the region's air quality that can be produced through data assessment. However, the resource requirements of operating a monitoring network are proportional to its size. Emission inventory data and air quality models can be used to interpolate air quality levels between ambient air monitoring locations.

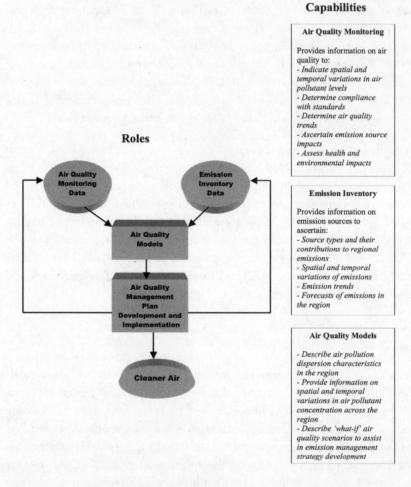

Figure 9.2: Roles and capabilities of air quality monitoring system, emission inventories, and air quality modelling.

Emission Inventory

An emission inventory is one of the cornerstones of a regional air quality management plan. It is an accounting of all air pollution sources within a geographical area, and it serves as a repository of information on:

- Type and number of emission sources

- Source location

- Source activity rate

- Air pollution control technology used at each source

- Quantity of pollutants emitted from each source

Typically, an emission inventory accounts for all anthropogenic and natural sources of air pollution. A complete emission inventory includes point (or stationary) sources, area sources, and mobile sources. In general, large industrial sources (e.g., petroleum refineries and thermal power generating plants) fall into the point source category. Area sources generally include smaller emission sources which are distributed throughout the region (e.g., gasoline service stations, printing shops, commercial and residential sources, and natural emissions from trees and other biogenic media). Individually, area sources are small emitters of pollutants, but collectively emissions from some area sources can be significant. Mobile sources are classified into two categories: on-road motor vehicles (e.g., cars, buses, trucks, motorcycles) and off-road sources (e.g., railways, aircraft, ships and boats, construction equipment).

Historically, emission inventories have included five common air pollutants: carbon monoxide (CO), sulphur oxides (SO_X), nitrogen oxides (NO_X), volatile organic compounds (VOCs), and particulate matter (PM). Lately, however, because of growing concern about specific local and global air quality issues, many agencies are also preparing emission estimates for 10 and 2.5 micron particle size components of total particulate matter (PM_{10} and $PM_{2.5}$, respectively), for different species of volatile organic compounds, for hazardous air pollutants and for greenhouse gases (CO_2, CH_4, N_2O), and ammonia.

Emissions from different sources are estimated by a number of source-specific methods. In recent years, because of the regional, transboundary and global nature of several air quality issues, emission inventory data compiled by one agency are shared and used by other agencies in order to address common air quality problems. Sharing of information requires that inventory data compiled by different agencies be compatible. In view of this, standard protocols and methodologies are being developed through international efforts.

An emission inventory system can be designed for any desired spatial and temporal resolution. Emissions can be estimated and reported for all sources within (1) an entire country, state, or province; (2) an air basin or airshed; (3) an urban administrative region; (4) each municipality within an urban area; or (5) small gridded areas covering a region, for example grids of 1 km by 1 km, or 5 km by 5 km. Usually, for a national or international inventory of emission sources covering a large geographical area, emission estimates are compiled using a "top-down" approach, i.e., based on average conditions of sources on a sectoral basis. This approach does not provide the detailed information on emissions from specific sources and the geographical resolution frequently required to address local or regional air quality issues. For these purposes, a "bottom-up" approach is pursued to obtain a better level of detail and more accurate emissions data for sources within a smaller geographical area.

Temporal resolution of emission inventory data is the characterization of emission rates over various periods of time. The general practice is to compile information on an annual basis for a calendar year. However, the inventory system can be designed to provide emission estimates for shorter periods, for example, on a seasonal, monthly, daily, or even hourly basis. For regional air quality modelling purposes, better temporally resolved emissions data are usually necessary.

For the purpose of AQMP development, an emission inventory for a particular calendar year is used as the "baseline" or "reference" year for emissions against which past and future emission changes can be compared. The emission inventory data for later years are compared with that for the baseline year to track progress in implementation of the AQMP.

Air Quality Modelling

Broadly speaking, an air quality model is a mathematical technique that provides an estimation of the ambient air quality characteristics of an air pollutant or pollutants at a desired location within a region. Several types of air quality models, simple and complex, are available for various pollutants and air quality issues. However, as most regional airsheds have unique meteorological conditions, physical features, and emission sources, region-specific air quality models are often developed using local data. Mathematical models are developed to simulate ambient concentrations of air pollutants monitored at different locations within the region. The credibility of a model is evaluated by comparing its results with actual air quality monitoring data. Development of a reliable regional airshed model is a time-consuming exercise, and requires considerable resources. However, once a model is developed, its further application becomes relatively inexpensive.

Forecasts of Regional Growth, Emissions, and Air Quality

A regional air quality management plan is usually developed for a designated period in the future. A typical planning period is 10 or 20 years from a current baseline or reference year. In order to determine what the future air quality situation will be in the region during the lifetime of the plan, it is essential to have information on projections of several major factors which influence future regional air quality: projected growth in population, motor vehicle use, industrial and economic activity, and associated air pollutant emissions. Based on this information, forecasts of emissions from the baseline emission inventory results can be made for different growth and emission reduction scenarios. Emission forecast data are used as input to regional air quality models in order to predict air quality outcomes under various what-if air quality management scenarios.

Air Quality Issues and Priorities for Action

Implementing an air quality management plan to provide cleaner air in a rapidly growing urban area is a very complex and costly venture. It is therefore important to ensure that resources are focused on the highest- priority air quality issues and the most cost-effective air emission reduction measures. Also, it may be beyond the capability or resources of air quality management agencies to simultaneously address all air quality issues within the period scheduled for the AQMP development and implementation. The general practice is to prioritize air quality issues and address them in a phased manner.

Assessment of air quality monitoring data and emission inventory results will identify the current air quality issues facing an airshed. Forecasts of emissions and air quality will indicate potential future issues. On the basis of current scientific information, each issue is assessed as to its potential impacts on human health and welfare, vegetation, materials, aesthetic matters, and global climate change. A common set of criteria allows determination of the relative severity of impacts of air quality issues currently facing the airshed, or anticipated in the future. Air quality issues are then ranked for prioritized treatment in the development of the regional air quality management plan.

Emission Control Strategy Options

The traditional air pollution control strategy, particularly in the case of industrial discharges to the air, has been the "command and control" approach. The regulator issues legislation or bylaws containing maximum allowable emission limits with prescribed penalties for non-compliance, and then monitors emission performance and prescribes fines or other penalties if it is determined that the emission criteria have been exceeded. While this approach seems fairly straightforward, experience has shown that it is difficult to gather scientific evidence proving non-compliance, and expensive to proceed through legal processes to apply penalties that are significant enough to encourage improved performance in the future. During the past 10 to 15 years, because of increased understanding of the complexity of air pollution and its management, there has been a shift from traditional regulatory approaches towards new ways of achieving emission reductions. Several alternative control strategies are being applied to reduce regional air pollution in jurisdictions around the world, particularly in North America and Europe. Experience to date indicates that when conventional regulatory tools are combined with other innovative approaches, overall emission reductions and air quality goals can be achieved in a more cost-effective and efficient manner. Brief descriptions of some innovative emission control strategies are provided below.

Alternative Emission Control Strategies

In order to bolster the effectiveness of the traditional regulatory approaches, several supplementary emission control strategies have been implemented in the past few years. The major criteria for assessment and adoption of an alternative strategy, relative to the traditional approach, are: environmental effectiveness, administrative and operational simplicity, stakeholder acceptability, and cost-effectiveness. Examples of alternative emission control strategies that have been applied to various sources are briefly described below.

Application of Economic Instruments

Economic instruments, or market-based economic incentives, for air pollution control include emission fees, emission reduction credits, tradable and transferable emission quotas, economic subsidies, and tax incentives. Application of economic instruments started in the 1970s and has been evolving continuously since then. For example, tradable permit systems for control of one or more pollutants are now in place in the US, Canada, and Europe [27]. To date this system is used primarily to reduce acid deposition (SO_2), ground-level ozone (NO_X, VOC), and ozone-depleting substances.

Because of the increasing concern over emissions of greenhouse gases and their impacts on the global climate, carbon taxes have been introduced in several European countries. Since the signing of the Kyoto Protocol on reduction of greenhouse gases, several countries have been considering tradable emission permits for both national and international applications in order to meet the respective emission reduction targets [28].

However, application of the appropriate instrument has to be determined for each specific situation and for the each source category and pollutant. When used together with conventional regulatory methods, economic instruments offer the promise of cost-effective action with incentive and flexibility to attain the overall emission reduction goal in a timely manner.

Source Operation Flexibility

Under the traditional approach, an emission source with several emission points within a facility is required to comply with permitted emission limits from each point individually. An alternative approach of limiting total emissions from the entire facility can be considered under certain instances. A facility-wide emission limit approach, also known as an emission bubble or cap, places a conceptual dome over the facility and treats it as one point source with maximum emission limits from the entire facility. The facility operator is authorized to use the most cost-effective mix of control techniques to comply with permitted emission requirements. This approach provides the facility operator with some flexibility to comply with regulatory requirements, and allows the operator to decide which emission points need to be controlled and how to accomplish this in the most cost-effective way.

Spatial and temporal emission reduction programs for specific sources also offer another potentially viable and cost-effective method of improving overall air quality within an airshed. For example, ground-level ozone is a summertime air quality problem. In most areas prone to such ozone smog episodes, the ozone concentration usually reaches unacceptable levels only on very hot days in the early to late afternoon. Some control measures, such as requirements for reduced gasoline vapour pressure to minimize evaporative emissions, have been targeted for implementation only in the summer season. Other measures, such as restricting the use of motor vehicles on very smoggy days, are introduced only over periods of several days during an air quality episode. The appropriateness of seasonal or episodal emission control measures should be considered only where such practice does not worsen air quality at other locations in the airshed or during other seasons of the year.

Pollution Prevention and Clean Technology

Pollution prevention methods are primarily preventative environmental management tools. As opposed to the traditional and reactive "end-of-pipe" control techniques, these approaches are geared towards controlling generation and emission of air pollutants proactively during production. There is an inherent danger of a misunderstanding of the word *prevention* within an environmental context, as in most cases these measures do not necessarily prevent pollution per se. Rather these actions minimize the generation and discharge of pollutants through a combination of selection of raw materials and production techniques, reuse of waste materials, and good housekeeping practices.

New production technologies, often referred to as "clean production," have also been developed to replace old processing and manufacturing practices. The primary objectives of these techniques are to produce goods in a cost-effective manner with minimum discharge of pollutants and less consumption of energy and raw materials. In recent years, several air pollution control agencies have also initiated technology or equipment certification programs. Under such programs, once a piece of equipment or a technology is developed to produce minimum emissions, the regulatory agency certifies it for use within the jurisdiction.

Precautionary Principle

The prevalent strategy for emission control has been mostly reactive, as it allows some emission of air pollutants from sources, irrespective of any long-term impacts of the residuals on health and the environment. There are instances where emission of pollutants has been allowed to continue even after some evidence of environmental damage has been identified, because there were uncertainties about the direct proof of a cause-and-effect linkage between particular pollutants and observed damages.

The concept of the precautionary principle is used to formulate policy based on a preventative approach in developing a long-term strategy for addressing local air quality and global climate change issues. This approach is based on the "better-safe-than-sorry" principle, and it proactively prevents emission of pollutants at the source when there is reason to believe that harmful effects or environmental damage is likely to be caused by the pollutants. Application of the precautionary principle in air quality management may be necessary under some circumstances to protect human health and the environment from potential adverse impacts of certain harmful substances.

Development of Emission Reduction Measures

After prioritizing regional air quality issues and deciding on the emission control strategies to be pursued, the next step in the planning process is to develop emission reduction measures for those air pollutants which are causing the most serious air quality problems. As illustrated in Figure 9.3, the development of emission reduction measures (ERMs) is an iterative process. The regional emission inventory is reviewed to identify those sources emitting air pollutants which must be reduced. A preliminary list of potential candidate sources for emission control is prepared on the basis of the type of air pollutant emitted, the emission rate, and the potential to apply further emission controls. The candidate sources are then subjected to detailed technical and economic assessment of emission reduction potential and costs, and the most promising measures are added to the AQMP priority list for emission control action.

Both stationary and mobile sources should be considered in this evaluation of candidate emission reduction measures. While the authority to regulate emissions from various sources may be shared among a number of levels of government, the air quality management plan should focus on developing the most effective proposal to attain the required emission reductions. Once the optimum plan is in place, the regional air quality planning agency can solicit the support of all levels of government to contribute their share of regulatory action to provide a successful AQMP implementation.

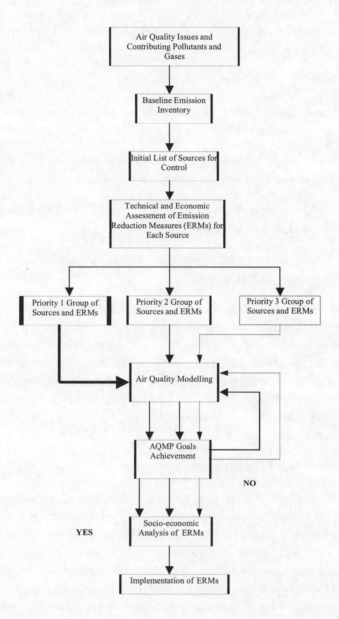

Figure 9.3: An iterative process of development of emission reduction measures.

Selection of Sources and Control Technology

Several important factors govern the selection of candidate emission sources and control technology:

- Should all source sectors be considered?

- Should all categories of stationary sources, irrespective of size and age, be considered?

- Should motor vehicle emission reductions include both tailpipe controls and measures to reduce motor vehicle use?

- Should emissions from all selected sources be reduced at the same time or at different times?

- Is there a need for any "contingency" ERMs for rapid implementation to meet the AQMP goals?

The availability of emission control technology is another most important factor in ERM selection. Generally, control technologies can be grouped in three categories: (1) well-proven and readily available commercial technologies, (2) technologies currently under demonstration, and (3) those still in the research and development stage. Based on the status of the control technology development, an ERM for a particular type of source could be considered for application over a short-, medium-, or long-term period.

Assessment and Prioritization of Sources

As shown in Figure 9.3, the next step in the ERM development process is technical and economic assessment of emission reduction measures for each emission source in the preliminary list. A set of common criteria is used to assess the relative technical merits of different control technology options for each emission source. Application of common criteria provides a fair and unbiased basis for selection of ERMs. Typically, the technical assessment of an ERM is made on the basis of the following criteria:

- Pollutants to be controlled

- Availability and applicability of control technology to the particular source

- Pollutant removal efficiency of control technique

- Cost-effectiveness of ERM

- Degree of impacts on health, environment and global climate change

- Potential impacts on other media, such as water and land

- Potential impacts on the effectiveness of other ERMs

The term *cost-effectiveness* usually means the economic efficiency of a particular emission control measure. It is defined as the total costs of an ERM incurred to reduce a unit quantity of emission of a pollutant, e.g., dollars per tonne of emission reduced. The total costs of an ERM include its initial capital cost and annual operating cost.

In addition to the above technical and economic criteria, the availability of regulatory tools for implementation of an ERM is another important factor that should be considered during its selection. If no regulation exists for implementation of a particular ERM, then enactment of appropriate regulation would be necessary.

Once the ERMs for the initial list of sources are determined, they should be prioritized into groups for scheduled implementation. The ERMs are usually prioritized on the basis of their ability to reduce the planned quantities of emissions, availability of technology, cost-effectiveness, ease of implementation, and equitable and fair distribution of selected ERMs among the regional sources. In some cases, a socioeconomic impact analysis of proposed emission reduction measures and/or a cost-benefit analysis of the draft AQMP is carried out to ensure that it meets all of the criteria for fairness and effectiveness.

Emission Reduction Measures

No discussion of the emission reduction measures for stationary sources of air pollution is provided here, as there are a wide variety of such sources, from large industrial facilities to residential fuel-burning appliances, each with a number of available emission control technology options. Consumer products (paints, solvents, adhesives, etc.) and off-road mobile sources (railways, aircraft, ships, and boats) usually come under provincial or national jurisdiction. Therefore, local authorities need to work jointly with senior government agencies to develop emission reduction measures for these sources.

Emission Reduction Measures for Motor Vehicles

Motor vehicles are the major contributor to urban air pollution, as well as one of the largest sources of greenhouse gases.

Control of vehicular emissions poses one of the most challenging tasks facing urban regions around the world. Although new vehicles manufactured today emit significantly less pollutants compared with older-model vehicles, reduced emissions from individual vehicles are being overshadowed by continuing growth in the number of vehicles and the total distance travelled by each vehicle. All levels of government have important roles in developing and implementing measures to reduce vehicular emissions.

Every major urban area has a unique set of transportation-related air quality problems. Therefore, an appropriate mix of control measures has to be evaluated for each urban area. The measures identified below are not a panacea for addressing air pollution from every urban motor vehicle fleet, nor are they exclusive of other strategies that are not discussed here.

It is commonly recognized that urban air quality, land use, and transportation are inter-linked. Emissions from motor vehicles can be reduced effectively only by considering a package of land use planning and transportation control measures, together with cleaner vehicles and fuels initiatives. Traffic congestion in many growing urban areas is worsening, exacerbating the problem of air pollution caused by motor vehicles. A variety of measures can be implemented to cope with traffic congestion, besides improving the existing transportation infrastructure, including provision of one-way streets, exclusive lanes for high-occupant vehicles (HOV) such as buses, carpools, or vanpools (i.e., HOV lanes), separate truck routes, bypass or ring roads to divert through traffic away from core business areas, bicycle lanes, and pedestrian pathways.

Transportation Demand Management

Transportation control measures can be broadly classified into three subcategories, namely, shifting to energy-efficient transport modes, transport infrastructure improvement, and transportation demand management. A shift towards energy efficient travel modes entails moving people in and out of an urban area with the minimum possible fuel consumption, and thus air pollution. Examples include provision of adequate and affordable public transit services, incentives for ridesharing in motor vehicles, and promotion of and incentives for using non-motorized transport modes, such as bicycling and walking.

In simple terms, transportation demand management consists of a range of relatively low-cost measures to make a transportation system more efficient by managing urban traffic within the constraints of the existing infrastructure. Besides improvements to traffic flow through measures mentioned above, there are other initiatives that can be categorized as "carrots" and "sticks." Examples of "carrots" include incentives to change the (1) amount of travel (e.g., by telecommuting), (2) time of travel (e.g., staggered work time, peak versus off-peak hours), and (3) mode of travel (e.g., carpool or vanpool, transit, bicycle, walk). Disincentives and penalties, such as parking charges, fuel and vehicle taxes, road tolls, fuel rationing and mandatory no-drive days, are examples of "sticks" that have been used in some cities to reduce single-occupant vehicle use and shift commuters and other urban travellers into more sustainable transportation choices.

Cleaner Vehicles

During the past three decades, governments in North America, Europe, and many other places have implemented stringent air emission regulations for new motor vehicles at the point of manufacture. This has resulted in significant advances in vehicle technology to make conventional fuel-burning vehicles (gasoline and diesel) less polluting and more energy-efficient. New low- and ultra-low emission vehicles have already been developed, and are being commercialized. It appears that the technology has nearly reached its limit of reducing emissions of air pollutants in any significant manner from conventionally fuelled vehicles. However, there remains the need to make them more fuel-efficient.

Manufacture of vehicles based on alternative technology, such as electric, hybrid, and fuel cell engines, has also begun and is gradually penetrating the market. This new generation of vehicles generates little or no pollution, but their cost is currently high. Further government requirements or incentives may be needed to increase the rate that the public adopts these vehicles for urban driving.

Vehicle Emission Inspection and Maintenance

Typically, older vehicles generate disproportionately more air pollutants than newer vehicles. A poorly maintained older vehicle can emit 100 times more air pollution than a properly cared for modern vehicle. Motor vehicles are manufactured to meet certain emission standards during their use over the vehicle warranty period. Proper maintenance of vehicles ensures that emission levels remain below those standards. Therefore, implementation of an appropriate vehicle emission inspection and maintenance program is an effective measure to ensure that vehicle emission control systems are maintained in good working order and do not emit an excessive amount of pollutants.

Old Vehicle Scrapping

In order to reduce the number of high-polluting old vehicles in the urban fleet, a vehicle scrapping program could be introduced. Under such a program, the owners of old vehicles can be given an incentive, either as money towards purchase of a new vehicle or as a public transit pass, in exchange for giving up the high-polluting vehicle for scrapping by the agency responsible.

Cleaner Fuels

Clean fuels are necessary to operate the new low-emission vehicles properly. In recent years, there has been considerable improvement in petroleum-refining techniques to produce much cleaner motor vehicle fuels. Lead, which is a significant health threat and a poison to the catalysts used in emission control systems, has been removed from gasoline. Reformulated gasoline with reduced sulphur and toxic constituents is commercially available, as well as low-sulphur diesel fuel.

Alternative transportation fuels such as natural gas, propane, ethanol, methanol, and bio-diesel are also available, and their use is increasing in many countries. While natural gas and propane have been used as a replacement fuel for some time now, the use of ethanol and methanol blended gasoline fuels is also increasing. These fuels produce less pollutants than conventional fuels. Appropriate techniques for conversion of older vehicles to run on alternative fuels are available, and new vehicles specifically designed to run on these fuels are being manufactured.

Public Awareness Program

The success of motor vehicle emission reduction measures depends largely on public acceptance and support for them. Many of these measures are aimed at changing the behaviour and/or lifestyles of citizens in the region. A public outreach program is a vital component of a successful implementation of various emission reduction measures related to urban transportation, especially those for transportation demand management. Local authorities must therefore provide a public awareness and education program about air pollution from motor vehicles, its effects on health and the environment, how the proposed measures will reduce pollution, and how individual and collective actions can lead to clean air for everyone.

Techniques that have been used successfully to raise awareness of the public include: written materials (question-and-answer fact sheets, brochures, and newsletters); media reports and interviews (radio, television, and newspaper); public forum; and community focus groups. Local authorities should decide which of these techniques will be effective, after taking into consideration the social and cultural aspects of the urban area. The public information program should be kept up-to-date through periodic review and revision, if necessary.

Smart Growth Land Use Planning

Land use planning is the process in which local governments plan for future growth in communities and determine what sort of development should occur within local boundaries. There are a wide range of issues that come to bear on the policies and practices of land use in large metropolitan areas. Three that are very dominant are transportation priorities, economic priorities, and cultural priorities. From the perspective of the city resident, these translate into "How can I commute to my job and travel about the city to access services, visit friends and relatives, and participate in religious, cultural, and recreational activities?"

Before the rise to dominance of the private motor vehicle as the key means of urban transportation in the middle of the 20th century, the traditional city was of a relatively compact form with a heavy dependence on walking and public transit. Development along main roads was generally mixed-use offices, shops and homes. Residents had access within a half-hour travel time to facilities and services which met most of their needs. The expansion of cities was achieved relatively slowly through the introduction of new public transit services.

The automobile-dependent city took shape after the Second World War when governments made road building a priority and the general public opted for a single-family home in the suburbs rather than an apartment or townhouse in the city. Within a half-hour, residents could drive 50 kilometres from the city centre, and this distance became the norm for many commuters. Today this trend has led to urban sprawl with traffic congestion, air pollution, and trip times that, for many commuters, are well in excess of half an hour.

Land use planners are now looking at different models for land use that are more sustainable over time. *Smart growth* is a term used in this recent form of urban land use planning. Smart growth land use planning focuses on the management of urban growth that will enhance quality of life and improve the efficient use of available resources.

Linking Land Use, Transportation, and Air Quality

In a typical North American city, motor vehicles are responsible for approximately one-half to two-thirds of the pollutants which cause the formation of ozone smog, and from one-third to one-half of the carbon dioxide emissions which lead to global climate change. Motor vehicle emission standards have been strengthened so that the automobile manufactured today produces 10 % or less of the smog-forming pollutants of automobiles of 15 to 20 years ago. However, total transportation emissions are unlikely to fall much further because of the continuing growth in the total number of motor vehicles in each urban area, and the fact that, on average, each vehicle is being driven more kilometres in cities, where rapid growth is accommodated by urban sprawl. Also, the trend to larger, less fuel-efficient sport utility vehicles results in increased carbon dioxide emissions.

Application of cleaner vehicle emission standards in 2004 will make motor vehicles even more pollution-free, but it is unlikely that auto-dependent urban areas with growing populations and increasing vehicle kilometres-travelled will experience cleaner air. Air quality improvements in these rapidly growing urban areas will depend on the introduction of sustainable urban land use planning approaches that reduce motor vehicle use by building more complete communities which enable residents to live, work, shop and enjoy recreation using transportation methods other than the single-occupant vehicle.

The air emission data presented in Table 9.3 show that wealthy Asian cities, such as Singapore, Hong Kong, and Tokyo, with high-density land use settlement patterns and efficient public transportation systems, have a per capita annual emission rate for smog-related pollutants of 30 kg per person compared with European cities at 101 kg per person and US cities at 252 kg per capita. Per capita emissions of carbon dioxide in wealthy Asian cities are also much lower than European, Australian, and North American cities. North American cities have much to learn from overseas cities about sustainable urban land use and transportation strategies to minimize air pollution.

	Annual per capita emissions (kg)	
	All smog-related air pollutants (NOx, SO₂, CO, VOC)	Carbon dioxide emissions from city transporation (private & public)
Developing Asian cities	89	837
Wealthy Asian cities	30	1,158
European cities	101	1.888
Australian cities	216	2.434
Toronto	233	2,789
US cities	252	4,536

Source: Newman, P., and Kenworthy, J., Sustainability and Cities, Island Press, Washington, DC, 1999.

Table 9.3: Per capita emissions of air pollutants and greenhouse gas in cities

Land Use Policies for Clean Air

A shift from land use planning for auto-dependent transportation solutions that usually lead to urban sprawl, traffic congestion, and unhealthy air pollution to smart growth land use planning begins by adopting land use and transportation policies to accommodate urban growth in a sustainable way. Such policies are built on four key criteria: economic efficiency, social equity, environmental responsibility, and human livability.

A policy for economic efficiency deals with the cost of urban development. Full cost accounting of all aspects of development options needs to be factored into the decision-making process. So, for example, it may be financially attractive to a large landowner to develop low-density single-family housing at a remote location on the fringe of the urban area. The city or private utility may not recognize the increased cost of providing streets, water, sewage, and electrical services to the subdivision. It is the homeowner and taxpayer who ultimately shoulder the cost of the original development and the ongoing costs of transportation to work, schools, shopping centres and recreational activities.

A policy for social equity is needed to ensure that personal income, family size, or cultural background does not disadvantage any group from securing a healthy place to live with good accessibility to employment, education, shopping and recreation, and other needed services.

There are many environmental issues related to urban land use that must be addressed to protect air quality and other aspects of the urban environment. The fundamental issue for regional air quality is to minimize the emission of air pollutants from transportation, and this usually means designing the city so that it is efficient to travel about on foot, bicycle, or public transit rather than in single-occupant vehicles. This approach will also be the most fuel-efficient option, thus minimizing emissions of carbon dioxide and other greenhouse gases that cause climate change.

Urban land use policies for livability are more difficult to define. Many people love their cars. However, the streets, highways, and parking areas needed to accommodate these beloved automobiles reduce the space available in the community for public areas such as parks, playgrounds, and general open space. When the motorists arrive home after a long commute from the office, they would prefer to have a home near such amenities so that they and their families can enjoy the community that they live in. Unfortunately, many suburban housing developments do not incorporate in the immediate area the key amenities that are needed to provide a livable neighbourhood.

Smart Growth Strategies

There are many smart growth strategies that can lead to an urban form that minimizes motor vehicle use and hence emissions from motor vehicles. In developing a land use planning strategy for a more sustainable urban form, it is important to recognize that some neighbourhood improvements may be immediately successful, whereas significant changes to urban form at the regional level may take 10 to 20 years to have a discernible effect on travel behaviour.

Some characteristics of urban form that have a positive influence on air quality include:

- **Higher-density development** — More compact neighbourhoods and regions facilitate transportation choices such as walking and cycling, and make public transit more economically feasible.

- **Mixed land use** — Incorporating housing together with employment, shopping, and recreational opportunities leads to shorter distances for commuting and other trips, and lessens the need for a second family car; with good public transportation services, it can eliminate the need to own a vehicle.

- **Transit accessibility** — Locating high-density commercial, shopping and residential centres around stations on major public transit routes can improve accessibility of services and increase transit ridership.

- **Pedestrian-friendly urban design** — Providing a pleasant street environment with attractive landscaping, benches, bicycle lanes, and other amenities will increase the desirability of walking and cycling.

Examples of Local Actions to Promote Smart Growth

There are many actions that support smart growth land use planning. Here are a few examples to provide a perspective on some of the things that a community or local government can do to reduce automobile dependence and air pollution.

- **Traffic calming** — The city of Hamburg has narrowed some four-lane roads to two lanes to create a safer and greener environment for pedestrians and cyclists.

- **Street safety** — The city of Portland, Oregon, has introduced traffic circles and speed bumps, resulting in a 50 % reduction in traffic accidents.

- **Bicycle priorities** — Copenhagen, Denmark has removed city centre parking and developed dedicated bicycle routes and facilities. The city provides 2,500 bicycles for free use in the inner city. One-third of the commuters arrive at city workplaces on bicycles.

- **Transit-oriented development** — The city of Toronto cancelled the proposed Spadina Expressway in the 1950s in favour of a subway line, and has emphasized transit-oriented development since that time.

- **More accessible and affordable transportation** — The state of Maryland's Smart Growth and Neighborhood Conservation Act will save remaining natural resources and focus development in existing communities and neighbourhoods where transportation and infrastructure is already in place.

- **Low-capital transit system** — Curitaba, Brazil, has developed a relatively low-cost bus system which includes dedicated busways as part of a citywide service that is closely integrated with land use policy.

- **Designated development area** — The city of Austin, Texas, is implementing a smart growth initiative which focuses growth in a high-density Desired Development Zone, and sets aside land in the Drinking Water Protection Zone that ensures the future water supply for the city and maintains habitat for endangered species.

- **Improved transit services** — The city of Ottawa operates a dedicated busway system to provide fast and efficient public transit.

- **High density town centres** — Regional town centres are being built in the Vancouver, Canada, urban area. They are served by light rail transit to provide high-density, mixed-use communities at strategic locations throughout the metropolitan area.

- **High density development and public transit** — Hong Kong and Singapore have developed very high density urban areas served by efficient public transit. Motor vehicle use is discouraged by taxes and fees, which impose high costs for automobile ownership and use.

SOCIOECONOMIC ANALYSIS OF AQMP

Improvement in urban air quality through implementation of an air quality management plan will incur costs as well as yield benefits to the region. The extent of the costs and who will bear them will depend on the sources targeted for emission reduction. Typically, as an AQMP recommends emission reduction measures for a variety of large, medium, and small sources involving all segments of the society, the costs of their implementation are borne, directly or indirectly, by all citizens in the region. An increase in direct costs of complying with emission reduction measures for industry, business, and the public is a general concern. This is mainly because of the lack of awareness among the parties about the "hidden costs" of uncontrolled air pollution and the potential economic benefits of clean air. Socioeconomic analysis forms an integral component of the development of an AQMP, as it evaluates the costs and benefits of the measures proposed and ensures their reasonableness and affordability.

Direct costs consist of expenditures for emission control equipment, motor vehicle emission reduction measures, and reformulation of products. The principal benefits of emission reductions will be to society due to improved air quality, which will result in reduced medical costs, increased agricultural yields, reduced damage to materials, and less traffic congestion. Improvements in the health and welfare of people and the environment as a whole, resulting in increased economic productivity in the region, are the indirect benefits to the community.

There are several methods available for socioeconomic analysis of emission control measures, but each method has its limitations. When applied to the same case, different methods can yield different results, and the estimates of costs and benefits may vary even by an order of magnitude. The primary reason for wide variations in estimates lies in the difficulty of assigning realistic monetary values to the costs and benefits of various measures. While direct costs and some benefits are measurable, several indirect benefits cannot be measured in economic terms. Many potentially adverse health effects of air pollution cannot be properly quantified, as there are both direct and indirect costs and benefits related to the state of human health. For example, loss of productivity and economic benefits because of absence from work can be due to ill health that is not necessarily caused by air pollution only. It is difficult to assign monetary values to reduced adverse health effects and risk of mortality because of improvement in air quality. It is also somewhat controversial, because assumptions are made about the monetary value of a human life. These issues are discussed in detail in Chapter 8. Another difficulty arises when estimating, in monetary terms, the intangible impacts of urban air pollution on the surrounding environment, such as visibility degradation and damage to ecosystems.

IMPLEMENTATION OF AQMP

Similar to the development of an AQMP, its implementation is an involved exercise. It is a multi-agency task, as no one organization has the jurisdictional authority or responsibility for putting in place all of the ERMs recommended. Therefore, a cooperative, coordinated approach, similar to that used during AQMP development, should be pursued during its implementation. Besides coordination of actions among the regulatory agencies, successful implementation of some ERMs will require working together with the private sector and the general public. Ways to involve stakeholders in the AQMP implementation process should therefore be established.

Implementation Priority

As an AQMP typically consists of a number of recommended ERMs, it is quite likely that these will have to be implemented in a phased manner over a period of time. It is appropriate to develop some criteria for prioritization of ERMs for implementation. The main objective for priority ranking of ERMs should be their effectiveness in achieving the emission reduction targets of the AQMP. As a general guide, the "low-hanging fruit," i.e., those measures that could be implemented relatively easily and with least cost, could be "picked" for priority implementation. However, choosing easy-to-implement ERMs first would leave some difficult, but often necessary, measures for implementation later. Moreover, implementation of all easy ERMs may not achieve the overall emission reduction goals as scheduled in the AQMP.

Tracking of AQMP Implementation

Achievement of urban air quality objectives can be a very long-term process. In measuring the progress toward implementation, periodic review of the development and enactment of legislation and regulations and implementation of the ERMs should be undertaken. Routine assessment of ambient air quality monitoring data and updated emission inventory results, as well as the use of air quality models, would be necessary to determine actual progress in meeting the AQMP goals of emission reduction and air quality improvement. Reports on the status of AQMP implementation should be prepared on a regular schedule for review by all stakeholders to determine the success or failure of the AQMP in meeting its goals.

From time to time, the air quality models should be used to assess the potential impacts of updated emission inventory forecasts on the future regional air quality situation. The results from such assessment could form the basis for any necessary mid-course revisions to the AQMP, and for a future AQMP update.

RESOURCE REQUIREMENTS FOR AQMP DEVELOPMENT AND IMPLEMENTATION

It is obvious that development and implementation of a regional air quality management plan is a long and complex process. It involves compilation, analysis, and assessment of a large volume of information by technical experts in several areas, such as air pollution engineers, air quality scientists, urban and transportation planners, economists, and outside consultants for special studies. Subsequently, it requires preparation of information materials for decision makers and stakeholder consultation, and holding of public meetings. All this entails significant resources in terms of staff involvement from various agencies and funding for external assistance and participation.

ENVIRONMENTAL STEWARDSHIP BY LOCAL AUTHORITY

Lately, the responsibility of local governments for management of environmental matters is shifting from the role of a regulator to that of a leader and partner. These agencies have the opportunity to set a good example by taking practical actions to reduce air pollution discharges from their own activities. Examples can be set by implementing "green" measures that replace the wasteful use of energy, raw materials, and products in public works and offices.

In order to reduce motor vehicle use, local authorities could launch a vehicle trip reduction program for their employees which promotes public transit use by offering incentives, and which discourages single-occupant vehicle use by facilitating rideshare in carpools and vanpools. Local authorities could introduce an improved maintenance program for their vehicle fleets, and should consider purchasing only less polluting alternative fuel vehicles when possible.

Local authorities can provide technical assistance and initiate joint demonstration projects with local businesses to facilitate modernization and cleanup of old polluting facilities. In particular, training could be given to employees of small and medium-sized facilities in reducing emissions from their activities. The operators of these facilities usually lack both the technical know-how and the financial resources to control emissions from their operations. These kinds of initiatives by local authorities would reduce emissions of pollutants responsible for local air quality issues. Such efforts would also put into practice the maxim "think globally and act locally" through concurrent reductions in greenhouse gas emissions.

PUBLIC CONSULTATION

Public consultation should be an integral part of the AQMP development and implementation process. In fact, effective public consultation should be a policy of the regulatory agency. The population as a whole has a stake in the quality of the air they breathe. It is each citizen's right and responsibility to be involved in the protection and enhancement of air quality for the benefit of present and future generations.

Public consultation is a two-way process. An informed public makes useful contributions to the development of a regional air quality management plan. Active public participation allows exploration of new and alternative, and sometimes innovative, ideas about AQMP issues. It may also enable early detection of potential problems with AQMP implementation.

Importance of Public Consultation

All levels of government have recognized the importance of public consultation in the development of environmental policies, pollution control strategies and management plans, and regulatory tools and measures. Different agencies have different ways of promoting and fostering citizen participation, and a few examples are provided below.

In Article 2 of the Comprehensive Air Quality Management Framework For Canada, November 1993, the federal and provincial ministers of energy and environment recognized that "wide consultation with stakeholders is important in the development of national and regional clean air goals, objectives, and policies, and in the implementation of strategies" [29]. Article 5.4 of the Framework also identified the need "to determine and implement a means of consulting with stakeholders outside of governments." Pursuant to the Framework, the "Towards a National Acid Rain Strategy" [15] and "Phase 2 Federal Smog Management Plan" [16] were developed in Canada through stakeholder consultation in 1997 and 2000.

The regional government of the Greater Vancouver Regional District, British Columbia, developed a stakeholder consultation process in 1991 as a part of its regulation development program [30]. In January 1992, the Lower Fraser Valley Air Quality Advisory Committee, a multi-stakeholder consultation group, was set up to assist the regional district with its AQMP development. Since then the Committee sponsors and partners have expanded to include the provincial and federal agencies with responsibility for air quality management in the Georgia Coast Cascade Air Basin. The committee is presently utilized by its sponsors and partners as a forum for consultation on different air quality issues of interest to the local citizens and stakeholders. On the other side of the country, the province of Ontario, issues discussion papers on its plans for management of air quality issues and invites comments from stakeholders [17].

In the US, under the Clean Air Act Amendments (CAAA) of 1990 the Environmental Protection Agency is required to publish proposed and final rules and invite public comment within a stipulated period. In accordance with the provisions of the US Federal Advisory Committee Act, a Clean Air Act Advisory Committee (CAAAC) is formed under the EPA Charter [31]. CAAAC is formed in the public interest and consists of representatives from various stakeholder groups of non-federal interests. It provides "advice, information and recommendations on policy and technical issues associated with implementation of the CAAA" and supports the EPA in the performance of its duties and responsibilities.

Various states and local authorities in the US have different mechanisms for public consultation. The Bay Area Air Quality Management District in California has an Advisory Council consisting of four committees, including an Air Quality Planning Committee [32]. The Advisory

Council has representatives from various segments of the population. The regional government agency of the South Coast Air Quality Management District (SCAQMD) in California has a Governing Board which adopts policies and regulations on air quality [33]. Prior to making any decisions that affect local residents and businesses, the AQMD is required to seek public comments and consider them through public workshops and a public hearing.

The Council of the North American Agreement on Environmental Cooperation, established by the partners in the North American Free Trade Agreement (Canada, Mexico, and the US, in 1994 created the Commission on Environmental Cooperation (CEC). Subsequently, the CEC established the Joint Public Advisory Committee, consisting of representatives from public and non-governmental groups, as the body to ensure public participation in the actions of the CEC. The committee is required to hold public consultations and reach out to the public who are interested in, and may be affected by, its work [34].

In the Air Quality Framework Directive, the European Commission provides directives to its member countries on stakeholder consultation during planning and implementation of environmental legislation [21]. The member countries also have their own regulations and procedures for public consultation during development and implementation of air quality legislative actions. For example, in the United Kingdom, the Department of the Environment, Transport and the Regions (DETR) solicits public input to national legislation through issuance of consultation papers [23]. DETR also provides guidance to local authorities for developing local air quality management strategies.

In Australia, the national government in agreement with the states enacted the National Environment Protection Council Act 1994, stipulating that all levels of government ensure public consultation before development of national "environment protection standards, guidelines, goals and associated protocols" and during environmental impact assessment processes [24]. Similar legislation has been passed by individual states. For example, New South Wales enacted the National Environment Protection Council (New South Wales) Act in 1995, and undertook extensive public consultation during development of "Action for Air," a 25-year Air Quality Management Plan for the state [25].

Under Section 31, Functions of Ministry, Environment Act 1986 of New Zealand, the Ministry for the Environment is required to ensure that "effective provision is made for public participation in environmental planning and policy formulation processes" in particular at the regional and local level [35]. The Canterbury Regional Council (CRC) is responsible for managing a diverse range of natural resources and associated environmental issues, including air quality. During the development of its regional plan to address air quality issues, CRC undertook a variety of public information strategies to seek public input. The strategies included a pre-planning survey of public awareness of air pollution issues, issuance of a discussion paper, media advertisements, mailouts to households, and presentations of the proposed plan to community groups [36].

One of the basic principles adopted at the United Nations Conference on Environment and Development held in Rio de Janeiro in 1992 was Agenda 21, which is a framework for a cooperative global action plan for environmental management and sustainable development. Chapter 28 of Agenda 21 recognizes the importance of public participation and cooperation in the development and implementation of "local Agenda 21" by local authorities. The chapter prescribes that, through consultation and consensus building with local citizens, community organizations and private enterprises, local authorities should acquire information necessary for formulation of environmental policies, regulations, and programs to achieve their Agenda 21 objectives [8].

Principles and Key Steps of Public Consultation Process

The most important principle behind public consultation is to maximize public involvement. Other important principles and features which need to be considered are as follows.

Fair and Equitable

In order to be fair and equitable, a consultation process should seek ways to reach diverse constituents in society, including non-traditional groups who are sometimes overlooked. Every effort should be made to communicate with as wide a public as possible. Different needs of various groups and cultures should be recognized and supported.

Efficient and Timely

Public awareness about air pollution and its impacts on human health and environment should be raised through distribution of information as widely as possible. The goals and objectives of the consultation process should be clearly defined and communicated to the public at the outset of the AQMP development. Necessary documents, reports, and notification of events should be provided to the public in a timely manner for review, active participation, and meaningful input. Records of all public meetings should be maintained and reports produced on a timely basis. Appropriate channels need to be developed for providing the public with such information, and authorities should use several means of communication to involve unorganized communities and individuals.

In order to facilitate and expedite the AQMP development with public input, local agencies may also consider other means of achieving the overall objectives of public consultation. An advisory group or a task force consisting of a cross-section of non-government stakeholders may be established to support the lead agency involved in AQMP development. This group can assist the agency in various aspects of the AQMP development and in preparation of public consultation materials for relevance, effectiveness, and transparency.

The task of compilation and analysis of important background scientific and technical information in support of the AQMP development is usually undertaken by the agency staff and subsequently peer-reviewed. Alternatively, it could be carried out by several working groups of experts in specific subject areas, and focus groups could be set up for public input.

Transparent, Accountable and Accessible

A trusting relationship between the local agencies and stakeholders is an essential feature of a successful public consultation program. Urban authorities therefore need to conduct their activities in an open and accountable fashion. To complement the transparency of the public consultation, an accountability procedure should also be designed. Additional background information should be provided to interested stakeholders upon request.

In certain circumstances, it may be necessary for the sake of efficiency and effectiveness to consult with experts on a particular subject matter, rather than with the public at large. However, the public should be given a clear context and rationale for such a decision.

Consultation Output and Feedback

The information obtained during consultation is to be regarded as stakeholder advice to the local agencies. The input from the public should therefore be reviewed and duly considered prior to decision making, participants should be apprised of the decisions.

Consultation Resources

Public consultation requires preparation of documents and communication materials, distribution of materials, and holding of public meetings. Adequate funding should be allocated for this purpose. In addition, due to financial constraints not all interested participants may be able to attend consultation meetings. Provisions for possible financial assistance to such participants should be duly considered.

Key Planning Steps

The process of consultation should be designed to reflect the particular circumstances at hand. Each situation needs to be tailored accordingly. Typically, the key steps involved in designing a consultation plan include: (1) identify the extent of consultation necessary, (2) establish consultation objectives and topics, (3) identify potential participants, (4) develop consultation methods and types of information materials needed, (5) plan consultation schedules, (6) record public input, analyze, and consolidate input in a report, and (7) seek post-consultation feedback from participants.

MEASUREMENT OF AIR POLLUTANTS

Most governments develop a network of outdoor air quality monitoring stations as a means of overseeing pollution levels. A typical air quality monitoring station will routinely measure the concentrations of the major outdoor air pollutants based upon the procedures first employed by the US Environmental Protection Agency (http://www.epa.gov/oar/oaqps/qa/monprog.html). These pollutants are ozone (O_3), carbon monoxide (CO), nitrogen dioxide (NO_2), sulphur dioxide (SO_2), lead (Pb), and particulate matter (PM). Specific size classes of PM itself may be measured, including total suspended particles (TSP), inhalable particles (PM_{10}), and fine particles ($PM_{2.5}$). The details of these size classifications are discussed in more detail in Chapter 2.

Specific monitoring locations may measure one or more of these pollutants at a frequency ranging from one measurement per minute to one per day. Together, multiple monitors may comprise a local monitoring network for a specific municipal area. Typically, the spatial coverage of a monitoring network is more thorough in more populated regions or in areas with specific air pollution concerns. Monitoring in rural areas is rare, except in the context of international monitoring networks to evaluate global atmospheric processes. Monitor location will depend upon the specific reasons for the monitoring program and the ultimate uses of the information. Background monitoring stations are the most common and are located so as not to be strongly influenced by specific sources. These monitors reflect the background contribution of many sources to the overall air quality and are often used to reflect long-term concentration trends (annual EPA Trends Report). Further, because most people do not live in close proximity to specific sources of air pollution, these stations will represent the concentration of air near many peoples' homes. Hotspot or source-based monitors are specifically located near air pollution sources such as industrial facilities or major roads. These monitors cannot be considered representative of regional air quality but do reflect concentration extremes. No routine programs exist for indoor air quality monitoring, except those conducted in industrial occupational environments. Measurements in non-industrial indoor locations are made in conjunction with research studies or in response to complaints from occupants. See Chapter 10.

REFERENCES

[1]   "Phase 2 Federal Smog Management Plan," Government of Canada, November 1997.

[2]   NILSSON, ANNIKA,"Greenhouse Earth," John Wiley & Sons Ltd., England, August 1992.

[3]   Intergovernmental Panel on Climate Change (IPCC) Working Group 1, 1995 Summary for Policymakers, World Meteorological Organization/United Nations Environment Programme, 1996.

[4]   Kyoto Protocol to the United Nations Framework Convention on ClimateChange, (http://www.unfcc.int/resource/docs/cop3/107a01.pdf).

[5]   Intergovernmental Panel on Climate Change (IPCC) Working Group 1, Third Assessment Report, Shanghai Draft 21-01-2001 20:00, January 2001.

[6]   "Depletion of the Stratospheric Ozone Layer: The Science, Impacts and Mitigation Measures," Air Resources Branch, BC Environment, Ministry of Environment, Lands and Parks, October 1997.

[7]   United Nations Environment Programme, Press Release — Governments Finalize Persistent Organic Pollutants Treaty (http://irptc.unep.ch/pops/princ5.htm)

[8]   United Nations Environment Programme, Chapter 28 — Local Authorities" Initiatives in Support of Agenda 21 (http://www.unep.org/documents/default.asp/ documentID=52&ArticleID=76).

[9]   "USA Air Quality Nonattainment Areas," Office of Air Quality Planning and Standards, Environmental Protection Agency (http://www.epa.gov/oar/oaqps).

[10]   "Eastern Canada Acid Rain Program," Environment Canada, 1985.

[11]   "Management Plan for Nitrogen Oxides (NOX) and Volatile Organic Compounds (VOCs), Phase 1," Canadian Council of Ministers of the Environment, Report CCME-EPC, 1990.

[12]   "GVRD Air Quality Management Plan," Greater Vancouver Regional District, December 1994.

[13]   "Canada–United States Air Quality Agreement, 1991," Environment Canada, 1991.

[14]   (a) "1985 United Nations Economic Commission for Europe Protocol (to the 1979 Convention on Long-Range Transboundary Air Pollution) on Reduction of Sulphur Emissions";

        (b) "1994 United Nations Economic Commission for Europe Protocol (to the 1979 Convention on Long-Range Transboundary Air Pollution) on Reduction of Sulphur Emissions";

        (c) "1988 United Nations Economic Commission for Europe Protocol to the 1979 Convention on Long-Range Transboundary Air Pollution Concerning the Control of Emissions of Nitrogen Oxides or Their Transboundary Fluxes," UN Economic Commission for Europe, Geneva, Switzerland.

[15]   "Towards a National Acid Rain Strategy," Report Submitted to the Canadian National Air Issues Coordinating Committee by the Acidifying Emissions Task Group, October 1997.

[16]   "The Canada-Wide Acid Rain Strategy for Post-2000. Strategy and Supporting Document," Federal/Provincial/Territorial Ministers of Energy and Environment, Halifax, Nova Scotia, October 1998.

[17]   "Supporting Document for Towards a Smog plan for Ontario," Discussion Paper, Ontario Ministry of Environment and Energy, June 1996.

[18]   "The Protocol to Abate Acidification, Eutrophication and Ground-level Ozone (AEGLO)," United nations Economic Commission for Europe, December 1999.

[19]   "Ozone Annex under the Canada–United States Air Quality Agreement, 1991," Environment Canada, December 2000.

[20]   "The Role of State and Local Governments" (http://www.epa.gov/globalwarming/visitorcenter/decision-makers/role.html).

[21]   (a) "Environment, Ambient — Air Quality" (http://europa.eu.int/scadplus/leg/en/lvb/128031a.htm).

(b) "Guidance Report on Preliminary Assessment under EC Air Quality Directives," R. van Aalst, L. Edwards, T. Pulles, E. De Saeger, M. Tombrou and D. Tønnesen, European Topic Centre on Air Quality and European Commission, January 1998.

[22]   "Environmental Protection Act 1990 (c.43)" (http://www.hmso.gov.uk/acts/acts1990/Ukgpa_19900043_en-1.htm).

[23]   "Developing Local Air Quality Action Plans and Strategies: The Main Considerations," Part IV The Environment Act 1995, Local Air Quality Management LAQM.G2(00), Department of the Environment, Transport and the Regions: London, National Assembly for Wales, March 2000.

[24]   "CLEAR THE AIR. National Heritage Trust Projects to Improve Urban Air Quality," the Commonwealth Government of Australia (http://www.environment.gov.au/epg/airquality/clear_the_air.html).

[25]   "Action for Air. The NSW Government's 25-Year Air Quality Management Plan," Air Pollution Section, Environmental Protection Authority, New South Wales Government, February 1998.

[26]   "Air Quality Management and Assessment Capabilities in 20 Major Cities," GEMS/AIR Environmental Assessment Report, UNEP/DEIA/AR.96.2, WHO/EOS 95.7, 1996.

[27]   (a) "Achieving Atmospheric Quality Objectives through the Use of Economic Instruments," Final Report of the Economic Instruments Collaborative, National Round Table on the Environment and the Economy, Canada, October 1993.

(b) "Integrating Economic and Environmental Policies. Green Paper on Greenhouse Gas Emissions Trading within the European Union," Commission of the European Communities, Brussels, 8.3.2000, COM(2000) 87 Final.

(c) "Economic Instruments for Pollution Control and Natural Resources Management in OECD Countries: A Survey," Organisation for Economic Co-operation and Development, ENV/EPOC/GEEI(98)35/REV1/FINAL, October 1999.

(d) "Market Approaches for Reducing Air Pollution," Features of the 1990 Clean Air Act, US Environmental Protection Agency, Office of Air Quality Planning and Standards. Report # EPA-400K-93-001. April 1993.

(e) "Regional Clean Air Incentives Market," Rule 2000. General, Amended October 20, 2000, South Coast Air Quality Management District, California.

[28]   "Using Tradeable Emissions Permits to Help Achieve Domestic Greenhouse Gas Objectives — Options Report," Tradeable Permits Working Group, National Climate Change Process, Canada, April 2000.

[29]   "A Comprehensive Air Quality Management Framework for Canada," Federal/Provincial/Territorial Ministers of Energy and Environment, 1994.

[30]   "Air — Stakeholder Consultation — Lower Fraser Valley Air Quality Advisory Committee Terms of Reference (981006)," GVRD Air Quality Department, Greater Vancouver Regional District (http://www.gvrd.bc.ca/services/air/consult/consult.html).

[31]   "United States Environmental Protection Agency Charter. Clean Air Act Advisory Committee," US Environmental Protection Agency, Office of Air and Radiation (http://www.epa.gov/oar/caaac/charter_of_caaac.html).

[32]   "Bay Area Air Quality Management District: Advisory Council: FY 00-2001," Bay Area Air Quality Management District, San Francisco, California, January 2001.

[33]   "How AQMD's Governing Board Works," South Coast Air Quality Management District, Diamond Bar, California, September 2000 (http://www.aqmd.gov/hb/govbd.html).

[34]   Commission for Environmental Cooperation, Joint Public Advisory Committee, CEC Secretariat, Montreal, PQ, Canada (http://www.cec.org).

[35]   "Environment Act 1986 127, II: Ministry for the Environment, 31 Functions of Ministry, and The Resource Management Act, 1991Clause 3," Ministry for the Environment, Wellington, New Zealand, January 1987.

[36]   "Canterbury Regional Policy Statement," Environment Canterbury, 1991 (http://www.ecan.govt.nz).

Chapter 10
Indoor Air Pollution

Michael Brauer

INTRODUCTION

As discussed in Chapter 2, for most air pollutants and for most people the majority of exposure occurs indoors. This is due to the simple fact that individuals spend the vast majority of their time indoors. This realization has led to an increased emphasis on the importance of air quality within indoor environments. Along with this new paradigm has been the change in residential and commercial building design within the past 30 years. As a way to improve energy efficiency, homes built since the 1970s have generally been "tighter," allowing for less heat loss but also for less frequent exchange of indoor air with air from outdoors. In larger buildings it has for some time been common to have air quality controlled by mechanical ventilation systems and not by individual openable windows. Coupled with these developments there has been an expanding use of synthetic building materials and multiple consumer products such as cleaning agents, air fresheners, and glues, which all release air pollutants into the indoor air.

Although the importance of indoor sources of air pollutants should not be neglected, one must also consider that infiltration of polluted outdoor air is also a source of contaminated indoor air, and that government regulation is mainly directed towards management of outdoor air quality. The management of indoor air quality is often at the discretion of building managers and the occupants of residential environments. Through informed decision-making about the design, use, and maintenance of indoor environments, individuals can directly influence their exposures. In this chapter the major indoor air contaminants and mitigation strategies are discussed. Detailed information on indoor air quality is available from a comprehensive handbook [24] and from several Web pages:

US Environmental Protection Agency (EPA) Indoor Air Quality
Program http://www.epa.gov/iaq/index.html
Contains public informational material, technical reports and
educational resources. Updated regularly, this is an excellent
source of information.

Indoor Air quality: The Inside Story
The full text of this US EPA informational book is available at:
http://www.epa.gov/iaq/pubs/insidest.html

Canada Mortgage and Housing Corporation
http://www.cmhc-schl.gc.ca/cmhc.html
A good source of research information regarding indoor air
quality in residences.

University of Minnesota — FAQ on Indoor Air Quality in
Schools http://www.dehs.umn.edu/iaq/school/
An excellent site for school indoor air quality issues, including
many useful links.

ENVIRONMENTAL TOBACCO SMOKE

Of all the indoor contaminants, environmental tobacco smoke (ETS) is
arguably the most important in terms of health risk in developed countries.
ETS has been determined to be a human lung carcinogen by the US
EPA based upon evidence from human epidemiological studies [1]. It is
estimated to be responsible for approximately 3,000 lung cancer deaths
annually in US nonsmokers. In children in the United States, ETS exposure
is associated with (US EPA estimate) 150,000-300,000 cases of bronchitis
and pneumonia annually in infants less than 18 months old and with
increases in the risk of otitis media (middle-ear infections) in preschool
children [2]. In Canada, ETS exposure is estimated to be a factor in 13%
of otitis media incidence [2a]. ETS irritates the upper respiratory tract
and is associated with a small but significant reduction in lung function in
those with prolonged exposure. ETS exposure also increases the frequency
of episodes and severity of symptoms in asthmatic children [3], and
may be a risk factor for new cases of asthma in children who have not
previously displayed symptoms.

RADON

Radon is naturally occurring gaseous radioactivity in soil. In homes built
in areas with high soil radon concentrations, the gas is emitted indoors from
the soil. The gas naturally decays into radioactive radon daughter particles
that can be inhaled. Even within areas of high soil radon concentrations,
there is substantial variability in indoor levels due to the ability of radon
gas to penetrate different building designs and the buildings' ventilation
characteristics. Concentrations in basements are usually highest due to
the proximity to soil and the surface area in contact with soil. A variety

of self-administered radon measurement devices are available for consumers. A useful resource which can help to estimate the potential for elevated indoor radon levels and the usefulness of monitoring is the Columbia University Radon project (http://www.stat.columbia.edu/radon/), which includes an algorithm that estimates probabilities of elevated radon concentrations for different home types throughout the US.

Elevated indoor radon levels have been associated with lung cancer, especially for individuals who smoke, and it has been estimated that radon exposure may account for 10-15% of lung cancer deaths in the US, primarily in smokers. Control of indoor radon can be accomplished by vapour barriers and sub-slab pressurization ventilation systems. A guide for consumers to reduce radon is published by the US EPA (http://www.epa.gov/iaq/radon/pubs/consguid.html).

BIOAEROSOLS

The indoor environment can be contaminated with a variety of airborne microorganisms such as fungi, bacteria, mites, viruses, and amoebae as a result of high indoor humidity, water-damaged indoor surfaces, reduced ventilation, and heating, and air-conditioning (HVAC) systems containing stagnant water. Surveys in Canada and the US indicate that 30-50% of homes have damp conditions which may encourage the growth of biological pollutants [5, 6, 7]. Control of microbial growth can usually be achieved with proper humidity control, prompt attention to water damage (materials need to be dried thoroughly within 24 hours) and building system design which minimizes intrusion of water or the presence of any standing water. Further, building design must allow moisture that does penetrate or that is generated indoors to exit the building envelope. Maintaining indoor relative humidity below 60% or below 70% when a building is occupied will usually maintain surface relative humidities below 65% thereby reducing the potential for microbial growth. As moisture can readily condense on cold surfaces, special treatment and attention may be required for such areas. Note that further reductions in humidity are required for control of dust mites, as described below. In buildings with mechanical ventilation, the system should be designed to minimize the possibility of standing water. Maintenance and cleaning of HVAC systems are also important for control of microbial growth.

For example, drain pans need to be physically cleaned periodically and water in cooling towers may need to be treated to prevent biological growth.

The mechanisms by which airborne fungi and bacteria may lead to adverse health effects have not been clearly understood. In some cases responses appear to be toxic and may result from toxic metabolites emitted by microorganisms or from toxic components of the organisms themselves. Toxic responses appear to be limited to specific microorganism species, among the most important for indoor air being varieties of *Penicillium, Aspergillus* and *Stachybotrys*. In other situations, responses are primarily irritation or allergic in nature. Allergens are discussed in more detail in the following section.

Several studies have consistently shown a strong and consistent relationship between home dampness and/or the presence of visible mould and respiratory health effects such as wheeze, cough, and bronchitis in children [7, 8]. Viable airborne mould levels have also been associated with symptom responses in a number of investigations. Recent research has evaluated several markers of fungal contamination and also evaluated mechanisms of action. $(1{\rightarrow}3)$-b-D-glucans and ergosterol, fungal cell wall components, are markers for total (viable and non-viable) fungal levels, as it has been suggested that viable mould levels may not account for all of the risk associated with indoor microbial contamination. Both ergosterol and $(1{\rightarrow}3)$-b-D-glucans have been associated with symptoms in a number of epidemiological studies [9]. $(1{\rightarrow}3)$-b-D-glucans has also been shown to stimulate humoral and cell-mediated immunity in laboratory studies, leading to the hypothesis that $(1{\rightarrow}3)$-b-D-glucans is a causative agent. Recent research has also shown that residential fungal contamination is associated with chronic stimulation of lymphocytes in children and that this association is not confounded by house dust mites [10]. Further, laboratory studies have indicated that spores isolated from mouldy homes stimulate macrophages leading to the production of inflammatory mediators [11]. Together these observations support a causal association between indoor fungal contamination and health impacts.

ALLERGENS

Approximately 20% of the population has allergic asthma or other allergic diseases [7]. Many of these conditions are caused or aggravated by exposure to allergens in indoor environments. In addition to fungi, among the most important indoor allergens are dust mites, pet allergens (dander, saliva), and cockroaches. Dust mites are one of the more important allergens due to their strong association in epidemiological studies with allergic symptoms and with demonstrated sensitivity. Dust mites thrive in places with high humidity, moderate temperatures, and an adequate supply of food (provided amply by human skin scales). Maintaining indoor relative humidity below 50% will help control growth of dust mites. Dust mite exposures can also be controlled by using allergen-proof mattress encasements, washing bedding/rugs in hot water, avoiding carpets and upholstered furniture, using a central vacuum (vented outdoors) or vacuums with high efficiency filters. Pet allergens are also important in North America as pets are found in over 50% of homes. Surveys indicate that 5-15% of the general population and 40-70% of asthmatics show indications of allergy to common pet allergens such as cat and/or dog dander [9a]. Close human contact accounts for the high prevalence of pet allergy. Cockroaches are ubiquitous and are also highly allergenic. Cockroach populations are highest in crowded urban areas, and are more difficult to control in warm countries.

Additional information on allergen exposure reduction strategies is available from the Lung Association (http://www.lungusa.org/asthma/asthomecon.html).

COMBUSTION PRODUCTS

Unvented or poorly vented indoor combustion products may also be important sources of indoor contaminants. Of these, the most important combustion products in indoor air of non-industrial buildings in developed countries are carbon monoxide and nitrogen dioxide. Carbon monoxide is a product of incomplete combustion, and high emissions generally occur when combustion devices operate poorly. At high concentrations, carbon monoxide exposure causes unconsciousness and death, while lower concentrations can cause a range of symptoms such as headaches, dizziness, nausea, and increased chest pain in people with chronic heart disease. Carbon monoxide is odourless, and individuals exposed to toxic levels are not warned by breathlessness or other symptoms before they become unconscious. Accidental exposure to CO is responsible for more than 200 deaths each year in the US [11a,] due primarily to poorly operated/maintained combustion-fuelled heating systems as well as fireplaces, the use of gas ovens for heating during power outages, and the warming up of cars in attached garages.

In contrast to carbon monoxide, nitrogen dioxide is a combustion product that is produced in any high-temperature combustion process, including those with high combustion efficiency. Nitrogen dioxide is a mucous membrane irritant that may lead to shortness of breath and difficulty inbreathing at high levels of exposure. Oxide of nitrogen (NOx) pollution from gas cooking has been shown to be important in relation to the frequency of episodes of lower respiratory disease in children of school age (see Chapter 4). Neas and his colleagues [12] studied a large cohort of 7-11-year-old children and found that mean NOx levels were significantly higher in houses with gas cooking, and levels were significantly higher in the kitchens than in the bedrooms. The authors concluded that a 15 parts per billion (ppb) increase in annual mean NO_2 was associated with a 40% increase in the risk of incidence of lower respiratory symptoms. A meta-analysis of 11 epidemiological studies yielded similar results, suggesting a 20% increase in the odds of a lower respiratory infection for children with a prolonged increase in exposure of 16 ppb NO_2 [12a]. It has also been suggested that continued exposure to low levels of nitrogen dioxide may increase the risk of respiratory infection. In contrast, a very carefully conducted study of NO_2 levels in homes of nonsmokers showed no evidence of any impact on the respiratory health of infants from birth to the age of 18 months [13].

In many developing countries, wood and other biomass as well as coal are burned without adequate ventilation indoors as cooking and heating fuels. Respirable particulate levels measured in these settings are typically 1,000-2,000 $\mu g/m^3$ depending upon the specific fuel, ventilation, cooking duration, and measurement interval [14, 15] (Table 10.1). These levels are 10-50 times above those observed in urban areas. The health effects of biomass smoke inhalation have been documented in developing countries where women and, in some cases, children spend many hours cooking over unvented indoor stoves. Exposure to biomass combustion products has been identified as a major risk factor for acute respiratory infections, the leading cause of infant mortality in the developing countries [16]. In addition to the risks of infants, the women who are cooking are also at risk for chronic respiratory diseases, adverse pregnancy outcomes, and lung cancer [14, 15].

Country	Conditions	Particulate concentration in kitchens (µg/m^3)
New Guinea	Overnight	200-9,000
Kenya	Highlands Lowlands 24 hours	2,700-7,900 300-1,500 1,200-1,900
India	Cooking – wood Dung Charcoal General	15,000 18,300 5,500 4,000-21,000
Nepal	Cooking – wood	4,700
China	Cooking – wood	2,600
Gambia	24 hours	3,600-6,800
India	Villages during cooking	3,600-6,800
Nepal	Villages during cooking Villages during cooking Villages during cooking	3,600-6,800 8,200 3,000

Table 10.1: Reports on indoor air pollution in developing countries.

VOLATILE ORGANIC COMPOUNDS

Volatile organic compounds (VOCs) are often implicated as a contributing factor to poor indoor air quality, especially in modern buildings in developed countries. VOCs are emitted from many furnishings, consumer products, and bioeffluents from humans as well as microorganisms [17]. In buildings where very high concentrations are found, it is often due to the presence of easily identified strong sources such as VOC-based finish materials, cleaning products, hobby and art materials, or newly installed building materials (carpets, paints, sealants, and adhesives). Emissions from most building materials tend to decrease rapidly when materials are new. In general, the older a building, the lower the VOC concentrations are likely to be.

A large number of VOC-emitting consumer products are commonly used in homes. Among the more common of which are glues, latex paint, woodstains, correction fluid, solvent cleaners, spot removers, electronic cleaners, and automobile cleaners [17a, 18]. Higher levels in homes were also associated with the presence of an attached garage (where gasoline vapour is emitted and where solvents and paints are likely to be stored), with the presence of drycleaned clothes and with drinking water that is contaminated with hydrocarbons. In this case, exposure to VOCs may occur due to volatilization of hydrocarbons during showering. Table 10.2 lists some of the common VOCs measured in office buildings, along with their source products.

VOCs are of concern because of the elevated cancer risks associated with exposures to many of these compounds and because of a complex series of responses involving neurobehavioural effects. These effects of mixtures of low levels of VOCs commonly measured in indoor air were first studied in the early 1980s in a groundbreaking series of experiments that uncovered human effects associated with VOCs at levels much lower than previously considered plausible. In controlled chamber studies, subjects exposed to mixtures of very low levels of VOCs experienced airway and eye irritation as well as attention deficits [19, 19a]. Other health effects include skin irritation, hypersensitivity reactions, and abnormal odour and taste.

Chemical	Source
Acetone	Paint, coatings, finishers, paint remover, thinner, caulking.
Aliphatic hydrocarbons (octane, decane, undecane, hexane, isodecane, mixtures, etc.)	Paint, adhesives, gasoline, combustion sources, liquid process photocopier, carpet, linoleum, caulking compound.
Aromatic hydrocarbons (toluene, xylene, benzene, ethyl benzene)	Combustion sources, paint, adhesive, gasoline, linoleum, wall coating.
Chlorinated solvents (dichloromethane or methylene chloride, trichloroethane)	Upholstery and carpet cleaner or protector, paint, paint remover, lacquers, solvents, correction fluid, dry-cleaned clothes.
n-Butyl acetate	Acoustic ceiling tile, linoleum, caulking compound.
Dichlorobenzene	Carpet, moth crystals, air fresheners.
4-Phenylcyclohexane (4-PC)	Carpet, paint.
Terpenes (limonene, α-pinene)	Deodorizers, cleaning agents, polishes, fabrics, fabric softener, cigarettes.

Table 10.2: Commonly encountered volatile organic compounds [20].

FORMALDEHYDE

Formaldehyde emissions indoors may result from household products and building materials as well as combustion processes such as smoking. Formaldehyde is a common ingredient in many manufactured products such as glues, pressed wood building products, cabinetry and furniture, and paints and sealants. Formaldehyde emissions from pressed wood products generally decrease as the materials age. New materials can be aged or "baked" at higher indoor temperatures to increase the emission of formadehyde prior to contact with building occupants. Formaldehyde exposure can also be reduced by the use of building materials and products which have no or low formaldehyde emission rates. It has also been suggested that coating formaldehyde-emitting materials with polyurethane will reduce the rate of formaldehyde emission.

In the 1970s many homeowners had Urea-Formaldehyde Foam Insulation (UFFI) sprayed in the wall cavities of their home for insulation. However, the UFFI emitted large amounts of formaldehyde into some of these homes and led to associations with health problems in residents. Consequently, UFFI is not commonly used any more. Homes insulated with UFFI previously are unlikely to still have elevated formaldehyde levels as the rate of emission decreases over time (unless progressive deterioration due to moisture damage or fungal activity is present).

Exposure to formaldehyde is a concern as it is a mucous membrane irritant that is also suspected of enhancing sensitization to future exposures to lower levels of formaldehyde and possibly other chemicals. There is also some evidence that formaldehyde may be associated with cancer, though there is no human epidemiological evidence of this.

SICK BUILDING SYNDROME/VENTILATION

Adjustment of ventilation rates in buildings is widely used to provide good air quality proactively, and to mitigate air quality problems associated with occupant complaints. The typical HVAC system is designed for occupant thermal comfort and to provide a minimal amount of outdoor air based on the use of the building and occupancy rates. The amount of outdoor air is usually determined according to the industry standards of the American Society of Heating, Refrigeration, and Air Conditioning Engineers (ASHRAE). Indoor air quality complaints are often linked to inadequate ventilation. In a 1993 NIOSH study of buildings with reported indoor air quality problems [21], 93 of 104 building evaluation reports contained at least one recommendation concerning HVAC design, operation, or maintenance deficiencies. Health studies have, for the most part, failed to establish definitive relationships between ventilation rate and symptom prevalence, except for ventilation rates well below the ASHRAE recommended levels.

CONTROL OF INDOOR AIR QUALITY

Maintenance of satisfactory indoor air quality can often be achieved by a hierarchical approach to potential sources. Source control is the most effective approach, followed by ventilation and then by active air cleaning. For example, it is much more effective to eliminate smoking in an indoor space than to use air cleaners to remove contaminants generated in cigarette smoke.

Source Control

Source control may entail simple avoidance of a source such as tobacco smoke; product improvement or substitution with a product that has lower emissions to indoor air (for example, low-emission interior paints or carpets); improved operation and maintenance of the building or appliances located in the building; source removal; aging of the building or furnishings (for example, fiberboard products which emit formaldehyde and other VOCs when new) prior to building occupancy; and effective climate control (for example, to reduce the potential for microbial growth). In general, reducing the indoor humidity to below 50% reduces not only the growth of house dust mites but also the growth of mould indoors. As described above, a series of preventive measures are effective in reducing house dust mite exposure. With regard to pet allergens, the only effective way of reducing exposure is to remove the pet from the home; frequent washing of the pet or application of chemicals has not been found to be useful, while the use of non-carpeted flooring or frequent steam cleaning of carpets is partially effective. Thorough cleaning and the use of insecticides are required to eliminate cockroaches from homes.

Ventilation

As ventilation is often present in buildings as a means to achieve climate control, it can also be used to dilute concentrations of indoor contaminants. Note, however, that care must be taken to avoid supplying an indoor environment with contaminated supply air.

This has occurred when the building air intake is located adjacent to parking lots. Where feasible, local exhaust ventilation is a more effective means than general ventilation to reduce the impact of specific contaminant sources. Common examples of local exhaust are kitchen range hoods to reduce the impact of particles produced in cooking and combustion gases produced by cooking with gas; bathroom fans to exhaust humid air; and local exhaust for copy machines and photo processors that emit VOCs as well as ozone.

As indicated above, a building HVAC system in primarily a mechanism for achieving thermal comfort but can also be used to effectively dilute pollutants generated by building occupants. Ventilation air requirements generally follow the standards of ASHRAE which specify amounts of ventilation air based on the size and use of the indoor space as well as the number of occupants.

Air Cleaning

Air cleaning, while often effective for smaller spaces, should usually be used when source control or ventilation is not effective or not feasible. Air cleaners may be portable models that can be used in buildings without mechanical ventilation systems or may be placed within the HVAC system itself — for example, high-efficiency filters or electrostatic precipitators [22]. In general, portable air cleaners are highly effective for particles, provided the cleaner is appropriately sized for the room to be cleaned. Air-cleaning devices for gaseous contaminants are much less effective and require regular maintenance to ensure that sorption media are changed regularly. Air cleaners may also have adverse effects themselves, such as noise generation, increased soiling of indoor surfaces from ion generators, and the redispersal or even production of indoor air pollutants — for example, the production of ozone by electrostatic precipitators.

The use of ozone (sometimes termed "active oxygen" in marketing documents) generators to improve indoor air quality has received widespread attention in recent years due to active marketing campaigns by producers of these devices. Ozone generators are not recommended for use in occupied indoor spaces, and even when used in the absence of occupants, their ability to improve indoor air quality has not been substantiated. In fact, one study has shown that very high ozone levels (4 ppm) are needed for the gas to serve as an effective biocide [23]. At this concentration, well above environmental and occupational standards, human health impacts are likely, and surface damage to indoor materials may also occur. As a result of these concerns, consumer advisories warning against the use of these devices indoors have been published by the several US states, the US EPA, and Health Canada (http://www.epa.gov/iedweb00/pubs/ozonegen.html).

REFERENCES

[1] Respiratory Health Effects of Passive Smoking: Lung Cancer and Other Disorders, US Environmental Protection Agency Report: EPA/600/6-90/006F.

[2] COOK, D.G., & STRACHAN, D.P., Summary of effects of parental smoking on the respiratory health of children and implications for research. Thorax 1999; 54: 357-66.

[2a] ADAIR-BISCHOFF, C.E., SAUVE, R.S., Environmental tobacco smoke and middle ear disease in preschool-age children. Arch Pediatr Adolesc Med 1998; 152(2):127-33.

[3] CHILMONCZYK, B.A., SALMUN, L.M., MEGATHLIN, K.N., NEVEUX, L.M., PALOMAKI, G.E., KNIGHT, G.J., PULKKINEN, A.J., & HADDOW, J.E., Association between exposure to environmental tobacco smoke and exacerbations of asthma in children. New Engl J Med 1993; 328: 1665-69.

[5] DALES, R.E., BURNETT, R., & ZWANENBURG, H., Adverse health effects among adults exposed to home dampness and molds. Am Rev Respir Dis 1991;143:505-9.

[6] BRUNEKREEF, B., DOCKERY, D.W., SPEIZER, F.E., WARE, J.H., SPENGLER, J.D., FERRIS, B.G. Home dampness and respiratory morbidity in children. Am Rev Respir Dis. 1989; 140(5):13636-7.

[7] POPE, A.M., PATTERSON, R., & BURGE, H., Indoor Air Allergens: Assessing and Controlling Adverse Health Effects. National Academy Press, Washington, DC, 1993.

[8] HUSMAN T., Health effects of indoor-air microorganisms. Scan J Work Environ Health 1996; 22:5-13.

[9] RYLANDER, R., Microbial cell wall constituents in indoor air and their relation to disease. Indoor Air 1998, Suppl. 459-65.

[9a] KJELLMAN, B., & PETTERSSON, R., The problem of furred pets in childhood atopic disease. Failure of an information program. Allergy 1983; 38:65-73.

[10] DALES, R., MILLER, D., WHITE, J., DULBERT, C., & LAZAROVITS, A.I., Influence of residential fungal contamination on peripheral blood lymphocyte populations in children. Arch Environ Health 1998; 53(3):191-95.

[11] HIRVONEN, M.R., NEVALAINEN, A., MAKKONEN, N., MONKKONENE, J. & SAVOLAINEN, K., Induced production of nitric oxide, tumor necrosis factor and inter-leukin-6 in RAW 264.7 macropages by Streptomycetes from indoor air of moldy homes. Arch Environ Health 1997; 52(6):426-32.

[11a] LIU, K.-S., PAZ, M.K., FLESSEL, P., WALDMAN, J., & GIRMAN, J., Unintentional carbon monoxide deaths in California from residential and other nonvehicular sources. Arch Environ Health 2000; 55 375-81. 2000.

[12] NEAS, L.M., DOCKERY, D.W., WARE, J.H., SPENGLER, J.D., SPEIZER, F.E., & FERRIS, B.G. JR., Association of indoor nitrogen dioxide with respiratory symptoms and pulmonary function in children. Am. J. Epidem. 1991; 134:204-19.

[12a] HASSELBAD, V., EDDY, D.M., & KOTCHMAR, D.J., Synthesis of environmental evidence: Nitrogen dioxide epidemiology studies. J. Air Waste Manage. Assoc. 1992; 42:662-71.

[13] SAMET, J.M., LAMBERT, W.E., SKIPPER, B.J., CUSHING, A.H., HUNT, W.C., YOUNG, S.A., MCLAREN, W.C., SCHWAB, M. & SPENGLER, J.D., Nitrogen dioxide and respiratory illnesses in infants. Am Rev Respir Dis. 1993; 148(5):1258-65.

[14] SMITH, K., & LIU, Y.,. Indoor air pollution in developing countries. In: Samet, J., ed., Epidemiology of Lung Cancer, Marcel Dekker, New York, 1993. Pg. 151-84.

[15] BRUCE, N., PEREZ-PADILLA, R., & ALBALAK, R., Indoor air pollution in developing countries: a major environmental and public health challenge. Bull World Health Organ. 2000; 78(9):1078-92.

[16] SMITH, K.R., SAMET, J.M., ROMIEU, I., & BRUCE, N., Indoor air pollution in developing countries and acute lower respiratory infections in children. Thorax 2000; 55:518-32.

[17] GODISH T., Sick Buildings: Definition, Diagnosis and Mitigation. Lewis Publishers, Boca Raton, FL, 1995.

[17a]WALLACE L., A decade of studies of human exposure: what have we learned? Risk Anal. 1993 13(2):135-39.

[18] WALLACE, L.A., PELLIZZARI, E.D., HARTWELL, T.D., SPARACINO, C., WHITMORE, R., SHELDON, L., ZELON, H., & PERRITT, R., The TEAM (Total Exposure Assessment Methodology) Study: personal exposures to toxic substances in air, drinking water, and breath of 400 residents of New Jersey, North Carolina, and North Dakota. Environ. Res. 1987; 43(2):290-307.

[19] MØLHAVE, L., Volatile organic compounds as indoor air pollutants. In: Gammage, R.B., & Kaye, S.V., eds., Indoor Air and Human Health, Lewis publishers Inc., Chelsea, MI, 1985.

[19a]KJAERGAARD, S., MØLHAVE, L., PEDERSON, O.-F., Human reactions to a mixture of indoor air volatile organic compounds. Atmospheric Environment 1991; 25A:1417-26.

[20] HEALTH CANADA Indoor air quality in office buildings: A technical guide. 93-EHD-166, 1995.

[21] CRANDALL, M., & SIEBER, W., The National Institute for Occupational Safety and Health Indoor Environmental Evaluation Experience. Part One: Building Environmental Evaluations, Applied Occupational and Environmental Hygiene 1996; 11(6):533-39.

[22] US E NVIRONMENTAL PROTECTION AGENCY, Residential air cleaning devices: A summary of available information. US EPA, Indoor Air Division. Washington, DC, 1990. EPA 400/1-90/002.

[23] FOARDE, K., VAN OSDELL, D., & STEIBER, R., Investigation of gas-phase ozone as a potential biocide. Applied Occupational Environmental Hygiene 1997; 12(8):535-42.

[24] SPENGLER, J.D., MCCARTHY, J.F., SAMET, J.M.,(eds.) Indoor Air Quality Handbook. McGraw-Hill, New York, 2001.

Chapter 11
Current Issues and Linkages

Robert B. Caton, Victor Runeckles, Bohdan W. Hrebenyk

To this point, we have emphasized the classic impacts of air pollution on human health, odour perception, and vegetation damage. In this chapter, we describe very briefly some contemporary and developing issues related to air pollution, and point out some of the linkages between and among them. The first issue, global climate change, is an extremely important subject, well documented in its own literature. We do not attempt to address it in detail. Rather, we outline some of the ways in which climate change is linked to conventional air pollution and air quality. Similarly, the descriptions of the other issues in this chapter are intended to show how they interact with one another and are all linked to the emission sources that also impair air quality.

AIR QUALITY – CLIMATE CHANGE LINKAGES

As this is being written, the Intergovernmental Panel on Climate Change (IPCC) has issued its Third Assessment Report. The IPCC Working Group on the Science of Climate Change (Working Group 1), in its Summary for Policy Makers, expresses increased confidence in its conclusion from the Second Assessment Report in 1995 that "the balance of evidence suggests a discernible human influence on global climate." The Third Assessment Report WG 1 Summary states with respect to the observed warming of the atmosphere: "There is new and stronger evidence that most of the warming observed over the last 50 years is attributable to human activities" [1].

The principal human-generated greenhouse gases that are implicated in causing atmospheric warming and resulting climate change — carbon dioxide (CO_2), methane (CH_4) and nitrous oxide — are emitted from many of the same sources that emit the pollutants that are important in impairing ambient air quality. Combustion of fossil fuels accounts for about 75% of the man-made emissions of carbon dioxide in the past 20 years, and fossil fuel production adds significant "upstream" emissions of CO_2 and methane (as well as nitrogen oxides [NO_X], sulphur dioxide [SO_2] and particulate matter [PM]). Fossil fuel combustion sources are also principal sources of NO_X, SO_2, carbon monoxide [CO], and fine PM ($PM_{2.5}$). Managing greenhouse gas emissions is thus closely related to managing the combustion sources that are involved in air quality management programs, including transportation (motor vehicles, air, rail, and marine), electricity generation, and space heating (see Chapter 2).

Air Quality Co-Benefits of Climate Change Mitigation

Improved air quality is being cited as one of the co-benefits of greenhouse gas mitigation [2, 3, 4]. Conversely, greenhouse gas emission reductions may accompany measures designed primarily to reduce emissions of common air contaminants (criteria air pollutants). Co-benefits (or "ancillary benefits," essentially interchangeably) are in addition to the direct benefits of avoiding the effects of climate change itself.

The benefits of avoiding global warming and climate change by reducing greenhouse gas emissions accrue globally, but the benefits of reduced common air contaminants accrue locally and regionally relative to emission sources because of the direct effects on air quality in the vicinity of the sources. The long-range transport of air pollutants in North America, Europe, or Asia, for example, extends the co-benefits of greenhouse gas and common air contaminant mitigation to the continental scale by reducing large-scale ozone and acid rain formation (see below).

A number of attempts have been made to estimate the air quality and other co-benefits of climate change mitigation, but this is a very inexact science. Resources for the Future, the US policy analysis organization, has estimated that in the electricity sector, the air quality co-benefits of meeting the Kyoto Protocol target for the US would be in the range of 5% to 15% of the direct greenhouse gas emission reduction costs [4]. Economy-wide estimates in the US and Canada have indicated that as much as 25% to 30% of direct expenditure costs might be offset by air quality and related co-benefits [3, 4]. In its Third Assessment Report, the IPCC Working Group on Economic and Social Dimensions of Climate Change (Working Group 3) [5] has declined to estimate the direct damage costs of climate change itself (a change of approach from the Second Assessment Report in 1995), but has extended its analysis of the value of co-benefits of climate change mitigation. In these analyses, human health benefits dominate the monetized estimates, but other potentially more valuable impacts, such as avoided ecosystem damage or loss of biodiversity, cannot be estimated reliably in economic terms yet.

Epstein [6] has provided a concise summary of the potential human health impacts of climate change. His review indicates that many important disease vectors might be enhanced significantly with warming of the Northern Hemisphere. For example, a 2°F global temperature rise by 2020 (relative to the average for the years 1961 to 1990) is estimated to extend the range of the organisms that transmit diseases such as malaria, dengue fever, and yellow fever so as to increase the risk of transmission of these diseases by up to twofold in populous, mid-northern latitudes.

Evidence for the reliability of forecasts of spreading disease occurrence from global warming comes from recent studies of the effects of short-term warming caused by extreme weather events associated with the El Niño Southern Oscillation. Regions in which extremely warm and/or wet conditions developed in response to El Niño (or the companion La Niña phenomenon) have experienced outbreaks of various mosquito-borne, rodent-borne, and water-borne diseases. The epidemiology of the arrival of the West Nile virus in the eastern US has documented the potential for weather-ecosystem enhancement of such disease vectors, especially for tropical diseases invading more northerly regions.

Although the potential spread of infectious diseases due to climate change has been widely hypothesized, it should be noted that climate is only one factor affecting the incidence of many diseases. Disease incidence can be mediated by a variety of biological, ecological, sociological, and epidemiological processes that may interact with each other and which may themselves be influenced by climate change [7]. For example, many vector-borne diseases (i.e., diseases associated with insects, ticks, mites, etc.) that were present in North America at the time of European colonization were eliminated in subsequent centuries because of broad-scale changes in land use, agricultural practices, residential patterns, human behaviour, and vector control. Thorough quantitative studies addressing the many interacting processes that affect disease incidence have not yet been completed, and at present it is premature to make broad generalizations about the potential effects of climate change on the spread of such diseases [8].

Air Quality and Climate Change Physical Linkages

Since air quality depends so directly on meteorological conditions for pollutant dispersion and transformation, it is logical to anticipate a physical connection between climate change and air quality. Most simply, many photochemical reactions that lead to formation of secondary pollutants, such as ozone and fine particles, are enhanced by warmer temperatures. When one examines the meteorology and chemistry of air pollution in detail, however, the effects of generally warmer temperatures are not simple. For example, as shown in Chapter 3, the formation of secondary fine particulate nitrates (e.g., ammonium nitrate) is very sensitive to temperature (and humidity). Higher temperatures may lead to a greater tendency for the gaseous ammonia and nitric acid precursors of ammonium nitrate to remain in the gas phase and not form fine particles.

Climate change will influence a very large number of variables that affect air quality. As described in the next section, on links with vegetation, climate change would lead to potentially significant changes in biogenic emissions of contaminants that are important in the chemistry of air pollution. Forests and wetlands, for example, would produce different fluxes of compounds such as reactive hydrocarbons and sulphur compounds that are involved in smog chemistry. Climate change would also change precipitation regimes that are important in both air quality impacts and acid rain phenomena (see below). Wind speed and duration patterns, which are very important in determining pollutant dispersion processes, would change. If increased warming were to create greater atmospheric instability and turbulence, for example, the potential for forming secondary pollutants such as ozone and fine particles could actually be reduced under certain conditions. That is, if warmer temperatures were to produce conditions that enhanced both formation rates and dispersion rates of pollutants, the result could be either exacerbated or improved air quality.

Seasonal, annual, and longer-term patterns of pollution would also be affected. It is impossible to predict reliably which direction this effect might take typically or on average in North America. When one takes into account the effect of climate change on cloud formation, which determines the amount of sunlight available to drive atmospheric photochemistry, it becomes difficult to predict whether the net effect of general warming would be to enhance or retard smog formation. Smog formation in North America is favoured by persistent, synoptic-scale stagnant anticyclonic ("high pressure") weather systems. The unpredictability at present of how climate change would affect the frequency, intensity, and trajectory of such weather systems compared with the influence of historical climate variability leads to the conclusion that smog episodes could either increase or decrease in severity as average temperature rises [8, 9]. This uncertainty is underscored by the climate models' predictions that the greatest temperature increases will be at northern latitudes and at night.

At present, no single existing model or modelling framework will address all of the required components for both climate change and air quality modelling. The specific type of change (local, regional, or global), the direction of change in a particular location (positive or negative), and the magnitude of change in air quality that may be attributable to climate change are not known [8]. Most air quality models focus on evaluating discrete episodes of elevated air pollutant concentrations lasting on the order of a few days, while climate change models focus on predictions of average climate conditions over longer time frames and much larger geographical areas. However, infrequent high air pollution episodes represent a small portion of the total pollutant exposure in a general population, and thus contribute very little to the total health effects from air pollutants [10]. From the perspective of climate change effects on air pollution levels and associated health effects, a rise in seasonal average temperatures, which leads to a small increase in seasonal average air pollution, may provide a better measure of the potential health effects of climate change than does the frequency of high air pollution episode days, which is the current measure used to evaluate the severity of air pollution levels. Consequently, coupling regional climate models to episodic air quality models may not be all that useful if the analysis is limited to the evaluation of climate effects on episodic air pollution levels.

Integrated air quality modelling studies will be necessary in future to assess the quantitative effects of global climate change on local, regional, and global concentrations of air pollutants [10]. Such models will need to incorporate variables such as the influence of climate change on future anthropogenic and biogenic emissions, as well as the effects of global climate change on local and regional meteorology [8].

Climate Change, Air Quality, and Effects on Plants

Figure 11.1 presents a diagrammatic summary of interactions among pollutants and their effects on plants. Climatic factors are on the left-hand side of the figure and air pollutants on the right. Ozone occupies a position near the centre because, on the one hand, it is a phytotoxic pollutant and, on the other, it is probably a greenhouse gas (GHG) whose increasing concentrations in the troposphere since pre-industrial times may now contribute significantly to the total radiative forcing of atmospheric warming, although this is not an IPCC conclusion yet — the jury is still out.

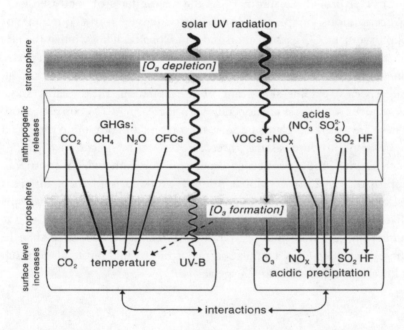

Figure 11.1: Summary of interactions among pollutants and their effects on plants.

Knowledge of the interactions is critically important to our understanding of the impact of air pollution and climate change [11, 12, 13, 14]. In order to provide the context in which to discuss these interactions, there follows a brief discussion of increasing CO_2 and temperature as components of climate change per se, and the impact of these changes on plants and ecosystems. To be complete, the discussion should address further interactions with ultraviolet-B (UV-B) radiation that is also changing as a result of stratospheric ozone depletion, yet another component of climate change. We gloss over this additional component here. Although much of the world's land mass is covered by native vegetation, most of the information available has been obtained from studies with agricultural crops and a few temperate forest tree species.

Plant Responses to Increased Carbon Dioxide and Increased Temperature

Carbon Dioxide

Table 11.1 provides a summary of the main effects of increased CO_2 concentrations on plants. Primary productivity is the outcome of photosynthetic CO_2 assimilation and it has long been known that the rate of assimilation increases with CO_2 concentration. Most plant species (including the major crops wheat, rice, potatoes, and soybean, and all tree species) exhibit significant photorespiration; these plants show large increases in assimilation rate with increasing CO_2 concentration. These are called C3 plants because the first major compound produced by their photosynthesis has three carbon atoms. In contrast, species such as the crops corn, sugarcane, and sorghum, which contribute approximately 20% of global primary productivity, have a different assimilation pathway. These possess foliar CO_2-concentrating mechanisms that result in photosynthetic carboxylation functioning close to CO_2 saturation, and little photorespiration. These are called C4 plants. In these, the rise in CO_2 assimilation rate is more rapid but tends to reach a lower maximum than in C3 species [15].

Plant response	Usual effect
Stomatal conductance	Decrease
Transpiration	Decrease
Photosynthesis	Increase (C3 > C4 species)
Photosynthetic acclimation	Variable (frequently, increase)
Growth rates (biomass & elongation)	Increase (C3 > C4)
Biomass & crop yield	Increase (C3 > C4)
Water-use efficiency (WUE)	Increase (C3 > C4)
Leaf area index (LAI, leaf area/unit ground area)	Increase
Specific leaf area (SLA, leaf area/unit weight)	Decrease
Root/shoot ratio	Variable (frequently, increase)
Branching & tillering	Increase
Fruit size, number, & seed/plant	Increase

Table11.1: Effects of increased atmospheric CO_2 on terrestrial plant species.

Long [16], Crawford and Wolfe [17], Luo et al. [18], and others have stressed that changes in CO_2 and surface temperature operate interactively with each other and also with other environmental factors. Numerous growth effects and physiological responses to increased CO_2 have been summarized in many reviews, including those by Allen [19] and Rogers and Dahlman [20] for crop species, Bazzaz [21] with respect to natural ecosystems, and Eamus [22] and Saxe et al. [23] for forest trees.

Temperature

With regard to growth, the optimum temperature range is one in which all the individual reactions and vital processes are collectively functioning optimally but not necessarily maximally. Different species have evolved with different ways of integrating their cellular-level responses, and the optimum growth temperatures for terrestrial species range up to more than 45°C.

"Temperature determines the start and finish and rate and duration of organ growth and development" [24], and individual features of plant development (e.g., shoot and root growth, flowering, pollen tube growth, fruit set, and seed development) have different specific temperature optima, so that increases in overall mean temperature lead to changes in the growth and development pattern of a species. Global temperature rise will therefore affect the interspecific relationships within natural communities [17] and the geography of crop production.

Carbon Dioxide and Temperature

A frequently observed CO_2-temperature interaction is that increased temperature enhances the CO_2-driven stimulation of photosynthetic assimilation in most plant species (including the major crops wheat, rice, potatoes, and soybean, and all tree species). This is probably because increasing CO_2 inhibits photorespiration more at warm than cool temperatures [25], and because negative feedback from the products of photosynthesis is reduced by the greater metabolic demands for photosynthates for growth at warmer temperatures [26].

However, growth and development processes are more variable in response to temperature than processes such as photosynthesis and respiration [24]. Hence the photosynthetic interrelationships with CO_2 and temperature do not necessarily translate into increased growth and yield. Thus there are reports of increased temperature either counteracting or enhancing the benefits of growth in increased CO_2.

The foregoing background has emphasized the complexity of the interactions of the fundamental climate change parameters CO_2 and temperature. This sets the stage for considering further complexity introduced by climate change–air quality interactions. Ozone is discussed as an example.

CO_2-Ozone Interactions

The effects of increased CO_2 on the impacts of O_3 on vegetation have recently been reviewed by Polle and Pell [27], who point out that CO_2 levels are reasonably constant over lengthy periods of growth, whereas O_3 presents a fluctuating stress with dramatic hour-to-hour and day-to-day variability.

Adverse effects of O_3 range from visible foliar injury (necrosis) in sensitive species and cultivars to more subtle biochemical and metabolic changes that ultimately manifest themselves as various deleterious effects on plant growth and development. The elevated CO_2-induced changes to some of the major effects of O_3 reported in the recent literature are variable from species to species — varying from synergistic to antagonistic. However, it is reasonable to say that for most species, elevated CO_2 reduces many adverse effects of O_3. Certainly, it appears that no synergistic or additive adverse effects on growth have been reported, although some physiological processes and features of growth may show additive responses. As Polle and Pell [27] point out, protection against one adverse effect is not necessarily reflected in protection against others.

There are still vast gaps in our knowledge of the various interactions of CO_2, temperature, UV-B, and O_3. The gaps will be filled only by extensive and costly systematic investigation, for without more basic information as input, even modelling can be of little help. This is particularly true if we ask: What effect will O_3 have on ecological changes, including species distribution and migration, that will result from increased CO_2, temperature, and UV-B? At the moment there is only speculation. Since poleward movements of native and agricultural species appear to be inevitable [28] and the problems posed by O_3 to plants are to a large degree geographically related to centres of human population with high fossil fuel consumption, the answer may lie in whether or not plant species and people migrate in step!

Although various computer simulation models have been developed for assessing the interactive effects of O_3, CO_2 and temperature, as reviewed by Kickert et al. [29], none has apparently yet been developed to assess the combined impacts of these factors with UV-B.

The Outlook for the 21st Century

Although the currently observed rates of change in atmospheric CO_2 and other GHGs may slow down as a result of international agreements, any deceleration in the rate of global warming will be gradual. The different scenarios forecast by the IPCC give some idea of what may be expected in the next century. With regard to air pollutants, as world population increases, centres of population become larger, and fossil fuels continue to provide the major source of energy, the concentration of tropospheric O_3 will continue to rise. The poleward shift of global isotherms will have significant effects on plant geography and the continuing abilities of present-day agricultural and forest production to be maintained in situ. With regard to native vegetation in particular, it seems likely that C4 species will increase their range of dominance in some parts of the world.

If these predictions are correct, and in spite of the extent of the investigations of the past decades, we are still poorly equipped to be able to predict how important the relative changes in CO_2, temperature, and O_3 will be to the sustained production of food, fibre and forest products. Uncertainties abound, among which Krupa and Groth [14] have identified the inadequate capture of the spatial and temporal variabilities of growth-regulating atmospheric parameters, the lack of realism of many experimental exposure systems, and the lack of multivariate investigations.

Because the contributory factors to climate change are clearly interactive, future experimental studies also need to be interactive. It is wrong to presume that computer simulation modelling will be able "to take care of the interactions," although their use may lead to the revelation of unexpected interrelationships. But they do not provide a panacea, because their outputs are still largely dependent upon univariate input data.

In summary, our present understanding suggests that, as far as tropospheric O_3 pollution is concerned, continuing increases in the CO_2 component of climate change are likely to be ameliorative for many (especially C3) species. However, concomitant increases in mean global temperature will probably decrease this protective effect. The global impacts of pollutants such as O_3 may well be dramatically changed by the indirect effects of increasing mean global temperatures leading to poleward shifts in both natural and agricultural vegetation with consequent changes in ecosystem structure. Since adverse tropospheric O_3 levels in particular are clearly related to the urbanization and "development" of an increasing global population, the consequences of poleward migration of vegetation on the impact of O_3 on food production and natural ecosystems will depend upon how the geographic distributions of sensitive species change in relation to the anthropogenic sources of pollution.

ACID RAIN

Like climate change, acid rain (acidic precipitation) is a complex subject with its own extensive literature (see Chapters 3 and 6 for an introduction). Only a brief outline of linkages is attempted here.

Acidic precipitation is formed in a complex system of chemical reactions in the atmosphere as pollutant precursors are transformed en route from emission sources to receptors — humans or ecosystems. Gaseous sulphur and nitrogen oxides become transformed into fine particulate sulphates and nitrates (Chapter 3) that have direct health effects, as described earlier (Chapter 4). These same pollutants can be carried long distances (tens to hundreds or even thousands of kilometres), scavenged from the atmosphere, and washed out by rain and (less likely) snow, to be deposited in remote locations. The fine particulate forms may also be incorporated into clouds as the droplets nucleate around them. The gaseous precursors are also transformed in the process of cloud formation and growth in aqueous-phase reactions within the cloud droplets, where they are oxidized to their acidic forms (sulphate and nitrate ions).

Ecosystems that do not have the capacity to neutralize the deposited acidity (through naturally occurring buffering) can become acidified. Forest and freshwater ecosystems may experience damage, so that biota that are dependent on them decline, or are affected directly by toxic effects of the acidity. Thus, the direct health and visibility impacts of fine particulate air pollution evolve into broader ecosystem impacts as the air parcels that carry them travel across continents. Air quality effects and ecosystem damage are connected across this continuum.

Acidic precipitation and deposition would be influenced by climate change both through possibly altered formation of sulphates and nitrates and by the intensity and geographic distribution of clouds and precipitation events. Again, it is impossible to predict how the potentially increased production of acidic pollutants in the atmosphere might be balanced by altered volumes of rain (or snow) that are predicted to be associated with climate change. Receptor ecosystems may be sensitive to the quantity of acidic pollutants delivered (loading) or to concentration (pH, ions), depending on their response characteristics. If climate change increases the total volume of water deposited as rain in a region, the effects of acidifying pollutants could be diluted, hence possibly mitigated; the reverse is true for regions that experience precipitation decreases. Changes in deposition patterns could also lead to increased acidifying impacts in regions that are currently less impacted.

VISIBILITY AND MATERIALS DAMAGE

Atmospheric aerosols — the mixtures of pollutant gases and fine particles that comprise smog — not only produce direct effects on human respiratory health but also impair the clarity of the atmosphere and deposit on and erode soil or valuable materials. Each of these subjects is important in itself, but here we gloss over materials damage and treat visibility very briefly. Ozone, SO_2 and fine particles cause damage to building materials, statuary, and other materials such as rubber by corrosion or soiling. These effects have appreciable economic value, but in studies of the economic value of air pollution impacts, they generally comprise a very small proportion compared with human health and the deemed value of impaired visibility.

Clarity of the atmosphere is measured by the visual range at which distant objects can be identified or at which their aesthetic value can be appreciated. Impairment of visual range — visibility degradation — is caused by the physical and chemical properties of aerosols that alter the optical characteristics of the atmosphere. Both gases and particles contribute to such effects, but the major impact is associated with fine particles, generally in the size fraction smaller than 1 micrometre. This size range coincides with the wavelengths of visible light, and particles in this size range are especially effective in scattering light in the atmosphere. Both this scattering effect and absorption of visible light by gases and particles contribute to the degradation of the clarity of visual images. The more distant the object, the greater the effect of light scattering and absorption and the more distorted the image.

Reduced visibility has an aesthetic value, which may be expressed in lost welfare value to an individual, or in harder economic terms, in lost tourism revenue to a region that is losing (or has lost) its view of scenic surroundings. Several studies in North America have shown that even citizens who live at a distance from scenic natural environments, such as the Grand Canyon or Banff National Park, place a significant value on the ability to see scenic vistas clearly. People who live near the scenic features not only express their personal willingness to pay to improve visibility but also experience the effect of reduced willingness to pay by visitors who are demotivated to visit because of poor visibility [30, 31].

The fine particles that contribute most to visibility degradation are also those that are thought to be most seriously implicated in respiratory illness (see Chapter 4) and acidic deposition (see above). Once again, the constituents of air quality impairment contribute to impairment of other environmental and economic values distant from their emission sources.

REFERENCES

[1]   INTERGOVERNMENTAL PANEL ON CLIMATE CHANGE Working Group 1, Third Assessment Report, Summary for Policy Makers, IPCC, January 2001.

[2]   CATON, R.B., & CONSTABLE G.A., 2000 Clearing the Air: A Preliminary Analysis of Air Quality Co-Benefits from Reduced Greenhouse Gas Emissions in Canada, The David Suzuki Foundation, Vancouver, BC. 23 pp.

[3]   ANALYSIS AND MODELLING GROUP National Climate Change Process, The Environmental and Health Co-Benefits of Actions to Mitigate Climate Change, October 2000.

[4]   BURTRAW, D., & TOMAN M., The Benefits of Reduced Air Pollutants from Greenhouse Gas Mitigation Policies, Resources for the Future, Discussion Paper 98-01 REV, November 1997.

[5]   INTERGOVERNMENTAL PANEL ON CLIMATE CHANGE Working Group 3, Third Assessment Report, Summary for Policy Makers, IPCC, February 2001.

[6]   EPSTEIN, P.R., 2000 Is Global Warming Harmful to Health? Scientific American, August, pp 50-57.

[7]   CHAN, N.Y., EBI, K.L., SMITH, F., WILSON, T.F., & SMITH, A.E., 1999. An Integrated Assessment Framework for Climate Change and Infectious Diseases. Environmental Health Perspectives 105(5):329-37.

[8]   PATZ, J.A., MCGEEHIN, M.A., BERNARD, S.M., EBI, K.L., EPSTEIN, P.R., GRAMBSCH, A., GUBLER, D.J., REITER, P., ROMEIU, I., ROSE, J.B., SAMET, J.M., & TRTANJ, J., 2000. The Potential Health Impacts of Climate Variability and Change for the United States: Executive Summary of the Report of the Health Sector of the US National Assessment. Environmental Health Perspectives 108(4):367-76.

[9]   HREBENYK, B.W., YOUNG, J.W.S., & MILLS, B.A., Background Report on the Effects of Weather, Climate Variability and Climate Change on Air Issues, Great Lakes Basin — Toronto-Niagara Region. Prepared for Environment Canada by SENES Consultants Ltd., May 1998.

[10]   HREBENYK, B.W., YOUNG, J.W.S., & MILLS, B.A., Atmospheric Modelling Capability Relevant to the Toronto-Niagara Region Study. Prepared for the Atmospheric Environment Service, Environment Canada, Downsview, Ontario, by SENES Consultants Ltd., 1999.

[11]   KRUPA, S.V., KICKERT, R.N., 1989. The Greenhouse Effect: Impacts of Ultraviolet-B (UV-B), Carbon Dioxide (CO_2), and Ozone (O_3) on Vegetation. Environ. Pollut. 61:263-393.

[12]   RUNECKLES, V.C., KRUPA, S.V., 1993. The impact of UV-B Radiation and Ozone on Terrestrial Vegetation. Environ. Pollut. 83:191-213.

[13]   LUO Y., & MOONEY, H.A., eds., 1999. Carbon Dioxide and Environmental Stress. Academic Press, San Diego, CA. 418 Pp.

[14]   KRUPA S.V., GROTH, J.V., 2000. Global climate change and crop responses: uncertainties associated with the current methodologies. In: Agrawal, S.B., & Agrawal, M., eds., Environmental Pollution and Plant Responses, Lewis Publ., Boca Raton, FL. Pp. 1-18.

[15]   HSAIO, T.C., JACKSON, R.B., 1999. Interactive effects of water stress and elevated CO_2 on growth, photosynthesis, and water use efficiency. In: Luo, Y., Mooney, H.A., eds., Carbon Dioxide and Environmental Stress, Academic Press, San Diego, CA. Pp. 3-31.

[16]   LONG, S.P., 1991. Modification of the Response of Photosynthetic Productivity to Rising Temperature by Atmospheric CO_2 Concentrations: Has Its Importance Been Underestimated? Plant Cell Environ. 14:729-39.

[17]   CRAWFORD, R.M.M., & WOLFE, D.W., 1999. Temperature: cellular to whole-plant and population responses. In: Luo, Y., & Mooney, H.A., eds., Carbon Dioxide and Environmental Stress, Academic Press, San Diego, CA. Pp. 61-106.

[18]   LUO, Y., CANADELL, J., MOONEY, H.A., 1999. Interactive effects of carbon dioxide and environmental stress on plants and ecosystems: a synthesis. In: Luo, Y., Mooney, H.A., eds., Carbon Dioxide and Environmental Stress, Academic Press, San Diego, CA. Pp. 393-408.

[19]   ALLEN, L.H., Jr,. 1990. Plant Responses to Rising Carbon Dioxide and Potential Interactions with Air Pollutants. J. Environ. Qual. 19:15-34.

[20]   ROGERS, H.H., & DAHLMAN, R.C., 1990. Influence of More CO_2 on Crops. Proc. 83rd Ann. Mtg., Air, Waste Management Assoc., Pittsburgh, PA, June 1990. Paper 90-151.1.

[21]   BAZZAZ, F.A., 1990. The Response of Natural Ecosystems to the Rising Global CO_2 Levels. Annu. Rev. Ecol. Syst. 21:167-96.

[22]   EAMUS, D., 1996. Responses of Field Grown Trees to CO_2 Enrichment. Commonwealth For. Rev. 75:39-47.

[23]   SAXE, H., ELLSWORTH, D.S., & Heath, J., 1998. Tree and Forest Functioning in an Enriched CO_2 Atmosphere. New Phytol. 139:395-436.

[24]   LAWLOR, D.W., 1998. Plant responses to global change: temperature and drought stress. In: De Kok, L.J., & Stulen, I., eds., Responses of Plant Metabolism to Air Pollution and Global Change, Backhuys Publishers, Leiden. Pp. 193-207.

[25]   JORDAN, D.B., & Ogren, W.L., 1984. The CO_2/O_2 Specificity of Ribulose 1,5-bisphosphate Carboxylase/Oxygenase. Dependence on Ribulose Bisphosphate Concentration, pH and Temperature. Planta 161:308-13.

[26] FARRAR, JF, Williams, M.L., 1991. The Effects of Increased Atmospheric Carbon Dioxide and Temperature on Carbon Partitioning, Source-Sink Relations and Respiration. Plant Cell Environ. 14:819-30.

[27] POLLE, A., & PELL, E.J., 1999. Role of carbon dioxide in modifying the plant response to ozone. In: Luo, Y., Mooney, H.A., eds., Carbon Dioxide and Environmental Stress, Academic Press, San Diego, CA. Pp. 193-213.

[28] INTERGOVERNMENTAL PANEL ON CLIMATE CHANGE, 1996. Climate Change 1995: The Science of Climate Change. Houghton, J.T., Meira Filho, L.G., Callander, B.A., Harris, N., Kattenberg, A., & Maskell, K., eds., Cambridge University Press, Cambridge, UK. 572 pp.

[29] KICKERT, R.N., TONELLA, G., SIMONOV, A., KRUPA, S.V., 1999. Predictive Modeling of Effects under Global Change. Environ. Pollut. 100:87-132.

[30] US NATIONAL RESEARCH COUNCIL, 1993. Protecting Visibility in National Parks and Wilderness Areas, National Academy Press, Washington, DC. 446 pp.

[31] PRYOR, S., STEPHENS, K., & STEYN, D., 1995. Visibility Perception in the Lower Fraser Valley. Prepared for BC Ministry of Environment, Lands and Parks.

Appendix I
Conversion Factors

Gas	Mol. weight	To convert	
		ppb to µg/m^3	µg/m^3 to ppb
		Multiply by	
NO$_2$	46	1.91	0.52
NO	30	1.25	0.80
HNO$_3$	63	2.62	0.38
O$_3$	48	2.00	0.50
SO$_2$	64	2.66	0.38
H$_2$S	34	1.50	0.67
CO*	28	1.16*	0.86*

* For CO, the factors are for ppm and mg/m^3.

All at 20°C.

Atmospheric particle strong acidity: 300 nmol/m^3 is equivalent to 15 micrograms (µg)/m^3 of sulphuric acid.

100 parts per billion (ppb) = 0.10 parts per million (ppm) = 10 parts per hundred million

To convert parts per hundred million to micrograms (µg) /m^3, multiply by 20 for ozone.

Appendix II
Standards and Guidelines

PARTICULATE POLLUTANTS

US EPA	PM10	Annual mean 50 micrograms/m^3
(1997)	PM2.5	24-hour max 65 micrograms/m^3
		Annual mean 15 micrograms/m^3
UK Objective	PM10	24-hour 50 microgram/m^3 as 97th percentile to be achieved by the year 2005.
	PM2.5	No objective
Canadian	Under Consideration	

World Health Organization (WHO) Guideline for Europe (1995): No numerical standard (see below).

The WHO 1995 Revisions, instead of suggesting a guideline and standards for particulates, provided Tables of Effects on which different jurisdictions could base their standards. Two of these are reproduced below:

Health Effect Indicator	Estimated Change in Daily average Concentration needed for given effect (in Micrograms/m^3)			
		SO_4	$PM_{2.5}$	PM_{10}
Daily Mortality	5% change	8	29	50
	10% change	16	55	100
Hosp. Adm. Resp. Dis	5% change	8	10	25
	10% change	16	20	50
Asthmatic B'dilator Use	5% change			7
	10% change			14
Asthma Exacerbation	5% change			10
	10% change			20
PEFR (mean popn. Change)	-5% change			200
	-10% change			400

Health Effect Indicator	Number of Subjects per million popn. Affected by 3 day long episode of PM_{10} at:		
	50 Micrograms/m³	100 Micrograms/m³	200 Micrograms/m³
Mortality	4	8	16
Hosp. Adm. Resp. Dis.	6	12	24
B'dilator use Asthmatics	1,400	2,800	5,600
Asthma Exacerbations	1,000	2,000	4,000

OZONE STANDARDS

US EPA (1997)	0.08 ppm measured over 8 hours . Average fourth highest concentration over a three-year period determining whether an area is out of compliance.
UK proposal	0.05 ppm as 8 -hour mean, measured as the 97th percentile, to be achieved by the year 2005.
Canadian	82 ppb for one hour
WHO Guideline	0.076 - 0.1 ppm for 1-hour
(1987 edition)	0.05-0.06 ppm for 8 hours
(1995 Revision)	0.06 ppm for 8 hours

SULPHUR DIOXIDE STANDARDS

Current US:	0.03 ppm Annual arithmetic mean
	0.14 ppm 24 hour mean
UK proposal:	15 minute mean: 100 ppb measured as the 99.9th percentile, to be achieved by the year 2005
Canadian:	Maximal Acceptable: 0.02 ppm Annual
(1971)	0.11 ppm 24 hour
	0.34 ppm 1-hour
	Maximal Desirable: 0.01 ppm Annual
	0.06 ppm 24 hour
	0.17 ppm 1-hour.
WHO 1987 Guidelines	10 minutes 0.2 ppm
(unchanged in 1995)	1 hour 0.12 ppm

CARBON MONOXIDE STANDARDS

WHO 1995 Revisions:	15 minutes - 90 ppm
	30 minutes - 50 ppm
	1 hour - 25 ppm
	8 hours - 10 ppm

These were designed to prevent an increase in COHb (carboxyhemoglobin in the blood) of more than 2.5%.

NITROGEN DIOXIDE STANDARDS

CANADIAN Guidelines	Maximal Desirable Annual Mean 60 micrograms/m³
	Maximal Acceptable 1 hour 400 micrograms/m³
	24 hour 200 micrograms/m³
	Annual Mean 100 micrograms/m³
	Maximal Tolerable 1 hour 1000 micrograms/m³
	24 hour 300 micrograms/m³
AUSTRALIA (National Environment Protection Council, 1998)	Averaged over one hour = 0.12 ppm (229 micrograms/m³)
UNITED STATES:	Primary: Annual Mean 100 micrograms/m³ California 1 hour 480 micrograms/m³
WHO (1998):	1 hour - 200 micrograms/m³ (0.10 ppm): 24 hour - 150 micrograms/m³ (0.08 ppm)

FORMALDEHYDE STANDARD

British Columbia Level B	1 hour microgram/m³ = 60
British Columbia Level C	1 hour microgram/m³ = 370

HYDROGEN SULPHIDE STANDARD

British Columbia	1 hour	Level A	7.5-14 micrograms/m³
		Level B	28-45 micrograms/m³
		Level C	42-45 micrograms/m³
	24 hour	Level A	4.0 micrograms/m³
		Level B	6-7.5 micrograms/m³
		Level C	7.5-8.0 micrograms/m³
WHO 1987 guidelines:	30 minutes:		7 micrograms/m³
	24 hours:		0.15 micrograms/m³

SUMMARY

The following table shows the ambient air quality standards/guidelines for Canada, the United States, and the World Health Organization. All concentrations are in ppm except Pb and PM, which are in mg/m³.

Pollutant	Averaging time	Canadian Level B Objective	(Proposed) Canada-Wide Standards[1]	WHO Guidelines[2]	EPA NAAQS[3]
SO_2	1 hr	0.34	NA	-	-
	3 hr				0.50[4]
	24 hr	0.11		0.048	0.14
	annual	0.02		0.019	0.03
Pb	Quarterly average				1.5
NO_2	1 hr	0.210	NA	0.106	-
	24 hr	0.110		-	-
	annual	0.050		0.021	0.053
CO	1 hr	30	NA	26	35
	8 hr	13		9	9
O_3	1 hr	0.082		-	0.120
	8 hr	-	0.065	0.06	0.08[5]
	24 hr	0.025		-	-
Particulate < 10 μm (PM_{10})	24 hr	50[6]		No guideline value (impact relationship)	150
	annual	30			50
Particulate < 2.5 μm (PM2.5)	24 hr		30	No guideline value (impact relationship)	65[7]
	annual				15

[1]A Canada-wide standard for PM_{10} was not put forward. Standards are: $PM_{2.5}$ = 30 μg/m^3 (24 hr, 98th percentile, averaged over 3 years); Ozone = 0.065 (8 hr, 4th highest reading, averaged over 3 years) (http://www.ccme.ca/3e_priorities/3ea_harmonization/3ea2_cws/3ea2.html).

[2]http://www.who.int/peh/air/airguides2.htm

[3]http://www.epa.gov/airprogm/oar/oaqps/greenbk/criteria.html Unless indicated otherwise, all US standards are primary standards designed to protect public health, including sensitive subgroups of the population. Secondary standards are designed protect public welfare, including decreased visibility, damage to animals, crops, vegetation, and buildings.

[4]Secondary standard.

[5]A 1999 court decision blocked the implementation of this standard. On appeal of this decision the US Supreme Court essentially upheld the original standard.

[6]British Columbia and Greater Vancouver Regional District Objective (no Canadian Objective).

[7]A 1999 court decision blocked the implementation of these standards. On appeal of this decision the US Supreme Court essentially upheld the original standard.

Glossary

Aerosol acidity: Acid aerosols, usually sulphates or nitrates lead to an increased acidity of the air, which may be expressed as an increase in hydrogen ion (H+) or, equivalently, a decrease in pH.

Aerosols: Sulphate or nitrate compounds formed from SO2 emissions or NOx emissions, accelerated by the presence of ozone.

Airway resistance: A measure of resistance to airflow during fast expiration or during quiet breathing.

Allergen: A substance such as pollen or other protein to which an asthmatic subject becomes sensitized.

Alveolar deposition: Deposition of particles in the lung.

Anthropogenic: As a result of man's activities. In the case of hydrocarbons, for example, vehicle emissions are anthropogenic but emissions from trees are biogenic.

Asthmatic subjects: Adults and children sensitized to allergens and with hyperresponsive airways. There is a genetic predisposition (atopic subjects), but non-atopic asthma occurs also in adults.

B cells and lymphocytes: Cells concerned in lung defences.

Baghouses: Process of passing smoke or fumes through a bag, thereby capturing the particles.

Black smoke: An old pollution index based on the blackening of a filter paper through which ambient air has been drawn.

Bronchitic: Individual with chronic cough and phlegm production.

Bronchiolitis: Inflammation of the small airways of the lung.

Bronchoconstrictor: Any substance or chemical such as SO2 that causes airway constriction.

Cardiovascular: Diseases or conditions involving the heart and circulation.

C-fibre system: A system of nerve endings in the lung that respond to irritants, usually inducing a cough or a feeling of "chest tightness." Stimulated by breathing ozone, for example.

Chronic bronchiolitis: Chronic inflammation of small airways of the lung, commonly due to cigarette smoking.

Chronic obstructive pulmonary disease: Chronic bronchitis, chronic asthma, or emphysema (lung destruction), leading to chronic difficulty in breathing.

Coefficient of haze: Measurement of particulate air pollution made by drawing air through a filter and assessing the degree of soiling.

COPD: See Chronic obstructive pulmonary disease.

Confounder: A risk factor that is related to both the exposure of interest and the outcome thought to be related to that exposure. Thus, for example, if temperature increase was related to the level of ozone and was also related to increases in mortality, it would be a confounder of the relationship between ozone and mortality.

Crustal windborne dust: Road dust or soil blown off the land; a feature of dry, dusty climates that contributes to PM10 values.

Dosimetry: The concentration of an inhaled substance that may be deposited in different parts of the lung.

Double negative: Often attributed to ill-education, but sometimes used in a cautionary sense.

Edema: Fluid in the tissues, often indicative of inflammation.

Epidemiology: The study of disease in populations.

Erythema: Reddening of the skin.

Extravasation: Fluid leakage, usually from the lung, when it may cause pulmonary edema.

Feed stock: The material used in the manufacture of something like cement.

FEF25-75: On a maximal fast expiration, the mean velocity of the portion of the expiration between 25% and 75% of the total.

FEV1: The forced expired volume in 1 second. This is a simple test of lung function, and can be used in anyone over the age of 6 or so. It is sensitive to airway constriction caused by any agent.

FVC: The forced vital capacity, or the total volume of an expiration after a full breath in has been taken. It is not limited by time.

Foliar: Some effect on leaves or needles.

Greenhouse gas: Gases that enhance the "greenhouse effect," such as CO_2 and methane.

Henry's Law: A gas law from thermodynamics dependent on solubility that relates the partitioning of a volume of gas as a vapour or in solution.

HONO: Nitrous acid or HNO_2, an pollutant produced indoors by unvented space heaters and outdoors by photochemical oxidation of NOx.

Hydrocarbons: A very large group of chemical compounds composed only of carbon and hydrogen.

Inflammation in the lung: Changes in lung fluid measured by washing out the lung, and indicated by increased protein and cell content.

Intercorrelated: Two or more variables may be correlated with one another, and this complicates their relationship to other parameters.

Ischemic heart disease: Heart disease caused by disease in the blood vessels supplying the heart.

"Kriging": A procedure whereby the anticipated concentration at a particular site (of drill samples or air pollutants) is calculated by weighting the values recorded at nearby sites according to their distance from the site in question.

Mast cells: Cells in the lung that contain histamine; their activities are increased in asthmatics and cigarette smokers.

Maximal oxygen uptake: The maximal uptake of oxygen that can be achieved on exercise.

Mediators: Substances that are released by cells that may exert effects locally or remotely.

Meta-analysis: Grouping together a number of studies of the same relationship to increase the statistical power of the whole series.

Monotonically: A straight-line relationship between two variables.

Morbidity effects: Effects on such indicators as hospital admissions, emergency visits, physician visits, or increased use of medication.

Morphological changes: Changes in tissue structure.

Mortality indices: Numbers of deaths per day. In air pollution time-series studies, accidental and suicide deaths are excluded.

Mucosa: The lining layer of airways or other surfaces.

Nasal mucosa: The lining layer of cells in the nose.

Neurogenic: Mediated by nerves.

Neurotransmitter: A chemical substance that stimulates nerve endings.

Nitrates: Aerosol nitrate compounds formed from NOx emissions.

Non-adrenergic fibres: Nerve fibres in the lung that do not mimic the effect of epinephrine when stimulated.

Non-cholinergic fibres: Nerve fibres in the lung that do not mimic the effects of methacholine when stimulated.

Outgassing: Process whereby volatile organic chemicals (VOCs) are slowly released from household products such as furniture or carpets, causing increases in hydrocarbon concentrations.

PAN: Peroxyacetyl nitrate, an intermediate compound formed in the photochemical reactions based on NO2 and hydrocarbons in the presence of sunlight. It is very irritating to mucous membranes, and is responsible for the eye irritation encountered in Los Angeles and Mexico City. Ozone does not irritate the eyes.

Peak expiratory flow rate (PEFR): A measurement of the maximal velocity of airflow. The subject takes a maximal breath in, then expires as fast as possible through an instrument (flowmeter) that will measure the peak velocity. The instrument is portable and can be used easily by adults or children in the home.

PM2.5: The particulate fraction of particles less than 2.5 microns in diameter.

PM10: The particulate fraction of particles less than 10 microns in diameter.

Polymorphonuclear cells: Cells that increase in number in the presence of inflammation.

Pulmonary arterial pressure: The pressure of blood in the pulmonary circulation through the lungs.

Regression equations: Equations that represent the best expressible relationship between two variables.

Respirable fraction: The fraction of inhaled particles that enters the lungs and may be deposited within them.

Respirable particles: Particles than can be inspired into the lung and deposited within it.

Robust: A statistical term indicating that an association between two variables remains significant when other variables are taken into account.

Scrubbers: Devices that remove SO2 from stack emissions, usually employing water-containing alkaline solutions.

Sick building syndrome: A pattern of symptoms complained of by workers in (usually recently constructed) buildings.

Spirometric lung function: Measurements of FEV1, FVC, FEF25-75, or PEFR.

Statistical modelling: Devising an equation using multiple variables that best expresses an association.

Sulphates: See Aerosols.

Tar sands refinery: A process of extracting hydrocarbons from tar-containing sands.

Threshold: Some value of a pollutant below which no measurable effects occur.

Tracheobronchial region: The portion of the human airway that starts at the larynx and branches in approximately 32 generations to airways about 1 mm in diameter.

Troposphere: The region of the earth's atmosphere below the stratosphere, between 10 and 20 kilometres above ground level; tropospheric ozone distinguishes the ozone at ground level from the ozone that exists in the stratosphere.

TSP: Total Suspended Particulate - all particles of whatever size are included. Because TSP is generally a gravimetric sample, the total amount is dominated by larger particles that generally are not respirable into the lung.

Vapour recovery technology: A process whereby the volatile organic compounds (VOCs) that would otherwise escape into the air when a gas tank is filled are captured.

Vascular congestion: Congestion of blood vessels.

Vascular resistance: The resistance to flow in a vascular bed.

Vmax50%: The flow velocity when 50% of a maximal expiration has been breathed out.

Vmax75%: The flow velocity when 75% of a maximal expiration has been breathed out. In older terminology, this was sometimes referred to as "Vmax25%." <DAVID: Should these be Vmax 50% and Vmax75% instead? The same query is found in Chapter 4, page 112>

VOCs: Volatile organic compounds.

Voluntary ventilation: The volume of lung ventilation (expressed in litres/minute) that a subject attains during exercise

Waferboard: Inside building material made from woodchips and resins pressed into boards under high pressures and temperatures.

Index

U